Praise for John Leslie's Previous Gideon Lowry Mysteries

LOVE FOR SALE

"Fast-paced, suspenseful. . . . Leslie represents a cross-sectional view of Key West society as his hard-hitting hero tenaciously investigates death and missing treasure and, in the process, unearths shocking secrets."
—*Daily Press* (Newport News, VA)

"John Leslie's intriguing, atmospheric Key West mysteries can be better than a trip to our southernmost city. . . . In [this] third Gideon Lowry mystery, Leslie's plotting is at its best."
—*Sun-Sentinel* (Fort Lauderdale, FL)

"The sultry island of Key West is the perfect setting for this steamy whodunit. The several turns and twists keep you on your toes. . . . Great story line, interesting characters, and P.I. Gideon Lowry makes this a first-rate mystery."
—*Rendezvous*

"Gideon Lowry is an easygoing Conch—a native of Florida's sultry Keys. . . . Lowry [is] interesting and believable, a guy you might like to hang around with if you ever hit Key West. . . . John Leslie imbues his tale with a calm menace."
—*The News-Leader* (Springfield, MO)

"An exciting tale; Leslie puts us on edge and dangles suspense to the final page."
—*Paradise This Week* (Key West, FL)

NIGHT AND DAY

KILLING ME SOFTLY

Books by John Leslie

Blood on the Keys
Bounty Hunter Blues
Killer in Paradise
Damaged Goods
Havana Hustle

Gideon Lowry Mysteries:

Killing Me Softly
Night and Day
Love for Sale
Blue Moon

Published by POCKET BOOKS

BLUE MOON

A Gideon Lowry Mystery

JOHN LESLIE

POCKET BOOKS

New York   London   Toronto   Sydney   Tokyo   Singapore

This book is a work of fiction. Names, characters, places and incidents are products of the author's imagination or are used fictitiously. Any resemblance to actual events or locales or persons living or dead is entirely coincidental.

 POCKET BOOKS, a division of Simon & Schuster Inc.
1230 Avenue of the Americas, New York, NY 10020

ISBN: 1-4165-0171-1

This Pocket Books paperback printing May 2004

10 9 8 7 6 5 4 3 2 1

Cover art by John Nickle

Printed in the U.S.A.

For Barbara,
who helped hatch the plot at dinner
one long-ago night in Missoula

BLUE
MOON

1

◇

Location, location, location. You've heard that before, haven't you, Bud?"

Staring above Frank Pappagallo's inquisitive gaze, I take in the framed photographs on the wall above his head—all the transformations this establishment has undergone over the years—and recognize them all. *Welcome to the Blue Moon, Key West's only five-star restaurant.* So the menu reads.

"Don't patronize me, Frank," I say. "I wasn't born yesterday." For the price of the food, the company could be more appetizing, I think. On the other hand, I'm not paying. On still another hand, I'm too old to have to listen to such crap.

"And I don't give a damn about real estate slogans," I continue, warming a bit to my own tirade. "I've lived in this town all my life. So what if somebody wants to pay me five times what the place is worth and ten, maybe twenty times what I paid for it God knows how many years ago. It's my home. I live there. What am I going to do, move every time some new pip-squeak with a fat wallet comes to town and decides this is it? The next hot spot. Location, location, location. They might as well hang a sign outside Key West changing its name to Location. How many times have you seen this place change, anyway?"

"Don't get sore, Bud."

Bud. My high school nickname. Hardly anyone from the old days calls me Gideon any longer. . . .

"Who's getting sore? I'm sixty years old, trying to live out my life and keep a little business going."

"I want you to do that, Bud. Everybody wants you to do that. But why in the middle of Duval Street?"

"Because it's my home, Frank. My home. Can't you understand that? I live here. I feel something for it. It's not just a place to do business. My life's here."

Frank sighs. "For half a million dollars I could take my life someplace else."

"That's the difference between you and me, Frank."

"I know it. And by the way, it isn't a new pip-squeak."

"Yeah, who the hell is it?"

"Fred Pacey's involved."

"Pacey's moving uptown? I thought he was happy making millions downtown."

I can see that Frank's smile is forced. He is uncomfortable. "Location. A higher-class neighborhood. Speaking of high-class neighborhoods, how do you like your dinner?"

"Twice-cooked pork. What's wrong, they couldn't get it right the first time?"

Now Frank looks hurt.

"I'm kidding, Frank. Seriously, I'm happy for Gaby. I've known her for a long time. When she first opened, it was rice and beans and fried plantains. Now look at the place. Starched linen.

Thirty-dollar bottles of wine. And food I can't even pronounce."

"Three blocks from where you live, Bud. When she first opened, she was paying a couple hundred dollars a month rent. Now it's five thousand. You don't make that kind of money serving rice and beans. Gabriella!"

"Hi, Frank. Look who you dragged in. Bud, it's been a long time. How have you been?" Gaby is tall, slender, with minty green eyes that survey me warmly. An old friend. She is wearing a simple dark blue dress with thin straps, her dark hair curling just above her bare shoulders.

"No complaints. We were just talking about the old days, Gaby, when you first started in the restaurant business."

Gaby smiles happily, putting a hand on my shoulder. "You were a regular." Her expression is open, honest. Never anything spoiled about Gaby, just as I remember her from so many years ago when we were close. She seems unchanged.

"I could afford to be," I say. "Now I've got to wait for somebody with deep pockets like Frank here to bring me in. He's trying to get me to sell my place."

"Don't make any deals until you've had dessert. Try the crazy *flan borracho*. It's flavored with Cointreau. It's on me. I've got to run. Enjoy your meal."

"She's something. You used to go out with her, didn't you, Bud?"

"Briefly. A long time ago."

"You old dog. I hear she's getting married."

"Who to?"

"Don't know. She's a looker though, isn't she, Bud? How old you think she is?"

"Mid-thirties. Somewhere in there."

"Her first, isn't it?"

"What?"

"Marriage."

"As far as I know."

"She's worked hard. Nose to the grindstone the last ten years or so to put this together."

I nod idly, lost in thought about Gaby. Remembering the way her body felt when she would come over some mornings after I'd played a late club date and, fresh from a shower, slide into bed with me.

"Anyway, Bud, you'll think about it?"

"Did Pacey put you on me, Frank? Is that what this is all about?"

"Please, Bud. You know me better than that. We go back, you and me. I wouldn't do that. I'm just the messenger passing along the word I hear on the street."

"That's good of you, Frank. The word according to Fred Pacey."

"He's buying up your block, Bud."

"For what? More T-shirt shops?"

"A mall. Upscale."

"You don't say."

Frank shrugs. I know he is terribly uncomfortable, that he isn't going to push this. "Bud, how about dessert?"

"I don't drink."

Frank laughs, relieved. "Gaby's got ice cream. Plain old vanilla."

"You know my weaknesses."

"He's already got the Cuban grocery store next to you."

"What?"

"Pacey. He's buying the little *groceria* next door to you."

A twinge of pain stabs my side. "I'll take the vanilla ice cream," I say.

Frank smiles weakly. "I'm sorry."

"Hey, it's only a neighborhood. What's the price?"

"I hear three-seventy-five."

"A steal."

"You're getting the idea."

"I don't think so, Frank. Like you say, I'm an old dog. Too old for these new ideas."

"You thinking at all about retirement, Bud?"

"What's to retire from? Nobody's beating the door down to hire a private detective these days. We're a dying breed. The Edsel of occupations."

"That's funny, Bud."

"I wish I could laugh with you."

"So you're sixty years old. Not a lot of work. But you've got some money saved and a house that's a gold mine. Why not take the money, get yourself off Duval Street, move in to some quiet noncommercial neighborhood. What's the sense of hanging on there? I don't see how you sleep at night, the traffic and noise all hours."

"I sleep just fine. Nothing on my conscience."

"You're a pistol, Bud."

"Drink your dessert, Frank. I enjoyed the meal but this discussion's given me a pain in my side. You don't mind, I think I'll take a powder, walk home and get my last view of Duval Street before the sidewalks get paved with gold and I can't afford to walk on them anymore."

2

◇

Three hundred and seventy-five thousand dollars. A lot of money for a grocery store no bigger than a small gas station, a mom-and-pop outfit selling Cuban mix sandwiches in waxed paper, a few condiments and canned goods, icy cold beer and soda, and the best espresso coffee in town. Locals come all day for a hit of *buche* or a *con leche* to jump-start the morning or provide a little pick-me-up during the day. The place is legendary. And now, apparently, it's closing. Selling out to make room for another mall. Upscale, according to Frank Pappagallo, a lawyer, my lawyer, who in the last few years has begun to specialize in real estate law. Frank seems to know when something is going to sell before the owner even knows his place is on the market.

Sad about Mom and Pop. But understandable, I suppose. Who can blame them? They're an elderly Cuban couple who run the place, with a little help from a couple of their grown kids. Over a quarter of a million dollars for a wooden shack with old wooden floors that are termite-eaten, the varnish long gone, the boards worn smooth under the constant tread of feet day in and day out for more years than I care to remember.

Frank. *Just the messenger,* he said. The pain in my side is like the dull, crippling sickness following a sudden blow to the groin. Spreading in waves somewhere below the rib cage and around to my lower back. A hell of a thing to eat a meal like that and feel like this afterward, I think.

Just the messenger. Maybe he is right. What the hell am I hanging on to here, anyway? Get out before I'm squeezed out. While I still have some leverage. Buy a little bungalow on the other side of town, out of sight of the commercial strip this street has become, and forget about it. Let Pacey have it. What is this absurd attachment to Duval Street, anyway?

At the corner is a traffic light, and I pause in my walk, leaning into the pain in my side with my forearm, as if I can somehow force it into a more manageable place, or dispel it altogether. It doesn't seem like indigestion, but maybe a couple of antacid tablets will do the trick. Fizz, fizz.

Past the juice bar, the art gallery, the ice cream parlor, and the all-night convenience store that gets held up regularly by crack addicts. None of this was here five years ago. And most likely none of it will be here five years to come.

And neither will I if Fred Pacey has his way. There is a light on inside, barely illuminating the windows with their crumbling gold lettering advertising the Lowry Detective Agency, but it is a welcome relief to step up on the porch and, after unlocking the front door, go inside and close the door on the world for a moment. Alone.

Sitting down in the swivel chair behind my desk, I find the antacid tablets in the top drawer and gulp a couple of them, then lean back in the chair, putting my feet on top of the desk. Staring at the ceiling. There is the click of paws on the wood floor as my tomcat comes in from the kitchen to check out my arrival. At least twenty years old, he is blind now in one eye and measures each move before he makes it. I watch as he slowly rubs a paw over his good eye, then pulls himself gingerly into the open lower desk drawer where he now spends so much of his time, also withdrawn from the world.

Nearly thirty years in this house, twenty of them with a cat who showed up uninvited on the back step one day and never left; a relationship that surprisingly has lasted longer than any of my three marriages.

The pain is spreading now like hot lava across my abdomen. Something is wrong. A couple of deep breaths, waiting, I now know futilely, for the antacids to kick in. During my life I've been spared illness. This kind of pain is foreign and therefore, perhaps, all the more forbidding.

Easing my feet off the desk, I realize that I'm moving much like the cat, staring now at the phone as I consider calling a doctor. Few of the local doctors are left, except for Doc Russell, who is ten years older than I and still practicing. Whenever I have needed some modest medication over the years, he has providently filled a prescription for it without making a big deal out of my reluctance to come to the office. I look up his home phone number. It is ten-thirty, and I am sure that I will wake him with a call at this hour. But he answers on the first ring.

"Bud, what's wrong?"

There is a certain huskiness to his voice and a faint slur in his speech. I wonder if he has been drinking and remember that Russell has a reputation for enjoying his cocktails, and for being quick with the knife.

"Doc, I've got a strange pain that seems to be getting worse."

"Where is it?"

I tell him.

He asks a couple more questions about my activities in the past twenty-four hours, punctuating each of my responses with an ominous *hmmm* before asking if I still have my appendix.

"No, you took it out when I was a teenager. Over forty years ago."

"Oh, I forgot."

"I would have forgot, too, except I've still got the scar to prove it."

Doc Russell chuckles. I find myself actually wincing aloud with pain. "Bud, you got a choice. Go to the hospital, or I'll come over and check you out and you may still have to go to the hospital."

"How serious is it?"

"I can't make a diagnosis over the phone." Russell sounds peeved.

"Well, then maybe you ought to come over."

The doc sighs. Then, I hear him in a muffled voice say something to his wife. When he comes back to me, he says, "Bud, I got to be the last MD in the country who will make a house call. And at damn near eleven o'clock at night, no less."

"At your age you don't need sleep."

"I'll be there in fifteen minutes."

I hang up. The pain has now taken on roller-coaster proportions. My skin is clammy with sweat. Never having been in the grip of any serious illness before, I begin to envision the end. But half an hour later, Doc Russell laughs, and says, "Bud, you got colitis. Get off the spicy foods. I'm going to put you on a diet, and in a week you'll be good as new."

3

$\Diamond$

I hope it wasn't something you ate, Bud." Gaby stands in my office the next morning, where I am stretched out on the old leather sofa. It has been a long night. The pain lasted into the early hours, and it was after three in the morning before I finally got any sleep.

"What are you doing here?"

"I came in when I heard that you were sick."

"Who told you I was sick?"

"Frank called me."

"How did he know?"

"You know Frank. He's a lawyer." Gaby smiles. "He hears everything. Sometimes before it even happens."

My lawyer. When I needed one. Fortunately, like doctors, that has not been often. Frank and I were born and raised in Key West. Friends, I suppose. Though, like he had last evening, he could get on my nerves at times.

"I've got to go on a diet. No more spicy foods. Cut out the coffee. First the alcohol goes. Then caffeine."

"It could be worse."

"Sure. I could take a vow of celibacy." Memories of Gaby from a different time play across my brain like a melody from some distant tune.

Gaby smiles, but looks away.

"I hear you're getting married," I say.

"Frank told you that?"

"Who else?"

"I've been meaning to talk to you for a while, Bud. In fact, when you're feeling better, I'd like for you to come and see me."

"Sure. Where you living now?"

"Up the Keys. On Sugarloaf."

"Nice." It was the country. Twenty miles out of Key West.

"It's quiet. After working in the restaurant late every night, it's a relief to get out there."

"You don't mind the drive?"

"No, it's a good transition."

I can't imagine it. Just the prospect of leaving Duval Street seems unsettling. The bell on the front door tinkles, and Frank comes in with a couple of carryout containers of coffee. It smells good. "I can't drink that stuff," I tell Frank.

"Sorry. I didn't know."

"I didn't either until last night. I've just been lamenting my new regimen with Gaby."

She smiles, bends down, and kisses my cheek. Her face is cool next to mine. "I've got to go," she says. "I meant it about coming up, though."

"Maybe tomorrow."

"Good. I'll keep the morning open." She turns toward the door. "Why don't you come for lunch?"

"Sure."

"Take care, Frank," Gaby says.

"Here, have a coffee," Frank tells her. "Get rid of the temptation."

Gaby laughs, takes the offered cup, and leaves.

Frank's dark hair, which I know he colors, is slicked down and still wet. He looks as if he has just recently gotten up. He also looks like he has a hangover. "Bud, what is this?"

"I suppose, Frank, what it is is age. Things start breaking down."

Frank shuffles around uncomfortably, blowing on the surface of his coffee. "How's your insurance, Bud?"

"What do you mean, how is it? What are you talking about, Frank?"

"I mean you're covered, aren't you?"

"Frank, I've got colitis, not cancer. Don't write me off yet."

"I'm just thinking ahead. If you ever had to go into the hospital, you've got plenty of coverage. That's all."

"I've got insurance, Frank."

"What's your deductible?"

"Frank, you're a pain in the ass sometimes. I don't know what it is. Three grand, five. I don't remember."

"That's high. Maybe you ought to reduce it."

"Then my premiums go up."

Frank takes a sip of his coffee, then puts the cup down on my desk. "Well," he says, "if anything happens you've got the house."

"Frank, we had this discussion last night. I'm not in the mood for it now. If Fred Pacey put you up to this, you've got a lot to answer for."

Frank holds his hands out as if he's pushing

something away from him. "Believe me, Bud. As your lawyer, I'm only looking out for your interests."

"That's big of you, Frank. Don't do me any favors."

The familiar hurt look comes over Frank's face. "Sure, Bud. I'm not pressing it. Anything I can get for you?"

"Yeah, a couple of scrambled eggs and some grits. That's bland enough."

"I'll go over to the drugstore and pick it up. After, we can play a couple hands of pinochle."

I haven't played pinochle since my first marriage, to Peggy, when we played with another couple every week. Over thirty years ago.

When Frank returns with the food, I eat half of it, then let him talk me into the card game. We play at opposite sides of the desk, Frank bantering while the cards are dealt. After an hour, I call a halt.

"Get out of here now," I tell Frank. "I don't need a nursemaid. I'm fine."

"All right, Bud. But call if you do need anything."

"I'll call when I need a lawyer."

Frank laughs nervously, and limps out the door.

4

◇

At eleven-thirty I go next door to the *groceria* and get a Cuban toast with cheese melted on it, and sublimate my desire for a *con leche* with a cold ginger ale. Pop is working the espresso machine, and I can see Mom making sandwiches beyond the opening in the wall to the tiny kitchen.

"Bud, someone tell me you been sick?" Pop says. He is a small man with thick salt-and-pepper hair combed straight back, always immaculate in a white shirt that looks as if it has just been washed and ironed.

"Nothing serious. Just got to change my eating habits."

Pop smiles and says something I don't hear against the roar of the espresso machine as he froths milk in a silver pitcher for a *con leche* for someone else. From the kitchen Mom pokes her head out the window and gives me a friendly wave.

When he puts the toasted cheese in its wax paper on the counter beside the *con leche,* I tell him I have heard he is selling the business.

Pop looks at me gravely. "Bud, what can I do? They come in here. They offer money, cash money, like I don't see ever before."

"Pop, they're offering you half of what this place is worth."

He lays his delicate hands on the counter. "Is a lotta money, Bud." Pop looks around the store, his business, as if taking an inventory and disbelieving what he finds. A few cans of black beans, some bags of rice. Staples. The cold colas and beer. I can see it in his eyes: Why would anybody want to pay that much money for this?

"I don't know, Bud."

"Think about it. You haven't signed anything yet, have you?"

He shakes his head. "They bringin' the contract papers tomorrow."

"You got a lawyer, somebody to represent you?"

Pop shakes his head. Mom comes out of the kitchen, wiping her hands on a tea towel. She's small, like Pop, her hair still dark, a pretty face with a dimpled chin. "I tell him," she says to me, laying her hand on my arm. "I tell him, Bud, wait. Don't hurry." She turns to Pop. "But he don't listen." She smiles affectionately despite the mildly scolding tone of voice.

Pop looks shamefully at me. "Maybe they go away," he says.

"They're not going away," I tell them. "They want to buy up this half of the block and put in a mall. They're fishing, seeing what they can get cheap before anyone knows what they're doing. They get you signed up, then they've got some leverage with me and the others along here."

"Who is it, Bud?" Mom asks. "Do you know?"

"I hear Fred Pacey's one of the front men. That's all I know. You want, I can have someone talk to you, give you a better idea what you've got here. At least if you're going to sell, get what the place is worth. Make them a counter offer."

Pop looks at Mom, who nods her head. "All right, Bud," he says. "We trust you."

The Cuban toast has gone cool by the time I get back to my desk, but it is bland and my stomach doesn't rebel. Frank, of course, is going to have a fit when he learns that I want him to intercede on behalf of Mom and Pop.

And he does. "You want me to what?" he demands when I reach him at his office.

I tell him again.

"I thought you had a bad stomach. You didn't tell me your brain was affected too."

I let that slide. "Frank, you're a lawyer specializing in real estate. You know what the market is in this town. All I'm asking is that you confirm that the little *groceria* next to me is worth more than Pacey is trying to pay for it."

"And what happens when Pacey gets word that I'm interfering in one of his deals, Bud? You got any idea what will happen to my career?"

"Pacey doesn't need to know. I'm not asking you to represent these people; just let them know what they've got and what it's worth."

"Bud, you kill me. Tell me how your friends are going to feel when they hold out for more money and Pacey decides he won't pay it. You think they're going to have a warm spot in their hearts for you then, Bud? Or maybe what you're doing is trying to queer this entire deal. Save your little shack on Duval Street, is that it?"

"Save it, Frank. And by the way, the Garcias are

supposed to sign a contract tomorrow. It would be good if you talked to them before that."

"Bud, you owe me one. And don't think I'll let you forget it."

"I knew I could count on you, Frank."

He hangs up without responding.

5

◇

It is October. For many in Key West this is a time of renewal. The end of summer and the beginning of the winter tourist season; a time of green. Halloween, in fact, will usher in the first great hordes of the season, who come to dance in the streets, costumed and uncostumed, sometimes even unclothed, during Fantasy Fest.

Driving up the Keys in my ancient Buick to see Gaby, I think about Frank's advice to sell out and get away from the madness. What am I clinging to? Yes, my roots are in this city, but it is barely a shadow of the place where I grew up. I now recognize vestiges of the old Key West only in strange moments—biking by an abandoned building that carries a memory and has yet to be renovated, or sometimes when the wind is just right and the oily scent of fish spawning is carried across the water. Moments that are too few.

The air coming in the Buick's open windows is less humid, the sun bright overhead in a near cloudless sky. Jets from the nearby naval air station roar overhead.

The first time I met Gabriella Wade was about fifteen years ago. She was in her early twenties and I would have been around forty-five. Gaby was a waitress in a rice-and-bean joint I frequented. Right away it was obvious that there was something different about her. This was more than just a job. Gaby lived for her work. She loved food. It was what she talked about. She'd put a plate of *picadillo* in front of you and come back after a few minutes to find out how you liked it. She did not want to hear that it was just good; she wanted to talk about it, analyze it. She would even suggest ways of improving it, various sauces that might enhance the flavors, sometimes bringing in something she had made at home.

Gaby was a hit. She made eating lunch an adventure, and it was not long before she was in the kitchen making her own brand of Cuban cuisine. Not the exotic fare she was now serving at the Blue Moon, but she was definitely on her way.

Single-minded, is how I think of Gaby. She liked men, but she was not interested in a serious relationship when she was younger. Didn't have time for it, she said. Out of fascination I took her out for dinner occasionally until eventually it became a weekly ritual. Dinner out. She taught me a lot about food, exulting over watching my taste buds change as she introduced me to more sophisticated food than I had been accustomed to. Sometimes she cooked, either at her place or mine.

It was after one of those dinners that we first slept together. I was an older man who posed no threat to Gaby's future. Good friends who occasionally slept together without a heavy emotional investment. All perfectly natural. It suited us both and became another ritual that went on for a couple of years, a passionate but limited affair that lasted until Gaby got her own restaurant, which took up more and more of her time and energy. We saw each other infrequently after that, although for years Gaby would call and talk, usually about her business, sometimes about herself, although it seemed to me then that there was little distinction between the two.

As I turn into her driveway that leads to a house I have never visited, it now seems impossible that more than a decade has gone by since we were together.

Gaby's home, like most of the houses in this area, is on stilts, concrete columns lifting the structure above the floodplain. It is a square, modest frame house surrounded by buttonwoods, silver thatch palms, and sea grape trees, all of which I recognize as indigenous to the Keys. No stately coconut palms or other exotics to crowd out the simplicity of the environment.

The house is remote; no sprawling residential feel to the area. Although other homes are around, they are distant; the nearest is a quarter of a mile away, located rather haphazardly. One of her neighbors, she told me jokingly, is a doctor. In case the lunch does not agree with me.

I can see why Gaby would view this place as a respite, a place to withdraw to from her responsibilities and the hectic life in Key West. It is quiet. The only sound is that of a woodpecker drumming against a tree limb and a few insects chittering.

Although an hour of travel time on a daily basis might deter others, I can understand, too, how she could get used to it, how it gives her time to clear her head, to begin to unwind or to prepare for the day ahead, depending on the direction she is traveling.

I touch the horn to announce my arrival and notice by the car's clock that I am fifteen minutes early. Anticipation? I have to admit that my fondness for Gaby has never diminished, that I am looking forward to seeing her now just as much as I did all those years ago.

There is no sign of her as I step out of the car. The air here is different. Lightly scented and clean; no dust, no fumes, a light breeze coming off the sea. I climb the steps up to the house, where a screen door leads to a screened-in porch. I knock and look inside. No sign of Gaby. I wait and knock again. "Gaby!" No reply.

The outside porch seems to wrap around the house, which is square, not large but comfortable, its construction typical of many early Florida homes that were designed to best capture the breezes before the advent of air-conditioning. I walk around the porch to the back of the house and take in the view, which is not apparent from the front.

About five hundred feet beyond the house is the sea, the Gulf really, dotted with its many mangrove islands, like small green hillocks on the blue horizon. It is low tide, the sandy bottom exposed briefly here and there, with wading birds marching stiff and silent across the edge of the tawny flats, while above larger birds drift on the thermals along the shoreline.

Between the house and the water is a low-lying area of bedrock and scrub. It is there that I see

Gaby. Or someone who I think is Gaby. She is
dressed in white, some kind of a jumpsuit with
long sleeves and gauntlet-style gloves. On her
head is a helmet, over which is draped a veil that
covers her face. She is facing a row of rectangular
boxes stacked on top of one another. Beehives.

I lift my arm and wave. She sees me, and when
she waves back, a swarm of bees lifts from around
her in a golden cloud, and she begins to walk
toward me, trailing bees, like a wake, until they
gradually settle back into their hives as Gaby
approaches the house.

6

$\diamond$

"You're early." Coming up the steps to the back deck, Gaby smiles as she pulls off the gloves, removes the helmet, and pushes her hand through her thick, dark hair.

"I'm not exactly on a tight schedule these days."

Gaby comes over and we embrace. It feels natural. She runs her hand up and down my back before stepping away. "Bud, how are you?"

"Fit as a Stradivarius."

Gaby laughs. "Doc Russell's still got the touch. Amazing. And he's almost as old as God."

"He thinks he is God."

"Well, if lunch doesn't agree with you, I'll call in Charley, my neighbor. He's young, with no bedside manner, but he's up to date on modern medical technology."

"He makes house calls, like Doc Russell?"

"I've never had to ask, but if it's an emergency, I suppose he would. We're kind of cut off out here, as you can see."

"I don't plan to put it to the test. By the way, when did you take up beekeeping?"

"Let's go inside. I'll start lunch and tell you about it."

Gaby takes my arm and leads me through a set

of sliding glass doors into the house. It is open, airy, and with just enough clutter of magazines, books, and papers around to give the appearance of comfort rather than disorder. A couple of deep-cushioned sofas face one another in the living room; a large bookcase is along one wall, a desk along the opposite wall.

Beyond the living room, we pass through the dining area and past a round oak table, on the way to the kitchen. Here, it is easy to see, is Gaby's life. The kitchen is bright, with windows facing south and east, lots of cupboards and countertops, and a butcher-block island with two barstools on one side of it.

"Sit down there while I go to work." Gaby pats one of the stools, and I sit down while she begins unloading things from the refrigerator. "I got into bees a couple of years ago," she says. "I'm surprised you didn't know that. I've been bottling and selling my own honey."

"You never do anything halfway, do you, Gaby?"

"What's the point? Life's too short to live it in half measures."

"But why bees?"

"Do you know anything about them?"

I shake my head, watching as Gaby dumps several containers of various vegetables, prechopped, onto the butcher block, then puts some olive oil and spices into a large frying pan on the stove and adds some of the vegetables once the oil is hot.

"The honeybee is really an amazing creature. A hive is a very orderly and organized place. Probably because all the work is done by females. They gather the nectar, build the combs, make honey, raise the young, defend the hive, and take care of the queen."

"Sounds exhausting. And, I suppose, the male is just lying around."

"Useful only in the spring, when they are pretty much just sex slaves to the queen."

"Not a bad life."

"Except once the queen entices them from the nest, the ones who mate with her die instantly."

"Is there a message here? Stay away from a lot of hard work and sex and you'll live longer? That doesn't sound like your philosophy, Gaby."

She laughs. "Hardly. I guess I'm just impressed by their production. The queen lays up to two thousand eggs a day before she dies. And the female workers have to make about twenty-five thousand trips between hive and flower to produce a pound of honey."

"Impressive. It puts that trip to and from the Blue Moon every day into perspective."

"Don't think I don't think about that." Gaby takes a whole yellowtail snapper from a bag of ice in one of the double sinks, puts it on the butcher block, and starts to fillet it.

"Is it a lot of work for you?"

"Not really. I've only got twenty-five hives. I make sure they are in good repair and check for disease. That's what I was doing when you arrived. I enjoy it. I like watching them. In some ways it's relaxing, and like I said, it certainly puts other things in my life into perspective."

"You don't get stung?"

"Sometimes. Not a lot anymore."

There is a note of pride in her voice.

"So what's this about you getting married?"

"I want a family, Bud."

"That's news to me. Have anything to do with those bees?"

"Now, don't make fun of me. You know how I am. I put that part of my life on hold while I was getting the restaurant going. It was the only way I could have done it. I've succeeded, and now I want to move on."

"That's pretty much the way I had it figured. Who's the lucky guy?"

"His name's Roy Emerson."

The name is unfamiliar to me. "Local?"

"His father was in the navy and the family lived in Key West a couple of years when Roy was a kid. They moved around a lot, but Roy always wanted to come back here, even though he had only a distant memory of the place."

"When did you meet?"

"Almost a year ago."

"What does he do?"

"He puts deals together."

"He what?"

"I know it sounds crazy. I guess he's sort of a broker. He brings people together, you know, buyers and sellers."

"It sounds kind of vague."

"Roy's like that. He's been all over the world. He's worked at a lot of different trades, he has money, but what he likes doing best is the deal. The art of the deal. Making the deal work, that's the way he describes it."

"All right."

"He's sweet."

"How old?"

"You sound like my father, Bud. He's thirty-five. A couple years younger than I am."

"No family?"

Gaby looks up from the fillet of fish. "He was married once. His wife died. No kids."

"Sorry. I guess I have more than a casual interest in your happiness."

"I know. That's all right." Gaby smiles. "Now, why don't you set the table. I'll just be a minute cooking these, and then we'll eat."

7

◇

The meal is simple. Delicious. As I eat, Gaby describes it for me bite by bite. Sautéed yellowtail in a tamarind tartar sauce, accented by red, yellow, and green peppers lightly cooked in ginger and garlic, with a side dish of plantain puree that she has brought from the Blue Moon. Nothing that I cannot eat.

Gaby pours herself a glass of white wine, California fumé blanc, lifting her glass to mine of water. "To your future," I say.

Gaby smiles, drinks. "How long has it been since you quit drinking?"

"About three years."

"Do you miss it?"

"Every day. I would love to share that bottle with you."

"Would you rather I not drink in front of you?"

"No. Facing down temptation is part of the price I pay for the years I was out of control."

"It's difficult for me to think of you like that. I didn't see it when we were spending time together."

"You're a perfectionist, Gaby. And hardest on yourself. I've never known you to be judgmental."

"The staff at the restaurant might disagree with that."

"I doubt it. I've watched you over the years. I think I know something about you."

Gaby puts her fork down, taking another sip of wine. "There's something you don't know."

"What's that?"

"You've probably never heard of Tay-Sachs disease, have you?" I shake my head.

"I'm a carrier."

I am stunned by this information, yet, never having heard of the disease, unable to grasp the severity of Gaby's revelation. "You never told me."

"There was no reason to tell you, or anyone. I'm not in any danger and neither is anyone I'm intimate with, but it's there, lurking like a deadly poison."

I say nothing. Gaby clearly has brought me out here to reveal this for a reason. I think I can guess what it is.

"It's partly why I've lived the way I have. Deferring a family life." She stares at me over the rim of her wineglass. "Tay-Sachs is rare. Infants who are born with it don't live beyond five or six. My brother died when he was five. My parents didn't know that they were carriers."

Gaby has talked little about her family. They were from Europe, I remember, and migrated to this country when Gaby was young. When she was in her teens, her mother died. I know very little about her father.

"You're afraid of having children?" I ask.

"I'm a carrier of Tay-Sachs. If I marry someone who is also a carrier, there's a one in four chance our children will have the disease. There's no cure."

"Have you told Roy?"

Gaby glances away quickly. "Jews are the people most at risk from Tay-Sachs."

"I never knew you were Jewish."

Gaby smiles. "See. You don't know me as well as you thought you did. I'm not religious. Quite the contrary."

"And Roy?"

"He's not a Jew."

"So you've got nothing to worry about."

"He was born in Louisiana. A Cajun. It's a weird coincidence, macabre even, that the one person I'd fall in love with and want to start a family with would be someone from the only other high-risk group for Tay-Sachs."

"You haven't told him, have you?"

"I've told him. Like you, he'd never heard of the disease. He scoffed at the idea that he could be a carrier."

"Can he be tested?"

"Yes, a simple blood test is available. He refuses."

"Why?"

Gaby sips her wine, looking thoughtful. Or thoughtfully lost. "Who knows? Why do many men refuse to be tested for HIV? Because they're afraid to confront their own mortality, or because they believe that it could never happen to them?"

We sit silently for a moment, the meal over. Gaby pours a half glass of wine.

"What are you going to do?"

She shakes her head. "What can I do? I was ten

years old when my brother died. I watched him. It was horrible. The symptoms showed up when he was only six months old. He went blind, and was paralyzed before he was three. His brain was literally being destroyed, the nerve cells eaten away."

Gaby pauses, shaking her head, her expression reflecting the painful memory all these years later. "I would never have a child if there was even a remote possibility he could suffer that way."

"Roy wants children?"

"He says he does. But I'm not sure. He's different. Like me he's independent and self-made. He started with nothing. Maybe that was part of my attraction. Seeing myself in him. I suppose that sounds narcissistic."

I reach across the table and take her hand. "Call it what you will. There should be more like you."

Gaby blushes. "You're too flattering, Bud. But if you were me, what would you do?"

"I don't know. But I'd be concerned that the person I was marrying wasn't more understanding."

Gaby nods. We don't speak for a while. Finally she says, "Well, let's move on to a happier subject." She stands up and begins to clear the table. Together we scrape the plates, clean the counters, and load the dishwasher. Comfortably domestic. Gaby talks about life out here, the remoteness and isolation that she enjoys. I watch as her spirit lifts, wondering to myself if this marriage is such a good idea.

"Coffee? An espresso?" Gaby hesitates. "Oh, sorry, Bud. I forgot. What about decaf?"

"Not for me. You go ahead."

I watch as she grinds the coffee beans. When

she has finished, I tell her about Mom and Pop. We are in the middle of discussing whether I should sell out when there is the sound of a car approaching on the gravel drive outside.

Gaby looks out the window. "It's Roy," she says. "I wasn't expecting him."

8

◇

Gaby and I stand side by side at the kitchen window, watching as Roy Emerson gets out of a black Mazda. He is tall and thin with a ruggedly handsome face, the kind of face one sees in cigarette commercials. Advertising the open spaces. A man's man. He is wearing jeans, a long-sleeved shirt, and dark glasses. He stands beside the car, a thumb hooked in the corner of one of his pants pockets, looking first at my car and then up at the house. He seems to stare into the window behind which we stand. Gaby touches my arm, moving away to the enclosed porch and the front of the house. "Roy," she says.

"Hey, honey." Roy's voice is deep, rich, relaxed, as if it were filtered through an old wooden whiskey keg. "You in there? I thought maybe you had company. I was in the neighborhood. Thought I'd just drop by." He has already started up the steps.

"An old friend," Gaby says. "Come in and meet him."

Roy gets to the top of the stairs, where Gaby stands holding the screen door open. He leans forward, kissing the top of her head, one hand nestling for a moment in the tangle of hair at the back of her neck. Several inches taller than Gaby,

Roy stoops even further and seems to whisper something in her ear.

Gaby turns away, blushing, to face me where I have been standing in the threshold between the kitchen and the porch. "Roy, this is Bud."

Stepping forward, I am sure that Roy has already seen me, although with his eyes hidden behind dark glasses it is difficult to tell.

"Bud?" He reaches out a bony hand. "I don't think I've heard Gabe mention you." The smile on his face is fixed, slightly crooked. He hangs on to my hand longer than I am comfortable with, gripping it tightly.

"Bud and I've known each other for years. We just don't see each other often. I invited him up for lunch." Gaby seems a little nervous, something I am unaccustomed to in her.

"You don't say." Roy finally lets go of my hand and steps back, still smiling, staring at me. "Whaddya do, Bud?"

"I'm a private detective."

"A shamus." Roy laughs and turns to Gaby. "Well, hon, I hope I'm not interrupting. This wasn't a business lunch, was it?"

"Oh, don't be silly, Roy." Gaby punches Roy in the arm, but I can see that she feels awkward, perhaps because we had been talking about him just when he drove up. "Bud was born and raised in Key West. He gave me some help when I went into business for myself. Also he plays the piano at one of the clubs in town."

"A genuine Conch," Roy says, rhyming *genuine* with *wine*. "Well, a friend of Gabe's is a friend of mine."

"He's recovering from an illness after eating in the restaurant a couple of nights ago. He was brave enough to take another chance on my cooking. I was just having coffee. You want some? Or a beer?"

Roy cocks his head to one side. "A hit of coffee. Sure."

"I should probably get back into town," I say.

"Don't rush off, Bud. I'm going to make some fresh coffee. You and Roy go out on the back deck, and I'll be right out."

"Do me the honor," Roy chimes in. "I've never met a private eye before. Tell me about it."

Before I can protest, Roy is heading across the room to the back deck, where I saw Gaby tending her beehives when I first arrived. Once outside we stand leaning into the deck rail, looking over the bay, Roy's fingers nervously drumming the rail.

"Nothing serious?" Roy asks, not looking at me.

"What?"

"The illness."

"Oh, no. A minor problem."

"Hospital?"

"No."

"Good. Avoid hospitals, I say. You want to get sick, go to a hospital."

There is nothing for me to say. Roy seems to have a personal issue here.

He continues to look at the water and the crooked smile never leaves his face. "The healthiest people in this country live the farthest from hospitals and doctors," he says. "Believe me. I've never been to a doctor. Look at Gabe. Never sick a day in her life."

I do not see any reason to point out that a doctor is her nearest neighbor. Or that she is the carrier of a deadly disease.

"You ever been out West, Bud?"

"Never."

"Big country out there. People live miles from any kind of medical facility. And they live a long time."

"Something in their diet maybe." I let a touch of sarcasm creep into my voice. But Roy seems to ignore it.

"Diet! That's not a word in anybody's vocabulary out West. They eat whatever they damn well want to eat. And plenty of it."

I let my own restricted diet pass. "You sound like you've spent a lot of time out there."

"Enough," Roy says, finally turning to face me. "But let's not talk about me. I want to hear what it is a private detective does."

"Right now he doesn't do a lot," I say.

"Pry a lot into other people's business, I guess."

"Mostly we just kick doors in. Shoot now and ask questions later. The way I imagine they do it out West."

Roy erases the smile for a moment. Then he laughs. "Now, Bud, don't get sore. Gabe would never forgive me. I didn't mean to needle you."

"Nobody's sore."

"Good." The smile came back. "You'll get used to me."

Somehow I doubt that possibility.

"Seriously, though," Roy continues, "you ever been shot at?"

"Yeah, I've been shot at."

"What happened?"

"He missed."

"But you've had that moment, looking down the barrel of a gun, thinking it might be your last."

Roy and I stand facing each other now. I am aware of my own portliness next to his slender, muscular frame. Staring up into his dark glasses, I wonder what it is Gaby sees in this guy. Roy suddenly offers his hand, and before I know why, we are shaking hands again. "I like you, Bud. You've got mettle. I like that in a man."

Without knowing what it was, I feel like I have passed some kind of test. Gaby comes out to the deck carrying a tray with two coffee cups, a bowl of sugar, and a small vase of flowers, which she sets on a table.

Roy goes over, kisses her again, and says, "I like your friend here."

Gaby looks toward me. I give her a smile. We both watch as Roy picks up his coffee, dumps two spoons of sugar, and stirs, then leans over and smells the flowers. "Nice. No coffee for you, Bud?"

"Don't drink it," I say, making sure I don't mention the dread diet.

Gaby stands next to Roy, sipping her coffee. When Roy has finished, he walks over to the deck rail and seems to be looking at something on the water. I watch a bee fly lazily around the porch, spinning a couple of loops around Roy's head. Roy lashes out with one hand and the bee disappears. Seconds later, Roy slaps at his neck. "Shit," he says. "The sonofabitch stung me."

Gaby puts down her coffee and goes to Roy. "You okay?"

Roy rubs at the sting. "Sure." He smiles.

"I'll get some ice to put on it."

"I'm fine," he says.

Gaby goes inside and comes back with ice wrapped in a towel. She holds it to the red welt appearing on Roy's neck. Roy smiles. "That sonofabitch packed a wallop. Was that one of yours, hon?"

Gaby nods, studying Roy, whose face has gone pale. "You sure you're okay?"

"A little weak. Maybe I'll just lie down a minute."

"I'm going to call a doctor."

"I'm fine. Just give me a minute." Roy starts to walk inside, taking a half dozen steps before he collapses on the deck.

9

◇

"Stay with him, Bud," Gaby says. "I'm going to call Charley. I think it's his day off. God, I hope he's home."

I kneel down on the deck beside Roy. Some drool oozes out of his mouth. I reach for his wrist and feel for a pulse. His skin is clammy, the pulse weak, a distinct odor coming from his body. I can hear Gaby on the phone. A moment later she is back on the deck.

"Charley's on his way."

"What's wrong with him?"

Gaby holds one of Roy's hands. "He must be allergic to bee stings. He's gone into anaphylactic shock."

Gaby shakes her head. "Charley's bringing some epinephrine." She kneels down beside me and takes Roy's hand. I wonder how Roy's going to feel about a doctor's presence. Right now he doesn't seem to be feeling much of anything; he's out like a light.

There is the sound of car tires crunching over the gravel out front and a skidding noise when the brakes are applied. Moments later, a young, confident-looking guy carrying a medical bag charges up the back stairs. Charley has a grim look on his face. He glances my way but does not speak.

With steady hands he opens the bag, takes out a syringe and a small, dark bottle; inserting the tip of the syringe into the membrane covering the bottle's neck, he pulls back the plunger on the syringe. "Roll up his sleeve," Charley says.

Gaby fumbles with the button on Roy's cuff, tears it, and pushes up the sleeve. The exposed arm has red blotches, some kind of rash.

Charley picks up Roy's arm, cradling it under his own, and searches for a vein. When he finds it, he slips the needle in and slowly pushes in the plunger. Roy's eyes flutter open and he immediately vomits.

Gaby sprints into the house and comes back with a glass of water and a wet towel, which she uses to clean Roy's face.

"What's your name?" Charley asks him.

"Roy," Roy says. "What's yours?" His voice has lost some of its timbre.

"Who's the president?"

"Clinton. I can't see too well." He seems to be gasping for breath. His eyes are hooded, unfocused.

Charley nods and turns to Gaby. "I called an ambulance before I left the house. He should go into the hospital for observation."

"Is he going to be okay?" Gaby asks.

Charley shrugs noncommitally, putting the needle back in his bag. He takes out a package of tablets. "Antihistamines. He should take a couple."

Holding Roy's head up, Gaby puts the glass of

water to his lips after Charley slips two of the antihistamines into Roy's mouth.

"His respiratory system has been attacked by histamines," Charley explains to Gaby ten minutes later as the sound of the ambulance cuts the stillness. "He needs to be in a hospital where he can have his heart and blood pressure monitored to make sure there hasn't been any damage. Two or three hours, and if he's okay, he can be released." Charley looks at me again.

"This is Gideon Lowry," Gaby says, introducing us. Charley extends his hand, giving me a perfunctory shake and a half smile, breaking away when the two uniformed paramedics come up the back stairs with a stretcher. Charley walks over to talk to them.

"What's happening?" Roy asks Gaby.

"You're going to the hospital for observation."

Roy seems groggy, weak. "Hospital?"

Gaby rests her hand on his arm. The medics come over, put the stretcher down, and begin to lift Roy onto it. He does not resist. "If you want, I can take you in with me," I say to Gaby.

She shakes her head. "I'll go in the ambulance with Roy." She watches as they carry him down the steps. "This has all been too much. What do you think it means?"

"I don't know, but I'd say Roy was pretty lucky that Charley was next door. I'm not sure he would have made it if he'd had to wait for an ambulance."

"Lucky," Gaby says. She stares out across the water. Then pulls herself together. "You can stay here if you want, Bud."

"You go on. I'll close the place up for you and then come into town. Call and let me know how he is."

Gaby smiles, gives me a brief hug, then takes off after Roy. Charley has gone with the medics. I listen as they load the stretcher into the ambulance and then skid on the gravel driving away. It is very quiet. I take the tray with the coffee on it inside, clean up the deck where Roy vomited, and pick up his dark glasses.

Not far from the glasses I notice something on the deck and walk over to it. It is a dead bee, presumably the one that stung Roy. I wonder if it is my imagination or is the little insect really smiling?

10

◇

The next day is idle. I have a club date, the first in several months, to play that evening at nine o'clock. After an early meal I show up at the bar at eight-thirty and find Ronnie, my favorite bartender, mixing drinks.

"Gideon Lowry," she says. "Welcome back."

Ronnie leans across the bar, and we brush cheeks. She is blond, with liquid blue eyes and a tender mouth. After five years she has become a fixture here, but despite the hours and the hazards of this sort of work, Ronnie remains without guile. She is good-natured; the late hours and often inhospitable clients never seem to wear her down.

"You behaving?"

Ronnie's lips tremble slightly when she smiles. "Ain't misbehavin'." She croons one of the frequent tunes I play. "Anyway I don't have time. Have you got your costume ready for Fantasy Fest?"

"I'm wearing it." In fact, I have on the same costume, khakis and a white shirt, that I have worn most of my life.

Ronnie laughs. "You still on the wagon?"

I nod, and she fills a tall glass with club soda, squeezing in the juice from a cut lime before putting the glass on the bar in front of me. A dozen or so people are drinking at the bar or scattered around the room, which, with its overstuffed chairs, is meant to give the feel of a large, comfortable living room. Ronnie goes off to mix a drink. At nine o'clock she switches off the CD as I mount the stage, where the black baby grand lurks like a baited trap.

Gershwin and Cole Porter are my repertoire. I lead off with "Love Is Here to Stay," and by ten o'clock a small camp following has ascended the seven stories to the club to listen, most of them middle-aged or older, but every now and then a younger face appears.

At eleven I take a break, go to the men's room, and find Gaby at the bar when I return.

"I just got away from the Moon," she says. "I thought I'd stop by and see you before heading home." Gaby looks tired.

"How's Roy?"

"That's really why I came. Charley was right. They held him for a couple of hours for observation. We took a cab back to my place and he spent the night."

"I hope he appreciated the proximity of a doctor."

Ronnie comes by, and Gaby orders a glass of red wine.

"I guess he gave you an earful of his views on hospitals," Gaby says when Ronnie leaves.

"I got the idea he doesn't much like them."

"He was acting really strange yesterday. I think he felt threatened by you."

"By me!" I laugh. "At my age I'll take that as a compliment."

"He asked me a lot of questions about you."

"I hope you didn't answer them."

"I did. Honestly. I've got nothing to hide."

"What about Roy?"

"How did he take it? He was fine. I think that bee sting actually scared him a little."

"I was wondering if he had anything to hide."

Gaby ducks her head. When she lifts it, we stare into each other's eyes. "I've been wondering the same thing."

"Since when?"

"A while now, I guess, but until the other day I don't think I was ready to acknowledge it."

"Tay-Sachs?"

Gaby nods. "You see, Roy didn't even know he was allergic to bees. And why would he? Charley said that people can react differently each time they're stung. Roy may never experience that again, but he's got a prescription for a kit with a syringe and an Epipen with the same drug that he can administer himself if it does happen again. Just a precaution."

"From what you told me about Tay-Sachs, it isn't that random. You either have it or you don't. Am I right?"

"Yes, Bud, but don't you see, I don't know anything about Roy. About anybody, really. Except what they tell me."

"Of course."

"You said something the other day about me."

"What was that?"

"That I'm a perfectionist. No half measures. If I get into something, I'm in it all the way."

"I believe that."

"Then it doesn't make sense for someone like me to marry a guy I've known for less than a year, does it?"

"Gaby, I can't answer that for you."

"I mean it doesn't make sense that I wouldn't find out as much as I can about him. Not just because of Tay-Sachs, but everything."

"What are you getting at?"

"I want to hire you, Bud."

"Gaby—"

"Wait. I want you to do a background check on Roy. I know it sounds cold and cynical, but I'm thirty-seven years old. I don't want to make a mistake. You know as well as I do the kinds of people this town attracts. You said it. I'm a perfectionist, and I want to know what I'm getting into. It's that simple. Will you do that for me?"

I drain the last of my club soda. "I don't like it, Gaby, but if it's what you want, I'll do it. You know that."

"Fine." She raises her glass. We touch.

"Let's talk in the morning." Gaby stands up to leave, reaches for money from her purse.

"It's on me."

She reaches up and kisses me. "I hope you don't find anything," she says, and leaves.

I am not sure what I hope. Back at the piano I strike a chord and flow into "Blue Moon." Left standing alone.

11

◇

Around midmorning the next day, just as I am leaving with my toasted cheese on Cuban bread, Frank Pappagallo walks up the steps to Mom and Pop's. "Bud," he says, "you've put me in the soup."

"What are you talking about?"

Frank is staring over my shoulder. I turn. Pop stands behind the counter, half a dozen people crowded in the little store, waiting on their orders for coffee and breakfast. Pop grins at us while operating the big four-cup espresso machine.

"Come on, let's go next door. You want to get yourself a cup of coffee?"

"I don't want to be seen in this place," Frank says. He is excited, nervous. But that's Frank. I have never known him when he was without an edge. Although he is only a couple years younger than I am, Frank is a guy who was never expected to live long. I have known him since high school. He is someone who very much wanted to be a player, to soar with eagles, but instead he has spent most of his life like a bird in a cage, hyper and flighty. Frank is not a bad guy and not particularly complex, except when he is trying too hard to ingratiate himself. Which he frequently is.

"Frank, you ought to get on the diet I'm on while you've still got a chance."

We are sitting in my office, Frank in the big easy chair on the client side of my desk. I put my feet up, lean back in the swivel chair, and study him.

"What are you talking about?" Frank says. "There's nothing wrong with me."

"You worry too much. About other people. Stuff you can't do anything about. Sooner or later you're going to give yourself an ulcer."

Frank pushes his lips out, then pulls them back, baring his teeth. "The old guy next door turned down the offer."

"You don't say." Pop has already told me, thanking me, really, for getting involved. He fully expects to sell the place, but for more money.

"I don't think you understand, Bud."

"Probably not."

"Pacey is pissed."

"There's another guy who needs to worry about ulcers."

Frank shakes his head.

"Forget about Pacey, Frank. He'll get his store. Pop will sell, but he'll get what the place is worth."

"The word is the financing on this project is down to the wire."

"So Pacey thought he could swindle Pop, stick it to the little guy, save some dough, is that it?"

Frank looks sick. "Bud, Pacey called me. He knows I went to see Pop."

"So a lot of guys see Pop. They get coffee there. Stop worrying, Frank. What did you tell Pop anyway?"

"I told him his place might be worth more than

what they were offering, but if he wanted to sell, he might have to wait to get that kind of money. The offer Pacey made was a reasonable one."

"Left yourself an out, huh, Frank?"

"I didn't think he would turn them down."

"Let Pacey up the ante. He can't just keep rolling over people the way he's done for years."

Frank shakes his head. "I don't think it's going to work that way." Something in Frank's expression troubles me.

"How is it going to work, Frank?"

He stares at me. I have never known why exactly, but I think Frank likes me. Maybe because before Carl died—my brother Carl, the state senator—he had the kind of power that Frank envies. Although they knew each other, Frank did not have access to Carl the way a guy like Fred Pacey had. So Frank was left to cozy up to the relatives, the bit players. Who knows? Maybe it was nothing more than longevity; we went back. Whatever it was, and whatever Frank's weaknesses, I did not think he would betray me. Needle, cajole, yes. But I was certain that I could trust him.

"It's hardball, Bud," Frank says, continuing to stare.

"Explain."

"There's nothing to explain. Pacey's going to put pressure on the coffee grinder."

"And just how is he going to do that?"

"I don't know. He has his ways. But it won't be pleasant for your friend."

"Wait a minute, Frank. Are you telling me that Pop's in danger? Threatened?"

"What I'm telling you, Bud, is that until you

butted in, the guy was ready to sell. So you bear some responsibility. Other than that, I don't know anything. All right?"

"Not all right. The first sign of any strong-arm tactics by Pacey, and I'll be in his face like a five o'clock shadow. You can tell him that, too. As long as you're spreading information around."

"Ah, Bud, don't blow up at me. I'm just trying to help, save everyone some difficulty. You can talk to Pop; he'll listen to you. Tell him to come back with a fair counteroffer and Pacey will listen. But not the top price he's asking. Pop won't get top price for the place, the condition it's in."

"'The condition it's in' is Duval Street. Location. Remember? You told me the other night that was all there was. Location."

Frank worries his lip a little more, then straightens his tie. Frank always wears a tie, one of those old-fashioned, preknotted, clip-on jobs, with a short-sleeved shirt and no jacket. The tie, red and green diagonal stripes, has a couple of stains on it. I would bet that it's twenty years old. "Forget it," he says. "Sometimes I don't know why I bother talking to you."

"You're my lawyer, Frank." I smile.

"You don't take advice."

"I'm stubborn."

Frank pushes up from his chair, groaning like a rusty hinge.

"Take care of yourself," I say. "You sound like a doddering old man."

"Around you that's the way I feel."

"Maybe if you weren't running interference for the likes of Fred Pacey, you could enjoy life."

Frank grunts, waves a hand in dismissal, and heads to the door.

When he has gone, I pick up the plastic cup Frank has left on the desk. The coffee, now the color of my khakis, has a thin scum floating over its surface.

12

◇

Gaby picks up the phone on the fourth ring, just as the answering machine clicks on. I listen to her recorded voice before she finds the switch, clicking the machine off. "I didn't wake you?" I say.

"No, I was outside watering the herb garden." She grows her own herbs for the Blue Moon.

During the two years that we saw each other, Gaby was always up early on those times when we spent the entire night together. She was not one to linger. There was always something to do. More than once I remember staggering up around dawn to find her experimenting in the kitchen. Breakfast on those occasions would be something special.

"You haven't changed your mind, have you?"

"About what?"

"What you came to see me at the club about last night."

Gaby laughs. "No, of course not."

"I didn't think so."

"You sound disappointed."

"Probably. It doesn't leave me in a very good position."

"What do you mean, Bud?"

"I mean, what if I find something out about Roy?"

"That's what I want you to do, Bud. I mean, if there is something, I should know about it."

"I know what you mean. You're in love with him."

"Bud, we have a wonderful relationship. A good time together, and he's very considerate of my time. Which, as you know, isn't easy."

"And if I turn up something negative?"

"Better to find out now than later."

Of course I knew that would be her response. Gaby is not one to change her mind once she has decided on a course of action. She does not see this as a betrayal, but prudence. And it is unreasonable of me, I suppose, to feel such foreboding about a job. But I do. "I'll need some information about him," I say softly. "His background."

"Whatever you need."

I ask her some questions and jot down the answers. Some of my questions she cannot answer, telling me that she will get back to me. I understand that she will have to ask Roy. When we hang up, I remain at my desk, studying my notes.

Roy Emerson was born in New Orleans on February 12, 1961. He is thirty-five years old. His father was in the navy, an aviation mechanic. He died about ten years ago. Roy's mother has remarried and is living somewhere in Florida; Gaby was not sure exactly where. Roy and his mother were never very close. There are no brothers or sisters. About his first wife, Gaby knew nothing. She thought they had lived in Jackson Hole, Wyoming, where Roy was involved in some kind of land speculation, but she was not clear on that either, at least not the exact dates and details.

Without a straight line to his past, or at least a solid point of entry, there really is little to go on. Roy has no deep ties to family that I can see, or any standing in a particular community. Most of his life he has moved around. He is without any sign of a continuous occupation, and that will make efforts to trace his path difficult at best, if not impossible.

Is it just coincidence, or has he lived this way for a reason? Just another footloose American trekking around the country in search of something, or someone. Typical wanderlust. Something I have never known. Without really knowing him, I have taken an early dislike to Roy Emerson, with or without the background details that Gaby has asked me to dig up.

I wonder whether it is my affection for her that has caused such a reaction to him. Maybe he was just as uncomfortable meeting me. He had come out that day unexpectedly and found Gaby entertaining me, a man he did not know. Gaby, I recall, had been somewhat ill at ease herself when Roy showed up.

Maybe Roy was simply jealous, feeling threatened, as Gaby told me later, and that was his way of reacting. For Gaby's sake I have to give him the benefit of the doubt, I suppose.

Until recently, I have done investigative work off and on over the years for the state attorney. After some political differences with the SA a few years back, that work ceased. I still have contacts in the office, however, and it is one of them, an older attorney there who has remained a good source of information for me, whom I now call.

"Bud, you old dog. How be you, brother?"

Will Seton has been in the SA's office for close to thirty years. He is approaching retirement age and has little to expect in the way of advancement or political favor from his position there. He is a willing coconspirator when it comes to dishing the current administration.

"Can't complain, Will. How's by you?"

"Oh, I can complain plenty. The word is, Bud, the head honcho here is on the way out. I know that should please you as much as it does me."

I, too, have heard rumors. After a decade in office, during which the present SA has run unopposed each election year, he is being challenged this year by a newcomer, someone from up the Keys, an unknown in Key West politics. Which in itself makes him refreshing. My own cynical outlook, however, tends to doubt his capacity against the political machinery here.

"You really think he can do it?"

"Between you, me, and the gatepost, Bud? *El jefe* doesn't have the stomach for it anymore. He's winding down, not putting up much of a struggle. My guess is, he's ready to bow out rather than answer some of the charges this upstart is bringing against him."

"I'm pleased to hear it." And it is good news. With a new SA on the throne, more work might come my way. Still, I know the perils of forecasting elections in this town. I will wait for the egg to hatch.

"What can I do for you, Bud? I assume this isn't a social call."

"I'm in a jam, Will. I've been hired to retrieve

some background on an individual who doesn't seem to have much of a past. He's not from around here, and I was hoping you might have some contacts out of state."

"What's the name?"

"Roy Emerson."

"Doesn't ring a bell."

"No reason it should. He's only been around here for a year or so and in no trouble during that time. Of course, this is also on the q.t."

"Understood, Bud. Where do we have to go?"

"Jackson Hole, Wyoming, for one."

"Good God! That's in another universe, isn't it?"

"Couple of time zones, anyway. Can you find someone in the DA's office out there to do some legwork for me?"

"I can try. Can't promise anything."

"Billable to me, of course, and pass along my phone number. We can deal direct."

"Sure. Anything else, Bud?"

"Not at the moment."

"Well, then, as the fella says. You have a nice day."

13

◇

Ironically, the last case I worked for the state attorney took me to New Orleans. Because of the nature of that case I have come to think of the city—unfairly, I suppose—as a place of betrayal. However, in the course of the investigation of a murder of a witness I'd been sent there to bring back to Key West, I met a cop I liked.

Sometime before noon and after repeated attempts to reach him, I finally get Dave Robicheaux on the line.

"Lowry. Sure I remember you," Dave says. His voice, like that of a bullfrog in a swamp at night, comes across the line deep and distant. "How'd that business back here get resolved for you anyway?"

"Not in my favor, I'm afraid."

"Sorry to hear that. It was unpleasant all around. I got to know the dead kid's sister. She took it pretty hard."

"I'm sure."

"What can I do for you, Gideon?"

"Dave, I'm trying to get some background information on someone who was born in New Orleans. I thought you might be able to help."

"Sure. Who is it?"

"A guy by the name of Roy Faulkner Emerson."

"It's got a literary ring to it."

"I'm afraid I don't have much more than that to go on. He was a navy brat. I don't know how much time they actually lived there."

"Birth date?"

I relay the information from my conversation with Gaby, including the Wyoming connection.

"He have a record?" Robicheaux asks when I am finished.

"I don't know. Since you're in law enforcement, I was hoping you could run him through the computer for me."

"I can do that. One of your people could do it in Key West just as well, though."

"We're a smaller town than New Orleans, Dave. I'm trying to avoid publicity."

"Got you. Anything else I should know?"

"You ever hear of Tay-Sachs disease, Dave?"

"Sure. It's rare, but we happen to be in a part of the country that's got a higher incidence of it. Nasty business. Any connection?"

"I'm not sure, but I'd like some medical background on Emerson just in case."

Robicheaux laughs. "You don't want much, do you, Gideon?"

"You big-city fellas have resources unavailable down here at the end of the road."

"Sure, Gideon. Give me a day or two and I'll get back to you."

"Thanks, Dave."

"Nothing. I'm sure you'd do the same for me."

"You know it, Dave. Anytime."

After giving Robicheaux my phone number, I

hang up, trying to think of any other leads I might follow. None come immediately to mind, so I decide to wait and see what comes back from Will Seton and Dave in New Orleans and head out to lunch.

October ushers in a different light, softer, less hazy than the hard glare from the summer sun that we have endured for so many months. Even though the weather is still hot, it carries with it a promise of relief. I can sense a change of moods. A kind of carelessness seems to have overtaken people. At the drugstore, where I sit at the counter, the banter is more relaxed, free from the edginess of summer.

When I return home, I see Pop standing in the doorway of the *groceria*. He has taken off the white apron that he wears constantly when he's working. He holds up a hand when he sees me. "Bud, can I talk to you?" he calls from the doorway.

"Sure, Pop, I'll come over."

"No, no. I come to you. Wait a moment."

He darts back into the store and returns a second later, practically running down the steps over to my place. I open the front door and let him in. He is obviously agitated.

"What's wrong, Pop?"

"Some guy come into the store and tell me I make a deal, I got to stick to deal. He got a contract for me to sign, the same one I tell you about the other day, Bud."

"You decided you weren't going to sell at that price, didn't you, after Frank Pappagallo talked to you?"

Pop nods his head. "The guy say I got to—"

"Wait a minute, Pop. What guy?"

"I don't know. I never see him before."

We are standing in the middle of my office. I put my hand on Pop's shoulder. "You didn't sign anything before you talked to me the other day, did you?"

"I don't think so."

"Then you don't have to worry. You're not obligated even if you made a verbal commitment."

"That's not what the guy says."

"Forget about him. He was just trying to scare you into signing that contract. Now, listen, Pop. I'm going to call my attorney and Fred Pacey for you. They can't pressure you like this. Who's running the store?"

"Orlando."

"Why don't you take some time off? Tell Orlando if this guy comes back to call me. I'll be around the rest of the afternoon. If he comes back when you're in the store, you call me. Okay?"

Pop nods. He must be seventy-five years old, and at the moment he looks every minute of it. "Don't worry. You want to sell, you sell on your terms, Pop."

He leaves. I sit down at the phone and try to reach Pacey. He is either not in, or not taking my call. I try Frank. "I'm telling you, Frank," I say when he answers, "I don't want Pop pressured. Pacey's already started. I tried to reach him, but he's not available. Tell him, Frank. Those tactics aren't going to work."

"Bud, I told you. There's nothing I can do. I'm out of this."

"You're the messenger, remember? So just deliver the message. And tell Pacey I'm taking a personal interest in this situation. Got me, Frank?"

"Sure, Bud," Frank says lamely. And sighs.

The rest of the afternoon I spend doing odd jobs around the house. At four I take a break and go across to the *groceria.* I'm pleased to see that Pop has apparently taken my advice; he's nowhere in sight. Orlando is working the coffee machine. He is a much younger version of his father. "Any more unwanted patrons?" I ask Orlando.

"Nothing. Mom and Dad went home. Me and my sister are taking over."

I give Orlando the thumbs up, take a hit of the cold ginger ale, leave a dollar on the counter, and go back home.

14

◇

Fred Pacey came to Key West on a millionaire's yacht when he was twenty years old. The millionaire, an attorney and Washington insider during the Nixon era, was, we later learned, gay. At a time when we were on the verge of losing the last shreds of provincialism, for some in town the homosexual was still a matter of curiosity and, sadly, too often animosity. Pacey was part of the all-male crew in the millionaire's flight from Washington when Nixon resigned. Whether Pacey was anything more than simply a crew member, I do not know. But what I do know is he did manage to borrow enough money from his benefactor to get a start in Key West at a time when Duval Street, three blocks beyond the waterfront, was little more than a shuttered ghost town.

Perhaps Pacey had a vision of Key West. If so, it could, at least in hindsight, be described in one word: familiarity. In Pacey's Key West there would be no surprises. Nothing, other than the weather, that could cloud or dampen the family vacation. Key West had theme-park potential written all over it. Any threat of chaos or unruliness would be replaced by order found in the world of retail outlets, where Pacey's image of a past Key West could be marketed and sold. Slogans on T-shirts, porcelain, and plastic, caricatures and cute drawings on scraps of driftwood, would replace the real thing.

I have always preferred to give Pacey the benefit of the doubt and to think that there was no vision, that in the early days he simply began a process over which he had little control, a hit-and-miss proposition that began with borrowed money and ended in bad taste and the homogenization of a community.

Whatever the case, in 1974 Pacey purchased a couple of buildings in the 700 block of Duval, where hardly anyone except locals ventured after dark. Three businesses existed there then: a down-and-out bar, a termite-infested flophouse, and a used-car lot, which did not have a vehicle on it worth more than a hundred dollars.

Undeterred, Pacey renovated the two buildings himself, creating a modest restaurant and guesthouse that offered an alternative to the higher priced joints downtown. He went before the city fathers, begged for some decent street lighting, called up a volunteer brigade to slap some paint on the crumbling structures that remained shuttered, and slowly began the restoration process of midtown.

Ten years after he first arrived, he owned most of the block. With the acquisition of real estate also came a reputation. He was a relentless landlord who would sacrifice any tenant whose business did not immediately flourish for one that he hoped would attract more tourists. Eventually, there was nothing more than T-shirt shops competing against one another, and Duval Street had become Pacey's creation.

He married a local woman, had a child, branched out into various other business ventures, and was generally successful, although frequently despised by those who worked for him. Yet despite all that, I have never heard charges more serious than greed and bad taste brought against Fred Pacey. Which is not to say that there should not have been. Most likely Pacey has just been good at covering his tracks.

For reasons that do not make sense, it now seems that he may have lost that ability.

Over the next couple of days, Pop tells me that the pressure has been reduced to a couple of phone calls a day in which someone tries to persuade him to change his mind. Pop tells me that he has thought about it and has decided to stick to his price. If they want to pay what the place is worth, he will sell. Otherwise, he has a good business that is supporting three families; why give it away?

A kind of jauntiness has come over Pop. He seems rejuvenated by the process of negotiating, and no longer threatened.

"Congratulations, hang in there," I tell him. "You can't lose."

He smiles when Mom comes out from the kitchen and takes my hand. "Thank you, Bud," she tells me, tears misting her eyes. "A true amigo."

I hope that is the case. A certain motive for self-preservation, part of a reluctance to give up the habits and traditions of thirty-odd years, I know, contributes to my desire to see the *groceria* remain where it is. A kind of last-ditch fortification against a tide that has not only turned but engulfed almost everything else around us.

Is it pride? Am I so opposed to everything that Fred Pacey stands for that I have chosen to draw a line in the sand, to be a last holdout, and convinced my neighbor to join me in a battle that I know we are doomed to lose? I cannot say. My belief is that Pop should be paid what his place is worth and not be cheated. Beyond that, it seems pointless to consider.

Late in the evening of the second day after I have phoned him, Dave Robicheaux calls from New Orleans.

"That was quick work," I tell him.

"An easy bit of gumshoeing, and no one shot at me," he replies, his rich Cajun accent peppered with laughter.

"What have you got?"

"Roy Faulkner Emerson was born in St. Catherine's Hospital on the date you gave me. There are no records of any run-ins with the law or indications that he is a carrier of Tay-Sachs disease."

Gaby, I think, will be pleased.

"I went a step further and called the National Institute of Health," Dave continues. "They keep extensive records of this sort of thing. Nothing on Emerson."

"Good work, Dave. I appreciate it."

"Of course, you understand you can't rule him out one hundred percent. There is always a chance someone could slip through the net."

"I understand."

"The guy could just have a simple blood test and be done with it."

"I know that. He's refused. Got a thing about doctors."

"One of those. Well, good luck, Gideon."

"Thanks again, Dave. I owe you one."

"I'll collect some day. So long."

15

◇

"I'm feeling a little guilty," Gaby says.

It is going on midnight. I had called her earlier and told her to call me when she had a chance, no matter how late. I can picture her now, seated at the wine bar in the entrance to the Blue Moon, staring out the window onto Duval Street, just as I am sitting behind my desk staring out at the same street a few blocks away. As we talk, I hear her taking sips of wine, trying to wind down from another hectic night.

"I wondered when that would set in," I reply, having just conveyed to her the information I received today from Dave Robicheaux in New Orleans.

"You thought it was wrong, spying on Roy this way, didn't you, Bud?"

I think about it for a moment, enjoying this time with her, late at night on the phone, something that we often did in the old days. "Let's just say I thought it could lead to complications. I'm glad it didn't."

"So I guess this means I can go on with my life, my plans." There is a change in her tone, a distance, as if she were talking from halfway round the world rather than five minutes away.

"It's a very rare disease, Gaby."

"I have it. At least the potential to pass it along to any children I might have."

"Without a blood test there is no guarantee, not a hundred percent, but the odds—" I repeat what Robicheaux told me.

"I know what the odds are. Negligible. What would you do now, Bud? Tell me."

I would wave good-bye to Roy Faulkner Emerson, I want to say. Brush him off like a mosquito. But I do not, cannot, say that. "I can't tell you—"

"Bud, please spare me." She sounds angry.

"All right. I would insist that he get a blood test. Make it a condition of marriage."

"And if he still refuses?"

"Then you have to make a choice."

Outside a car goes by, its radio tuned to an all-night jazz station. Moments later I can hear the same tune as the car passes in front of the Blue Moon.

"You're right," Gaby says. "I know. I'll tell him tomorrow."

I feel a kind of elation, as if I have won a victory even though it is meaningless, without a trophy. "Good luck."

Gaby stifles a yawn. "I'd better get up the road. Thanks for your help, Bud. What do I owe you?"

"Nothing. I just made a couple of phone calls. Someone else did the work."

"Well, at least let me buy you dinner. Why don't you come in tomorrow night? Maybe I can take an hour and we could eat together."

"That would be nice."

Once we hang up, I am restless, feeling some

tension in the air. I remain for a time at my desk, then wander out into the kitchen and drink a glass of water. After playing the piano in the bedroom for a while, I stretch out on the bed and try to read. Then get up and pace.

Finally, at one o'clock, I go to bed and lie in the dark with my eyes open before drifting into a light sleep with consciousness lurking somewhere nearby. Images I cannot quite grasp seem to float just beyond my eyes. Coupled with strange sounds and sensations. I wake, then ease back into a dream.

In the club at the piano, it is crowded. And smoky. Appropriately, I am playing "Smoke Gets in Your Eyes." Gaby is there with someone I do not recognize. She is angry, either with me or the person she is with. She screams while I pound away at the keyboard, trying to overpower her, before I realize that she is not screaming at all, but singing.

I wake up. The room is dark, darker than usual. Fog seems to crawl across my vision. Not fog. Smoke. I struggle up, still gripped by the dream and sleep, and rush into the kitchen, where I throw open the back door just as a small explosion erupts in the *groceria* next door and flames leap from a hole in the roof, lighting up the night sky.

For precious seconds I am mesmerized by the lascivious flame, like lightning tongues licking against the darkness. The noise of the fire itself is surprisingly loud, and just beyond the roar, I can hear the more delicate crackling sound of old, dry timber as it feeds the hungry blaze. And then there is the smell, a combination of charcoal and burnt coffee, which, more than anything else, propels me back inside and into my office, where I dial 911, watching as the insidious smoke creeps inside.

The stream of water from my garden hose attached to a spigot at the back of the house is useless against this conflagration that grows, like some huge ancient beast, feeding on itself. All I can do is spray water on the roof and sides of my place, wetting everything down, hoping to delay the inevitable, while ash and glowing embers rain down on me like sparks from a Fourth of July celebration.

The scream of sirens barely pierces the noise of the fire. But soon there is a cascade of water pouring into the *groceria* and over the roofs of the adjacent buildings, including my own, as I stand drenched in the backyard, wearing only the boxer shorts I was sleeping in, still spraying water from the garden hose.

Firemen in heavy lime-colored helmets and jackets and black rubber boots begin swarming everywhere, some trailing hoses, others carrying axes. One of them approaches me. "Is anybody in there, Bud?"

I do not recognize him. "I don't think so. No one lives there." I realize I do not even know what time it is.

"Everybody out of your place?"

I nod, thinking about my cat, half-blind Tom, and wonder if he's okay.

As the fire begins to abate, the smoke increases, thick, dark clouds of it roiling up like thunderheads against a summer sky.

16

◇

It is five o'clock in the morning. Almost three hours have elapsed since I called 911. Although my place is untouched by the fire, when I go inside to find a pair of khakis and a shirt, everything is wet and smells of smoke and burnt wood. The electricity is off. Locating a flashlight, I make a quick search through the house to look for the cat. He is in none of his familiar places.

Outside, fire and police personnel fill the block, their vehicle lights still flashing, the great canvas hoses snaking across the street and sidewalks, while one lone fireman continues to douse the ruined *groceria,* presumably to prevent flareups, even though the inferno has been contained. The crowd, held back by a roadblock on either end of the street, begins to diminish as the firemen start the clearing-up process.

I am standing in the street when I see Pop hurrying up Duval. He has the look of a man who has witnessed Armaggedon. Standing beside me, he cannot take his eyes off the charred shell of the *groceria.*

I put my arm across his narrow shoulders. His face is gaunt, the white whiskers brittle in the flashing colored lights.

"What happen, Bud?" he asks in a tired, thin voice, without looking at me.

"I don't know, Pop. I was asleep. The smell of smoke woke me. When I went outside, I saw the roof explode."

Pop's jaw clenches. He lifts his hand and looks up at the dark sky. As if he could find some answer there, or accuse God. "Who did this?"

Until now it is a question that no one has bothered to ask. Was it an accident or arson? With the cleanup beginning, however, an investigation should follow. In fact, as Pop and I stand here, helpless, the question hanging between us, the fire chief walks our way, the tops of his black boots rolled down below his knees, his heavy jacket hanging open.

"Bud, what a bitch. It could have been worse, though. Five minutes later and we would have lost a couple more buildings." His face is streaked with sweat and grime. "Pop, I'm sorry. We did the best we could."

Pop does not, or perhaps cannot, speak. Over the years the chief must have had as many cups of *con leche* in Pop's place as I have. The loss of the *groceria* is the loss of a landmark.

"I understand that you called in the alarm, Bud. What happened?"

I repeat what I have just told Pop.

"You weren't aware of anything suspicious before you went to bed?"

I think back on my conversation with Gaby, then the hour or so I remained up before turning in. "Nothing," I tell him, shaking my head.

"Pop, everything okay when you closed up?"

Pop nods.

"Any electrical problems you're aware of?"

"No. I unplug everything except the coolers before I go home at night. The inspector come six months ago. Everything is good."

Someone calls the chief's name. He turns, then looks at his watch. "It'll be light in an hour. We'll start our investigation then," he says. Then walks away.

Pop and I remain fixed, watching as the firemen begin winding the big hoses back onto the trucks.

"Bud, you think this fire start because I don't sell?"

Sooner or later it has to be asked. The question of a reason for arson has been in the back of my mind, one I would rather have waited to deal with once the sun was up, the street cleaned up, and, beyond the remains of Pop's charred business, life on the block returned, as much as humanly possible, to normal. I want the chief to find evidence of a couple of crack addicts getting high behind the *groceria,* or even some faulty wiring. Anything but evidence of deliberate arson, which for both Pop and me will point in one direction. Fred Pacey. And at that time I will have to begin to live with blame, taking responsibility for interfering in Pop's decision not to sell. I am not yet ready to face that prospect.

"We don't know if it's arson yet," I tell him. "Let's see what their investigation turns up."

Pop does not say anything, but I can tell from the set of his jaw that his mind is already made up.

Dawn is breaking when I reenter my home to take stock of the damage. Which seems to be nothing that a major cleanup and paint job will not repair. But that, in itself, is a daunting task, knowing that it will be months before I am even rid of the smell of smoke. I begin to pick up soggy bits of paper and wipe a mop over the floors, leaving the doors and windows open.

At seven-thirty I give up and go to the drugstore for breakfast. People glance up when I enter, their expressions no doubt mirroring my own. Every conversation is concerned with the fire.

"Bud," one of the waitresses says. "I hear they saved your place."

"I got lucky, Mary."

She puts some coffee in front of me. I am on my second cup when Frank Pappagallo shows up, taking a seat at the counter on the stool next to mine.

"Bud, thank God you were spared."

I look at him in such a way as to let him know that the irony of his choice of words is not lost on me.

"Bud—"

"I'm not in the mood to talk about it right now, Frank."

"You got insurance, though?"

I nod. The next thing on my agenda will be to call my agent.

"Bud, you need help, a place to stay until yours is cleaned up. We've got a spare room with your own bath. Beth and I'd be honored—"

"Thanks, Frank. That won't be necessary." Until now, I have not thought that far ahead, although it does seem unlikely that I will want to stay in my place for the next few nights. The strain of sitting here now is too much, remembering Frank's warning earlier in the week. Rather than say something I may regret, I take a few more bites of food but leave without finishing my breakfast.

17

◇

The morning is filled with insurance agents, a team of fire investigators, and gawkers. The block is now open to a steady stream of the curious, who parade around outside, staring at the ruins. I answer the investigators' questions and sign papers while at the same time I try to reestablish some order. From time to time I look out a window and see Pop and his family trailing through the debris like scavengers.

Shortly before noon, Gaby appears. She comes in the open front door and without speaking puts her arms around me. We stand like that for several seconds, the fragrant scent of her hair and skin mixing with the smell of cold burnt wood and smoke that now seems so much a part of me.

"Bud, I am so sorry." Gaby steps back, taking hold of my hand while she looks around the office. "This is awful. What happened?"

As we walk through the house and out the back door to look at the *groceria,* I repeat what has become a litany for me now. When she sees the charred shell of Pop's place, Gaby's hand goes to her mouth. She takes a deep breath, then asks what everyone wants to know, "Why?"

I shake my head. "No one knows yet. Or if they do, they aren't telling me."

Gaby seems to want to flee from the sight, and I follow her back inside. She is wearing shorts, a T-shirt, and sneakers. I have mopped up the kitchen, and we sit down at the table. "What are you going to do, Bud?"

I shrug. "Fix the place up and go on with my life. What can I do?"

"I mean immediately. Are you going to do the repairs yourself? Do you have insurance?"

I nod.

"Why don't you hire someone, then? Get out of here for a while until it is back to normal."

"Where would I get to, Gaby? My life's right here in these rooms."

She taps the table with her fingertips. "I thought about it on the way in this morning, after I heard the news. Bud, I've got a spare room. You're welcome to it for as long as it takes to get your own life back to normal."

"That's sweet of you. But I couldn't."

"Why not?"

"I wouldn't be comfortable with strangers working here when I wasn't around."

"You could come in during the day and be here."

It sounds tempting, certainly more appealing than staying with Frank. And I have been thinking of getting a room someplace for a few days. "I wonder how Roy would feel about that?"

"It doesn't matter. Besides I'm gone much of the time and you would be alone."

"I'll think about it, Gaby."

"Do." She stands up. "Now, what about dinner tonight? We have a date, don't we?"

"Sure."

"Good. And if you decide to stay, I'll give you the key and you can drive up afterwards."

"You're an angel, Gaby."

"Hardly. Now, I must run."

When she has gone, I sit down at the phone and call a couple of old-timers I know, guys who have basically retired from the building trades but who will do some odd jobs, part-time work occasionally. I find Gaby's suggestion that I get someone to do the renovations appealing. After the fire and a nearly sleepless night, I am tired, depressed, and not exactly drawn to tackle this project myself. It would do me good, I reason, to get away from here for a while. Bill, one of the guys I call, is available and says he could start whenever I want him. He will drop by this afternoon, he tells me, to assess what has to be done.

Before going to lunch, I gather up several changes of clothes to take to the drop-off laundry, realizing I have made my decision to take Gaby up on her offer. On my way out I see Pop standing in front of his place.

"Any word yet?" I ask him.

He shakes his head. "They won't tell me nothin', Bud. I don't know."

"I'll call the chief this afternoon." Again, I feel a stab of guilt, wanting to do something to help Pop get through this. "I've got someone coming over later to look at making repairs. You want, I can have him take a look at your place, too."

Pop shakes his head again. He seems despondent. I would like to draw him out, let him talk, but I do not know where to begin. "What about insurance?" I ask lamely.

"Some. Probably not enough."

He looks up at me then, his dark brown eyes liquid, staring. Hopefully it is only my imagination, but, I think, perhaps even accusatory. I start to walk away with my laundry.

"Bud."

I turn back. "What is it, Pop?"

"They call me again."

I do not have to ask who, merely wait. I know what is coming.

"They make an offer."

"What kind of an offer?"

"No good. Below even the first one."

Damn it! What have I done? It is time to talk to Fred Pacey.

18

◇

The Blue Moon is crowded when I arrive for dinner at eight-thirty. There is the clatter and clink of silver and glasses above the rhythmic hum of conversation when Gaby greets me at the door with a kiss on the cheek, then leads me to a table for two in the rear. "Someone else is going to take over the hostessing for the rest of the evening," she says with a smile. "Just give me a minute and then I'll join you." She hands me a menu. "By the way, I recommend one of the specials tonight. Citrus planked salmon with mango mustard glaze, cucumber-and-onion salad with black squid rice." Gaby winks and hurries away.

She knows that I am and will always be a meat-and-potatoes kind of guy. After looking over the menu with the planked salmon and dolphin coated in plantain with a tamarind tartar sauce, I decide on the grilled skirt steak, content knowing that Gaby will understand and that I am going to get a lesson in, as well as a taste of, the other items, too.

When she returns to the table with an uncorked bottle of wine and is seated, we toast. "To your future," she says, clinking her wineglass against my glass of water. "And yours," I reply.

"What did you decide about my suggestion?"

"I'm going to take you up on it. I've got a bag with a couple of changes of clothes in the car outside." In fact, though the clothes are clean, I can still smell the residue of smoke on them, and myself.

Smiling, Gaby lifts her glass again. "I didn't think you would do it."

"I didn't think I would, either."

"I told Roy that I'd offered the invitation."

"How did he take it?"

"Remarkably well. I think he's a little shame-faced about the way he acted the other day and with what happened to him. Anyway, he's gotten very busy and won't be around much."

I nod, not at all disappointed with that news. "I also hired someone to come and do the repairs. I'll be spending most days in town, though."

"Bud, please feel free to come and go as you wish. For as long as you need it, my place is yours."

"You're very generous."

"We're old friends. You'd do the same for me."

I nod, remembering with some pleasure that at one time we were more than old friends. Gaby, perhaps aware of the drift of my thoughts, changes the subject. "What about the fire, Bud? Have you heard anything?"

"I called the chief this afternoon. He says they won't release any information until the investigation is concluded."

Gaby leans across the table. "Rumors are going around that it was set deliberately."

"Why?"

"Some developer wants to put a mall in there. They're trying to get the property cheap."

I nod. In Key West it does not take long for rumors to fly. I am not surprised to hear this, but what does surprise me is that Fred Pacey's name is not mentioned. "Anything's possible," I respond noncommittally.

"Isn't that why Frank Pappagallo brought you to dinner here the other night, Bud? To try to talk you into selling your place."

"It was mentioned."

"Bud, you could have died in that fire."

A thought that has never been long out of my mind. I have not told Gaby that it was not only the smoke but a dream of her that woke me last night. Somehow it seems like too intimate a revelation to make to her, especially in my present circumstance as her houseguest.

"What do you think I should do?"

"I don't know. Do you really want to go on living on Duval Street? It's only going to get worse."

I look at her questioningly.

"I mean the development," she says. "This street's really no longer a place to live, is it?"

"Maybe you're right."

We order dinner, and then Gaby tells me about her wedding plans. Now that Roy has agreed to the blood test, she has decided to step up their plans, which Roy has wanted to do all along. Any lingering doubts she might have had seem to have been replaced with excitement. A new venture. A new life.

When the food begins to arrive, Gaby, true to form, tells me all about it, insisting that I taste each and every item. Halfway through the steak, however, I feel myself beginning to fade.

"Bud, you must be exhausted."

I have to admit that I could use a good night's sleep.

Gaby tells me where she has hidden a spare key to the house, and after finishing the meal, I set off up the Keys, while Gaby stays behind to close up.

The fresh air coming in through the Buick's open windows feels good; for the moment at least, the smell of smoke is absent. Twenty minutes later I am in the spare room, where Gaby has made up the bed. Unlike last night I have no trouble falling asleep.

19

◇

During the next couple of days Gaby and I seldom see one another, and when we do, it is only in passing. I spend the days in Key West overseeing the repairs, and the evenings at Gaby's, where, in peace and quiet, I can consider my options and make a decision about whether or not to put my house on the market.

Late in the afternoon of the third day, when I have lingered longer than I expected, long after the carpenter has left, the phone rings. It is Will Seton at the state attorney's.

"Bud, glad to catch you. Sorry to hear about the fire. I didn't know if you'd be living there or not."

"I'm in and out a lot. What's up?"

"That matter you asked me to look into?"

In all the confusion I have forgotten my call to Will. Or at least put it out of my mind now that Gaby seems satisfied with Roy's medical background, leaving nothing more to pursue.

"Everything's pretty much been resolved there," I say.

"Oh?"

"My client's concerns have been answered, Will. I appreciate your effort. I hope I didn't put you to too much trouble."

"Bud, you might want to call the investigator with the DA's office in Jackson Hole."

Some nerve ending tweaks just behind my eyes. "What's it about, Will?"

"I didn't get all the details, but I told him you might call. I vouched for you, and he'll be glad to fill you in. In fact, I think he wants to talk to you."

"How about giving me a clue?"

"Probably better you talk to him directly, Bud," Seton replies. "The guy's name is Don Cameron. I've got his number right here."

I write it down.

"He's expecting you to call."

"Thanks, Will. It sounds ominous."

"I don't know what you're after here, Bud. It's none of my business, but if you've got a client who is interested in Emerson, I would make that phone call."

We hang up. I sit there amidst the sawdust, stacks of lumber needed to repair siding that has sustained more than smoke damage, paint cans, and carpenter's tools. The fading smell of smoke is gradually being replaced by paint thinner. I feel unsettled. I have done what Gaby asked me to do. I should call her, I suppose, and tell her about Will Seton's suggestion before I do anything. It is her decision. But Gaby has already confessed that she feels guilty just going as far as she did in spying on Roy. If I do anything, I think, I am going to have to do it on my own.

As a friend, I owe it to Gaby to protect her. But reaching for the phone to dial the number Will has given me, I have a sense of foreboding, of stepping into uncharted waters where I risk losing everything.

Relieved when there is no answer in Jackson Hole and an answering machine comes on, I hang up without leaving a message.

Driving back up the Keys to Gaby's, I try to put it out of mind. It is possible to rationalize that everyone has something in his past that he would just as soon have forgotten. Without cause it is none of my business to go prying into Roy Emerson's life. It is Gaby's business. But because of her, I know that tomorrow I will again try to make that call.

When I turn into the drive, I am surprised to see both Gaby's car and Roy's. For an instant I think of turning around and heading back into Key West, but it is too late now, anyway, because Roy is standing on the porch, waving when I pull up.

"Bud, come on up. Have a drink. It's Gabe's day off, and we thought we'd surprise you with dinner."

Roy's rangy body presses against the porch rail while he stands grinning down at me. He looks somewhat mischievous, no dark glasses, the corners of his mouth curl upward, reminding me of a dog's expression as the animal waits for its food to be put down. Ready to devour. Gaby comes out on the porch and Roy sweeps her up against him in one arm. She laughs. "Hi, Bud."

I climb the stairs to the deck, feeling like an intruder. Roy offers his hand, and I take it, expecting a wisecrack that fortunately does not come.

"Roy got freed up unexpectedly," Gaby says. "I thought we would go out, but he insisted we cook here. You don't have plans, do you, Bud?"

"No. I'll wash up and join you."

In my room, I strip off my T-shirt, shave in the

adjoining bathroom, wash under my armpits, and put on a clean shirt before going into the kitchen, where Roy and Gaby are preparing dinner.

"What about that drink now?" Roy says.

"Bud doesn't drink," Gaby intercedes.

"Oh." Roy seems disappointed. "Well, something?"

"Some club soda. I'll get it." It is one of those moments when the desire for alcohol is overpowering.

"Bud, I haven't really seen you. You doing okay out here? Anything you need?"

"Gabe told me about the fire," Roy chimes in. "What a bummer."

"The place is shaping up," I say. "Another couple of days and I should be able to get back in."

"You don't have to rush it, Bud." Gaby is tearing lettuce leaves into a salad bowl while Roy prepares some steaks for grilling.

"I'm not rushing, but I do have to get back to work."

"What are you working on?" Roy asks.

Taking a hit of club soda, I watch him. He is different from the last time I saw him. More congenial. Less combative. But I sense that he is trying, working at it. And, of course, hiding something. "Nothing of any interest," I say. "Mostly just paperwork."

Gaby glances quickly in my direction.

"I thought detective work was supposed to be exciting," Roy says.

"In books maybe."

Roy carries the plate of steaks outside to the grill.

"See?" Gaby whispers to me. "He's not such a bad guy."

Over dinner they talk about their wedding plans, and Roy quizzes me about music. His knowledge of jazz is good, and we spend the rest of the meal talking about musicians. Something I would not have expected, and I am surprised. He suddenly seems more human, not a bad guy at all. Tomorrow I will find out for sure when I call Don Cameron in Wyoming.

20

◇

His wife was killed in an accident out here about five years ago," Don Cameron says from Jackson Hole, Wyoming, where I reach him the following day around noon Key West time.

"What happened?"

"No one's quite sure." Cameron's voice is without inflection, a monotonous recitation as though he were reading from a long text, anxious to get to the end. "They were hiking in the Tetons on the Idaho side in an area called the Devil's Staircase. It's a steep, rocky climb, most of it right out in the open. It was late summer, and a thunderstorm came up fairly suddenly, something that happens a lot around here. Karen—that was Emerson's wife's name—she was standing out on the edge of a rocky pinnacle near the top when lightning struck about ten feet from her. Something happened. The ground shifted, a little rockslide or something; anyway she lost her footing and fell. Tumbled about a thousand feet, bouncing off rocks, to her death at the bottom."

The only time I was ever in the mountains, or saw snow, was the two-year stint I did with the marines in Korea back in the fifties. Since then I have seldom left Key West. I am a waterman, only comfortable when I am near the sea. Just listening to Cameron describe this situation sends a chill through my body. I have heard of the Tetons, seen pictures of them, snowcapped and with meadows of wildflowers, but just imagining someone actually climbing there fills me with apprehension.

"What about Roy?"

"Well, he claims he was still climbing when it happened. That he was about a hundred yards behind her. Karen was raised around here. She was an expert climber and she knew these mountains like the back of her hand."

"You don't believe him."

"Karen's family didn't believe him. They're ranchers. They own a lot of land around here and they carry some hefty influence. They insisted on an autopsy. As you can imagine, her body was pretty battered from the fall. The autopsy was inconclusive, but there was the possibility that some of those bruises came before she fell."

"Meaning, you think she was pushed."

"I don't think anything. I was hired to investigate. There wasn't enough evidence to bring charges against Emerson, so the family hired me to dig into it. Understand, we're going back five years, now."

"Find anything?"

"Nothing substantive. Plenty that was circumstantial."

"You still on the family payroll?"

"It's a matter now of kind of keeping tabs on Emerson. He left here about a year after the accident. And began moving around a lot. Until eighteen months ago I was able to keep up with him, then he disappeared."

"About the time he showed up here."

"That's what I gather. I was grateful to hear from the SA down there. Is Roy in some trouble?"

"I'm not sure," I say. "His fiancée asked me to do a check on him."

"Fiancée, huh? Well, I'm glad to see he's following his usual pattern. Is she rich?"

Gaby, I assume, is well off. Rich is another category. "Comfortable, I would say."

"What with the life insurance policy and all, Roy inherited close to two hundred grand from Karen."

"Well, he was married to her."

"For six months."

"That isn't a lot of money these days."

"Precisely." Cameron lets his response hang.

Gaby's decision to speed up their wedding date was Roy's idea, I remember. "You mentioned other circumstantial evidence."

"Another accident. This one a drowning. Only he didn't marry her. They were engaged, though. Roy borrowed a bundle for a deal he told her he was working on. They were alone, a picnic near some isolated lake. She went swimming, the water was cold, she got cramped up, and before he could get to her, she was gone."

"In the Tetons?"

"No, this was in Idaho over near Sun Valley. He seems to like resort areas."

"And no inquest?"

"The woman had no close family. The inquest showed the cause of death to be drowning."

I try to imagine how I will approach this with Gaby. She knows about the wife who died, but I wonder how many of the details she knows, exactly what Roy has told her. Gaby would probably laugh at what Cameron has given me. "What's your continued interest in this?" I ask Cameron.

"I told you. Karen's family is paying me. They think he's going to strike again and that sooner or later he'll mess up. They may not be able to pin him for their daughter's death, but they damn sure want to get him. I can tell you they weren't happy that I'd lost his trail."

"I'm not sure what I can do. For personal reasons, I'm going to have a hard time taking this to my client and getting her to believe it. She's in love with him. And she's already feeling bad about spying on him to the point I already have."

"You're in a tough spot."

"What would you do?"

Cameron hesitates for the first time. I can hear what sounds like a match being struck, Cameron inhaling smoke from a cigarette. Finally, he says, "If I was in your boots, I'd make a trip out here. There's people you can talk to who can put all this in perspective rather than me just summarizing it for you on the phone. It would at least give you a feel for the situation, maybe make it easier to decide how to handle it from your end. Me, I don't think there's any doubt. Emerson's going to hit again. Just a question of time. I guess you've got to figure out your responsibility to your client before that happens."

Gaby. I picture her out there, alone in that house, remote. See her walking up from her beehives, smiling, telling me all about how bees mate, the queen leading the drones on a suicide mission. Gaby's something special. Not just a client.

"You decide to fly in here," Cameron says, "let me know. I'd be glad to meet you. Get you pointed in the right direction."

21

◇

While Bill the carpenter bangs and saws in the next room, where he is replacing the damaged paneling, I sit at my desk, stunned. It is difficult enough in this business to deal with the plight of strangers, but when someone like Gaby, someone I know and love, is threatened, the emotional toll is higher. Especially under these circumstances.

After talking to Don Cameron, I am left to pick my way through a course of action. It is clear that I can say nothing about this conversation to Gaby. At least for the moment. Not only would she laugh at me, but by confronting her right now with information like this, it would only call into question her own judgment, which would, in turn, anger her enough to drive a wedge between us. A wedge that would serve only to drive us further apart if she then confronted Roy—whatever the outcome of that confrontation might be.

In order to help Gaby I will need to continue to see her, to get her to confide in me about the time she spends with Roy. To spy on her, in other words. And, I will probably also need to make that trip to Jackson Hole. If for no other reason than to confirm in my own mind that Roy Emerson is indeed the threat to Gaby that Don Cameron imagines him to be.

While I am trying to sort this out, Frank Pappagallo shows up.

"Bud, you busy?"

"Do I look busy?"

"A little spaced-out maybe."

"I was thinking, Frank. You ever try it?"

"I just stopped by to tell you the news, in case you haven't heard."

"I haven't."

"It's unofficial, but the word on the fire is it was arson."

"Why am I not surprised? Any word on who did it?"

Frank shakes his head. "Listen, Bud, I talked to Pacey. He absolutely denies any knowledge of it."

"You didn't expect him to admit to it, did you?"

"It isn't his m.o., Bud. Pacey's a lot of things, but he's not into burning people out."

"I'm sure you know how he works better than I do."

"I hear you put up at Gaby's place for a while."

I nod.

"You met the guy she's marrying?"

I try to keep the interest out of my gaze as I stare at Frank. "Yeah, why?"

"Just curious, Bud. He's working for Pacey, you know."

As a distraction I gather up some paper clips from my desk. "I didn't know that."

"Emerson, that's his name. He's going to close some deals for Pacey, and, so I hear, he's investing some of his own money in the project."

I sweep the paper clips into the top drawer. I wonder if Gaby knows about this. "That's interesting."

"Yeah, I guess it is. Well, I don't want to hold up your thinking. Just dropped in to chat."

"Sure, Frank."

"Any of those thoughts have to do with selling?"

I shoot Frank the evil eye and watch him back toward the door. "Just asking, Bud."

"Don't push me, Frank. It won't work. You'll be the first to know when I make my decision. I don't want you to lose any sleep, or a commission."

Frank waves, and before reaching for the phone, I watch as he scoots up the street in his familiar, slightly disjointed walk.

I catch Gaby at home just as she is about to come into town.

"Everything okay, Bud?"

"I just called to thank you for dinner. And also for the use of your place. I'm going out of town for a while, so I'll be out of your hair now."

"Bud, you're not in my hair. You know that. I've hardly seen you. I told you that you're always welcome here."

I find myself thinking that may not always be the case.

"Wasn't Roy sweet last night? He isn't so bad, now, is he?"

I resist telling her just how bad he may be. "What's he up to these days?"

"He's signed on to some real estate projects that he has hopes for."

"Investing?"

"Roy seems to have a lot of irons in the fire. I can't keep up with all of them. I know he's invested in some things and turned some quick profits. He seems to have a knack for it."

"So financially he's okay?"

"I think so."

I try to laugh. To make a joke of it so that it does not appear that I am prying. "How about you? Are you getting involved in that world?"

Gaby laughs, too, more spontaneously than I do. "I confess," she says. "I've gotten the bug, too."

I cannot, of course, ask her how much she has invested and if she has simply given money to Roy to handle for her. "I hope you're doing well."

"So far, so good."

I want to tell her to be careful, to instill some sense of danger, but I know at this point it would be useless. And so I rely on platitudes, and then wish her luck.

"Dud, it's unlike you to leave Key West. How long will you be gone?"

"I'm not sure. Not long I hope. I'm working on a case, so it's hard to say."

Thankfully, Gaby does not ask where I am going and I am spared lying to her. When we hang up, I feel leaden, weighted to my chair, knowing that I am not looking forward to this, neither the flying, which I have a dread of, nor what awaits me at the other end of the country.

22

◇

The flight west is full of perils. Financial. Emotional. And not the least, physical.

On such short notice it has cost a small fortune for a round-trip ticket to Jackson Hole, Wyoming. Without a client, the expenses of this trip, of course, are all on me. Why am I doing it? To help an old friend, sure. But it is more than that. Not only do I want to protect Gaby, I also want her not to marry Roy Emerson. I know that now. Regardless of what I find out about him in Wyoming, whether he is a murderer or simply a cad, I am convinced that he is wrong for her, and I have taken it on myself to prove it. Why? Not for the first time it occurs to me that I might be in love with Gaby myself.

In the years since we were together, she has matured. The girl is gone and the woman who has replaced her is more absorbing, even more provocative. The little time we have spent together recently has produced an awkward response in me, sparking a desire that I am sure, whatever the consequences of this trip, will not be reciprocated. Nevertheless, I am determined to proceed.

Some thirty thousand feet beneath this hollow

aluminum tube in which I have placed myself, I see the terrain below unfold like a slowly riffled deck of cards. The color, the texture and topography, all so foreign and remote. Once we have left the sea behind, I am, in a sense, at sea—baffled by the hills and gray wooded thickets that eventually distend into flatness and evenly marked plots of tilled earth, brown and barren, punctuated occasionally by ribbons of highway, a town, or a lone river coursing like thread, weaving the jumbled continent together like some haphazard suture sewn by a drunken doctor.

A baby cries. Someone in the row behind me sneezes. Behind the steady drone of the engines and my blocked ears, sound is strangely muted. A bank of video monitors suspended from the ceiling plays out a soundless movie while the flight attendants ply the aisle performing their strictly regimented acts of hospitality. Flying is no fun. People packed together randomly in a pressurized tin for the purpose of getting from A to B, some working on laptop computers, others reading newspapers or doing puzzles, asleep or chatting with strangers who will quickly be forgotten the moment we depart this unnatural environment.

We are chasing the sun, crossing time zones as the light outside grows brighter. At three o'clock we are scheduled to land in Denver, where I have a two-hour layover before catching my flight to Jackson Hole.

An early, unseasonal snowstorm has blanketed the Mile-High City, the pilot announces over the intercom from the cockpit. And indeed, as we cross into Rocky Mountain time somewhere over western Kansas, the world outside the plane turns gray and menacing. Thin gray clouds prevent my first view of the mountains we are approaching.

The fasten-seat-belt light comes on overhead at the same time that a bell sounds on the intercom system, and the pilot returns to announce that we will be experiencing some turbulence. Five minutes later the aircraft begins to buck, buffeted by downdrafts, unseen forces of nature, and all I can think of is that there is no visibility as we hurtle toward those high mountain ranges. Every creak and groan and change in the pitch of the engine seems to signal doom. Even the movements of the flight attendants, as they scurry back and forth picking up refuse and locking up tray tables, suggest trouble. As more babies begin to howl, the situation in Key West that has put me on this flight seems minimized, and I begin to think that I have been too impetuous. I would like a drink.

The video monitors suddenly go blank, flickering snow for several moments before being replaced by the image of a smiling, confident attendant who appears to explain the procedure for landing. But in the noise and chaos it is impossible to hear anything she says.

I stare out the window. We are descending. Watching the clouds as we surge through them and adjusting to the change in our flight path angle, I feel as if we are going faster, out of control, and when the whirring vibration of the landing gear comes on, I am certain we are speeding toward oblivion.

Images begin to appear through the clouds. I can see highways, signs of life, solid ground. We are flying across a valley, punctuated by mountains. The day is gray and dark, and I see snow for the first time in forty years, falling against the yellow-tinted mercury lights along the roads as we drift downward. For the first time in the past half hour I begin to feel that there is a measure of control being exerted over the aircraft.

When the tires thump against the runway, before gripping and settling into the tarmac like giant claws, I exhale as the engines reverse, realizing that I have been holding my breath for the past several seconds. We are down. Safe. And I have two hours to prepare myself for the next leg of this questionable journey.

Once inside the terminal, I stare at another video monitor with departure information, searching for the boarding gate for the flight to Jackson Hole. After finding it, I slide into line at the nearest fast-food joint and wait for ten minutes to get a soft drink.

In less than eight hours I have been transplanted to another world. The casual T-shirt, shorts, and sandals look of Key West has been replaced with coats, suits and ties, and more cowboy boots and Stetsons than I have ever seen outside the movies. There is something in the air, a kind of density that is unfamiliar even at this altitude. Gravity. Or perhaps it is just the grayness and cold that I am so unaccustomed to.

For half an hour I simply sit and stare at the foreignness of it all before finally trudging off on what seems like a two-mile hike to my gate.

23

◇

It is approximately a two-hour flight from Denver to Jackson Hole. I am relieved when, forty-five minutes after takeoff, the clouds disappear and we are flying in blue skies once again. So despite the agony of the previous flight, I feel a certain level of confidence return once I can see what is below us. And that in turn induces sleep, which is broken only by the announcement from the cockpit that we are beginning our descent into Jackson Hole.

As I open my eyes and look out the window, I am stunned. We are flying parallel to and at eye level with the craggy peaks of the Grand Tetons. Compared to the arrival in Denver, this is clear, clean, and majestic. The mountains are so close that I can see individual patches of snow just below the chiseled rock faces sloping away from the peaks. It somehow seems too perfect, postcard perfect.

Once we are down and inside the airport, I see that perfection imitated everywhere. Not only on the postcards that are in racks all over the place, but in the clothing designs and ceramic pottery that fill the gift stores. I am back in familiar territory, the world of tourism, albeit with a western motif.

Standing near the baggage carousel for our flight is a guy holding a cardboard sign with my name on it. He is about six feet tall in cowboy boots and a well-worn Stetson. Except for the droop of his handlebar mustache, his face is expressionless.

"Don," I say. "Gideon Lowry." We shake hands.

"Yeah, I kind of picked you out of the crowd as being from Florida," Don replies. There is something mechanical about Cameron. Maybe because nothing registers in his face when he speaks, and his mouth, hidden behind the mustache, barely moves.

"The tan?" I suggest.

"That, and you look like a detective."

"I didn't know we had a look." I certainly would never have thought of him as a detective.

"Yeah, something in the way you were taking in everything. I could tell. You don't miss much. What have you got in the way of luggage?"

The carousel is revolving now, and I spot my canvas satchel, grabbing it as it comes around. "This is it."

"Travel light," Cameron remarks. "I like that in a man."

I follow him outside to the parking lot where his Jeep Wrangler is parked and toss my bag in the back. The air is crisp, dry, the temperature somewhere in the sixties, I would guess, which for Key West would be quite cold. Here, I am sure, it is nothing. Indian Summer, Cameron tells me as I climb into the passenger seat.

"Must be quite a change for you," Don says once we are on the highway heading into town.

"I grew up in Key West, and I don't travel much. This is all new to me."

"I thought so," Don remarks elliptically. "Same for me. I've been around here all my life. Wouldn't know anything else."

I would guess Cameron to be in his fifties, but it is hard to tell. His face is round, seamless, so much of it hidden beneath the hat and the mustache.

"I've got you booked in a hotel in town. Nothing fancy. You want to change, you're welcome. Figured you'd probably be tired and want to rest tonight. Tomorrow I've got you pretty much booked up."

"That's fine."

Cameron drops me on a side street in front of the hotel in downtown Jackson Hole, telling me he will meet me here at eight o'clock in the morning, then drives off with a laconic half wave.

I stand there for a moment, feeling as if I have been plunked down in a westernized version of Duval Street. The sidewalks are wooden planks, but the shops are the same mix of T-shirts and upscale clothing outlets. Hundreds of people prowl along with cameras around their necks, eating ice cream cones, and gawking. In place of the trains and trolleys clogging the Key West streets, here it is stagecoaches. Tour busses stand at curbside, their rumbling motors spewing forth fumes, ready to gather up sightseers.

The hotel is a two-story frame building that seems not to have been touched by the renovation that has clearly claimed the rest of the town. The lobby is small, with a scuffed hardwood floor and a couple of well-worn Indian rugs around the desk and the sitting area, which consists of an old leather couch, a couple of rocking chairs, and a coffee table holding several magazines. On the walls are some mounted animal heads, deer and elk.

Behind the desk, an elderly woman has me fill out my reservation card, then hands me a key, giving me directions to my room on the second floor.

It is spare, one curtained window overlooking a back alley and the mountains beyond. There is an iron-frame bed, a mirrored dresser with a chair beside it, and, on the wall, a print of a lone cowboy riding off into the setting sun. I drop my bag on the chair and stare out the window.

It is almost nine o'clock by the time I get cleaned up and go out in search of a meal. I manage to find a café that seems to cater to locals, where I can have a steak without robbing a bank to pay for it.

Afterward, I wander around the town, trying to get the feel of the place, a sense of what it was that attracted Roy Emerson here in the first place, concluding that it must have been the real estate offices, which are as numerous as fleas on a dog. Another similarity to Key West.

By eleven o'clock, exhausted, I return to the hotel and collapse into bed, sleeping dreamlessly until the early morning, when I get up to take a leak and close the window. I have not been so cold since I left Korea. By dawn I get up, stand under a hot shower, and head off for breakfast at seven-thirty to the same café where I had dinner.

I find Don Cameron perched on one of the counter stools.

24

◇

Cameron looks up, his Stetson pushed back on his head, and I see that he is nearly bald. He nods briefly as if he were expecting me, then picks up his mug of coffee. "So you found us," he says, before drinking.

"Dinner was pretty good here last night, and the price was right."

"About the only local hangout left around here any longer."

"Tourists?"

"They've taken over everything. Not a business around that doesn't cater to them. I don't understand it. You think they'd come out here, they'd want to see something real. But no, they want it all dressed up, want it sanitized."

"We've got the same problem in Key West."

Don turns to face me, studying me for a moment. Except for a necklace made of animal claws, large claws, he seems to be wearing the same clothes he had on when he met me at the airport yesterday. Looking into his eyes, I can still read nothing in his expression.

A waitress comes to take my order. Don turns back to his newspaper folded on the counter beside his coffee cup. There is a vending box outside the door, and after placing my order, I go out and get a paper of my own.

For twenty minutes we sit side by side, reading our papers and eating. When we have finished, the waitress takes our plates and refills Don's coffee mug. Don turns and says, "You a drinking man, Gideon?"

"Gave it up a few years ago."

"May be coming to that myself. I feel like a pack mule kicked me upside the head this morning. Then dragged me across a sheep pasture."

"Don," the waitress interrupts, "you've just been living alone too long. Time you got married."

"Tried it once and it didn't work."

"Try it again," the waitress says.

"You proposing, Velma?"

"You're too hardheaded, Don Cameron. That mule needs to kick you a few more times and soften you up some." She smiles and hurries away with her coffeepot.

We leave some cash on the counter and step outside. Don pulls his Stetson down on his forehead, looking at his watch. "I'll pick you up in front of the hotel in about fifteen minutes. We've got about a half-hour ride to where we're going, and we're supposed to be there at nine o'clock."

"Where's that?"

"A ranch outside of town."

The light jacket I am wearing—in fact, the only jacket I own—is not warm enough. Even though the sun is shining, the temperature is in the mid fifties. On the way back to the hotel I stop in a store and pay too much for something warmer, a canvas coat with a plaid wool lining.

Back at the hotel I drop off the jacket in my room, make a pit stop, then go back down to the street.

Don is already waiting, his Jeep parked at the curb. "A little cold for you," Don says, looking at the coat as I get into the Jeep.

"Ah, well," I say, mocking my own weakness, "the blood thins in Florida."

"That's what I hear. Another month or so up here and you'll be drinking antifreeze." Cameron neither laughs nor smiles at his joke, staring straight ahead as he guides the Jeep along the narrow streets, where the business community is preparing for another day of tourism.

"You want to fill me in on where we're going, and why?"

Cameron stops at a light, turns on the left-turn signal, and we sit listening to its steady rhythmic click. "The Hargreaves hired me to keep track of Roy Emerson when their daughter died. I believe I told you I did that up until about a year and a half ago, when I lost track of him. He just seemed to disappear."

The light changes to green, and Don turns onto the highway I remember from yesterday coming in from the airport.

"Roy was married to their daughter, I think you told me."

"That's right, Karen. The only girl in the family, and the old man doted on her."

"And they were only married a short while?"

"Yep, about six months. Until she died."

"And the Hargreaves think Roy killed her."

Don mumbles something that I don't hear in the noisy cab of the Jeep.

We pass the turnoff to the airport, clipping along the straight valley road at a steady sixty-five, the whine of the Jeep's motor vibrating up through the floorboards. Cold air seeps in through the cracks in the canvas top. Five minutes after we have passed the airport, Don slows, making a right-hand turn onto a dirt road that can be seen stretching out for miles in front of us into low, tree-covered hills.

Barbed-wire fence encloses the grasslands on either side of the road as Don drives slowly over a ribbed-steel cattle crossing. Two great vertical logs at either side support a crossbeam in which the letter *H* is burned in a circle at its center. The Jeep bounces along the road, a cloud of dust trailing behind us.

Once we enter the foothills, the road becomes more rutted, twisting and turning, and for the next ten miles Don does not speak as he concentrates on his driving.

By the time we come to another of those log entrances, this one with a slatted wooden gate, I feel completely lost.

The sky is a deep blue and looks like something I could swim in. A few puffy clouds are low to the ground. Beyond the gate is a two-story log house, the logs a worn, rusty red. A long-haired dog comes loping toward the gate, barking. Don speaks to it, and the dog stops barking, but does not advance further down the lane toward us. Instead, he stands there watching us, his black, wet muzzle sniffing the air.

An old barn sits opposite the house, and as we drive in, a tall, thin guy with sloped shoulders comes out the wide double doors and follows us as Don drives up to the house.

"They're nice people," Don says, shutting off the ignition. "You're going to like them."

The way he says it, I don't think I will be given much choice in the matter.

25

◇

Robert "Bob" Hargreaves is tall, rangy, slightly stoop-shouldered, with eyes almost the same color as the Wyoming sky. He wears jeans, a white western-cut shirt, and a narrow-brimmed Stetson that is in somewhat better condition than the one worn by Don.

Standing on the side lawn facing the Tetons, we shake hands. Hargreaves smiles, but his eyes contain a hint of suspicion; his leathery face with its narrow hook-shaped nose is as expressive as Cameron's is absent of expression. I would guess Hargreaves to be close to seventy.

"Come on in the house," Bob says, "meet my wife and get a cup of coffee."

Don and I follow Hargreaves up the steps of the side porch, where there is a dinner bell atop a wrought-iron pole. The entire setting reminds me of any number of western movies I have seen.

We step inside a large kitchen with a long wooden table capable of seating a dozen people. "Ruth," Bob calls out. He takes his hat off and puts it on an antler rack just inside the door. His hair is thick and perfectly white.

Moments later a woman enters the kitchen,

says hello to Don, and offers me her hand as Bob introduces us.

Like her husband, Ruth is slender, well kept, with short, gray hair and friendly dark eyes. She wears a peach-colored shirt-style blouse tucked into a long denim skirt. Silver bracelets adorn one arm. "Go on in the front room," she tells us, "and I'll bring out some coffee. Would you like something to eat?"

"Thanks," I say, "but I just had breakfast. And I don't drink coffee."

"Anything else?"

"A glass of water would be fine."

"You got any of those good cinnamon rolls, I wouldn't say no to one," Don says.

Ruth laughs as Bob ushers us into the living room, a vast room with a beamed ceiling, wide plank floors covered with colorful Indian rugs, two leather couches facing one another in front of a wide plate-glass window framing the ever-present Tetons. At one end of the room a stone fireplace big enough for a small man to stand upright in has the still-glowing embers from a recent fire. A bar complete with barstools occupies the opposite end of the room, and suspended above it all, from the centermost ceiling beam, a wagon-wheel chandelier.

"Quite a place," I remark as we sit down on the couches, Bob and Don sitting opposite me. Don crosses one leg over the other and puts his hat on his knee.

"My grandfather built it in the mid 1800s," Bob replies proudly. "Except for four years away at school and a brief tour in the army, it's the only home I've known. We've added onto it and of course modernized over the years, but essentially it's the same place it was a hundred and fifty years ago."

Ruth brings in a tray with a silver coffee urn, four cups, and a plate with a couple of cinnamon rolls dripping with melted butter.

"Will that keep you going, Don?" Ruth asks.

"Until lunch," Don replies.

Ruth shakes her head, hands me a glass of water, then sits on the couch beside me and begins to pour coffee. "Don is like family," she explains. "In fact his own family had the ranch next to ours for many years."

"Until it was foreclosed," Don says.

There is a brief silence before Bob speaks. "Well, we're all going down the drain," he says, "with the government cutting grazing land and the price of cattle what it is. Not to mention taxes as the land gets more valuable to the recreation community."

Ruth finishes pouring and passes out the coffee.

"What are you going to do?" I ask, thinking about my own small crisis at home, whether or not to sell out in the face of the unstoppable march of tourism.

Bob's head droops forward on his chest for a moment. Ruth stares at him. "Don't know," he says. "And don't guess it makes too much difference, since we won't be here, anyway."

"Oh, don't be so morbid, Bob." Ruth puts a roll on a saucer and hands it to Don. "What he means is," she says, turning to me, "is that we've got two sons, and neither one of them is much interested in ranching."

Bob lifts his head. "Karen would have been the rancher. She loved this place."

Ruth shakes her head. "Honey, you know a woman can't run a spread like this."

"She could have. If she'd had the right man helping her."

"That girl knew what she was doing when it came to horse sense," Don remarks.

"She ought to," Ruth says, "she was raised on one. But riding a horse isn't all that ranching is about; you know that, Don Cameron."

"Well, I don't know. Women are different these days, Ruth. They can pretty much do whatever they want to do, even if it is traditionally a man's job."

"That's right," Bob echoes. "Karen could have managed this place, and I was ready to let her."

"What do your sons do?" I ask.

Bob waves a hand in the air. "They're in town. One of them's gone into real estate, and the other's practicing law."

"They're both good boys," Ruth adds somewhat defensively. "It can be a real hardship out here at times. Cut off from people, from any kind of a social life." She sounds wistful.

"If you want to call what Jackson Hole's turned into a social life," Bob says.

"Oh, honey, you know what I mean."

Bob nods, smiling at his wife. "You don't have any complaints at this late date, do you?"

Ruth smiles back. "None. But in that regard I think I can perhaps understand the boys better than you can."

Don has finished his cinnamon roll and wipes

his mustache on one of the paper napkins Ruth gave him. "Gideon here knows Roy Emerson," he says. "He's down in Key West about to get married again."

Hargreaves stands up and walks over to the picture window, standing with his back to us, part of the scenic mountain setting now. "I'll see that man in hell," he says so softly I can barely hear him.

Ruth puts a hand to her eyes, shaking her head.

26

◇

Getting up from the couch, Ruth walks to the fireplace and returns with a framed photograph. "This is Karen," she says, handing me the color photo of a pretty young woman standing in a high meadow with snowcapped mountain peaks behind her. She is wearing shorts and hiking boots, the straps of a backpack clearly visible around the shoulders of her sweatshirt. She carries a walking stick. Despite the snow on the mountains, the meadow where she stands is filled with wildflowers in bloom.

"She knew the Tetons like the back of her hand," Bob Hargreaves says, turning from the window. "She had hiked and climbed in these mountains ever since she was old enough to walk."

Like her mother, Karen has an oval face. Her hair is blond, cut shoulder length and pulled back from her face with a red band. She is smiling. There is nothing in her expression to suggest anything other than youthful excitement and confidence. She appears happy and in good health.

"That was one of the last pictures of her ever taken." Ruth pours more coffee into Don's cup.

"Who took the picture?" I ask.

"Roy." Ruth barely whispers the word, as if it is forbidden.

"Were they married then?"

Ruth nods. A quietness has come over the room. I try to imagine Bob and Ruth's life here now in this big house, remote, alone.

"How did they meet?"

Bob moves away from the window and walks toward the kitchen.

"Karen's brother introduced them. Jim." Ruth continues to speak in a hushed tone of voice.

"Which brother is that?"

"The one in real estate."

Don picks up his coffee cup and carries it into the kitchen. As Ruth tells me how Roy and Karen first got together, I can hear the indistinct voices of Don and Bob conversing in the other room. Roy, Ruth tells me, was in some development deal that her son Jim had an interest in. Ruth has forgotten the exact details, it was more than five years ago, and anyway she thinks the deal fell through.

"How long after they met before they got married?"

Ruth looks down, smoothing her skirt. "About a year, I think."

"And how long were they married?"

"Six months."

I think of Gaby. She, too, has known Roy only about a year. "What happened?"

Don has already given me the details of Karen's death, but I listen again as Ruth repeats essentially the same information. A hiking trip on the Idaho side of the Tetons in late summer. A sudden thunderstorm with Karen standing on a rocky pinnacle when lightning struck not far from her. Something happened. She lost her footing. And fell. Nearly a thousand feet straight down. Ruth does not look at me. Her voice breaks.

Staring at the picture of Karen I hold in my hands, I find it difficult to imagine her terror. She seems so composed, so sure of herself. In that way, at least, like Gaby.

"And Roy wasn't around," I say.

Ruth shakes her head. "So he said."

I continue to study the photo while Ruth appears to withdraw inside herself. Bob and Don reappear from the kitchen. Bob walks with a distinct gait, as if his knees are bad. "I can tell you this," he says, going to stand by the fireplace, where he examines the many photos that are lined up there. I assume most of them must be of Karen. "She would never have been standing out there in the open, exposed, when a storm was blowing across. A year doesn't go by around here that somebody isn't struck by lightning. Usually a tourist, someone inexperienced in the mountains. That wasn't Karen."

"What would she have done?" I ask. "Caught out like that."

"Found a rock, a ledge, a cave. Someplace to crawl in or under. She would not have just been standing there."

I nod. "What do you think happened?"

Leaning against the mantel, Bob Hargreaves shakes his head. "I know what happened. The sonofabitch pushed her."

"Bob," Ruth says.

It is unclear if she is admonishing him for his language or the accusation, but her husband does not respond.

"What would his motive have been?" I ask. "Why did he push her?"

Bob and Ruth look at one another. Don moves back around to the couch facing me. "Roy took out a life insurance policy on Karen against accidental death," Don says. "A hundred grand."

"He had also borrowed that much, or more, from her after they were married," Bob adds.

"Karen had that kind of money?"

"All the kids had a trust fund. When she turned twenty-one, Karen had access to a quarter of a million dollars."

"What did Roy want the money for?"

"Investments."

"Did Karen talk to you about it?"

"We have always tried not to interfere in our children's lives," Ruth says. "Karen didn't consult us about it. We found out only after her death."

"Did you get the money back?"

"No," Bob says sharply. His blue eyes have turned to ice. "And we won't get Karen back, either."

"You requested an inquest?"

Don clears his throat. "It was inconclusive, Gideon." He stares at me as though he has more to say but is reluctant to say it, and it is clear that he wishes I hadn't brought the subject up again. I assume out of deference to the Hargreaves.

"Then no charges were brought against Roy, I take it?"

They all shake their heads. "He left town about

three months afterwards," Don says. "Once the paperwork was done and he had collected on the insurance."

We sit in silence again. My mind turns back to Gaby, and I picture Roy standing on her deck, railing against doctors and hospitals, while extolling the folks in this part of the country for their independence from medical institutions. I also begin to picture him alone with Gaby, remote and isolated. I wonder what I am doing here.

"You're probably wondering what can be done, why I thought it would be a good idea for you to come out here," Don says.

"It did cross my mind."

"We think he's going to strike again, that Karen's death wasn't an isolated event but part of Emerson's m.o."

Hargreaves limps back over to the window. "We may not be able to get him for Karen's murder, but . . . well, we understand from Don that you were checking up on him."

"Roy is planning to get married again. His fiancée wanted some medical history on him. I provided that. This other came right out of the blue."

Bob smiles understandingly. "After Karen's death we hired Don to investigate. You probably know that."

I nod.

"But he's got a job with the DA's office. There was only so much he could do."

"At this point there's only so much anyone can do," I reply.

"But you're living in the same town now. You know the woman he wants to marry."

Again, I nod.

"We wanted to meet you, talk to you. Which is why I asked Don to try to get you out here. You must have had some concern because you were willing to come all the way up here on your own."

I don't say anything. There is a long silence.

"Well, we want to make it worth your while. I'd like to pay for your expenses and hire you to do what Don here was doing, keep track of Emerson as long as he's in your part of the country. Maybe we can save someone else."

"Save someone?" I ask. "Or, bring him down for what happened to Karen?"

Hargreaves turns away, staring out the window. Don sits stroking his mustache. Ruth carries the tray back into the kitchen. "Maybe it looks that way to you," Bob says. "It's true, we want to see justice served."

"Without clear evidence against him?"

Don clears his throat again.

"We're not asking you to do anything illegal."

"I had to make sure," I reply.

"Believe me, we don't want to see anyone else go through what we have."

"I don't either," I say.

27

◇

In low gear Don Cameron's Jeep grumbles and growls along the rutted road back toward town. Don does not speak until we reach the blacktop a couple of miles from the Hargreaves's home. A check for a thousand dollars, folded once, reposes nicely in my shirt pocket.

"Didn't I tell you they were good people?" Don shifts into fourth gear as the wide-tread tires begin to whine against the smooth blacktop.

I agree they seem like good people. There is something about Bob Hargreaves, some quality in him, that resonates with me. "At their age, isn't it tough living all alone up there?"

"You get used to it." Something in Don's voice sounds a little wistful. "The winters are the worst. Hell, forty years ago you could get snowed in for three months. In bad winters there were a lot of times I had to ride a horse to school. Now the roads are pretty much kept clear and you can get to town whenever you want. But Bob and Ruth like it up there. They don't really come down any more than they have to."

"I guess that your families were close."

Don grunts. "I've known the Hargreaves all my life."

"When did you move into Jackson?"

"When I was fifteen. My old man died and left us with a lot of debt. It was just my mother and me to work the ranch, so we didn't have much choice. We sold what we could to the Hargreaves and the creditors got the rest. My mother went to work in a bank in Jackson. Summers I worked for the Hargreaves."

Some little whisper of an idea trips across my brain. "How well did you know Karen?"

Don turns his head sharply toward me for a second, and I sense that I have touched a raw nerve. "We were friends even though she was ten years younger than me."

Something in his manner prompts me to tell him about Gaby. When I finish, we ride in silence for a while. "Curious," Don finally says.

"What's curious?"

"I was crazy about Karen." Cameron looks out the side window, watching a guy in waders fly-fishing in a stream.

"I thought maybe you were."

"For a few years we spent a lot of time together. Friends, you know. We had a lot of the same interests, but when it came down to anything more than that, the age difference was just too much."

"But you had hopes."

Don shrugs. "The heart mends."

I recall the conversation with the waitress earlier this morning. "But you never found anyone else like her."

Don runs a hand over his bushy mustache. "Never."

"Did you meet Roy?"

Don shakes his head. "Didn't want to. But by the time he came on the scene, Karen and I had gone our separate ways, anyway."

"What was her attraction? To Roy, I mean."

"I've thought about that. Karen loved it here, this valley, even with all the changes. She never grew tired of it, or cynical, the way some of the rest of us have. I guess she was able to adapt better than I ever could. That isn't to say she approved of what was happening here, but she knew how to live with it, and make the most of it. Me, I would just retreat, go back to the mountains and live much the way Bob and Ruth do now. If I could. Karen, on the other hand, wanted to be in on everything. She liked newcomers, welcomed their ideas. I think that was what it was with Emerson. He came from the outside world with a different point of view and plenty of charm. Damned if I know what it was, but Karen fell for him."

Just like Gaby. "Do you think she really would have run the ranch?"

A nerve in Don's jaw twitches, pulling at one side of his mustache. He nods. "I think so. I doubt that Emerson would have lasted."

"But she couldn't have done it on her own."

"She would have had help."

"From you?"

"The offer was always there."

We ride in silence again for a while. "Tell me about the necklace," I say.

Don lifts a hand and fingers the claws around his neck. "From a bear," he says. "The last one I ever shot."

"You're a hunter?"

"Nope. The year my dad died a rogue griz got into our cattle and killed a couple of the heifers. I tracked it down and shot it." Don speaks matter-of-factly, slowing the Jeep as we approach the intersection with the highway into town. "Today you hardly ever see a griz around here. Some over in the park, in Yellowstone, of course, but with all the development around Jackson, they're getting pushed out like everything else. A dying breed, I guess you could say."

"Like you and me, maybe."

Don turns and looks at me. "Maybe," he says. "People have gotten so used to seeing nature bottled and corked that they forget there is still stuff out there that can kill you."

It is approaching one o'clock when we reach town. Don suggests lunch, and we go back to the same café where we had breakfast.

"I take it you've got something lined up for this afternoon."

"Yep," Don says. "I want you to meet Karen's brother Jim."

"The one in real estate?"

Don nods as the same waitress who served us this morning approaches. "Let me guess," she says. "Chicken fried steak."

"Gravy on the mashed potatoes," Don answers.

She looks at me. I have never eaten chicken fried steak. "Double that order," I say.

28

◇

Snake River Realty is a chic, weathered frame building sandwiched between an art gallery and a factory outlet clothing store. The windows of the gallery are filled with large, lifelike paintings of Indians in headdresses and war paint, and on pedestals beside them bronze sculptures of cowboys on broncs—modest imitations of Remingtons.

The realty office is like all realty offices everywhere, functional, without unnecessary accoutrements. It is instead entirely devoted to the business of selling houses. One front window panel is given over to color pictures of properties for sale, some with "sold" in bright red letters stamped diagonally across their faces. A quick glance at the price list reveals that Jackson Hole has more than tourism in common with Key West.

Inside, a secretary is seated at an unadorned desk. When she looks up, Don tips his Stetson. "Don Cameron," he says. "We've got a one-thirty with Jim."

The secretary, a middle-aged blond woman wearing a fringed shirt and a bolo tie with a large turquoise clasp, looks at her watch, then picks up the phone, speaking into the receiver, her chin tucked down, in a voice apparently meant to be heard only by whoever is on the other end of the line. When she hangs up, she looks up, smiling brightly, with little half moons of flesh appearing on either side of her mouth. "He'll be right out," she says.

Don seems nervous, uncomfortable, as if he feels out of place here. I can't say that I blame him. Five minutes later, when I hear a door opening and closing, we both peer expectantly down the hallway leading toward the back.

"Don, how you doing? Long time no see." The man who appears, offering his hand, first to Don, then me, is tall, slender, dressed in a business suit with a white shirt and tie. Shiny tasseled loafers on his feet replace the ubiquitous boots.

"Gideon Lowry," Don says. "Jim Hargreaves."

Except for the hawklike nose and sky blue eyes, Jim appears to have little in common with his father. He projects a certain sophistication at odds with the easygoing western informality that seems so much a part of his parents and Don Cameron. Behind the suit and cool eyes, I sense some unexplored tension in Hargreaves.

"Let's go back to my office," Jim says. "Can I get you anything?"

"Nothing for me," I reply.

Don shakes his head.

"Carla, hold all my calls."

The secretary nods, while using one lacquered thumbnail to squeeze a mint from a paper roll.

Hargreaves's office is large enough to accommodate a desk and a conference table. On the table are several blueprints. Hanging on the walls, framed black-and-white photographs depict Jackson Hole in its various stages of development. Hargreaves pushes the blueprints to one end of the table and sits down at the other end, Don and I taking seats opposite one another on either side of him.

"We were up at the ranch earlier," Don says.

"Mother called and told me." With a forefinger Jim worries the cuticle of his thumb. He looks at me. "She said Dad hired you to look into Karen's death."

"I gather that's been pretty well examined," I reply. "What they hired me to do is keep an eye on Roy Emerson."

Hargreaves shakes his head disapprovingly. "You probably won't agree, Don, but I think this whole thing has gotten to be rather obsessive on their part."

Cameron lifts his Stetson and runs a hand over his smooth head, dropping the hat on the table. "I don't know about that, Jim."

"Karen's been dead five years now. There was never anything except Dad's hang-up on this issue to keep this pursuit going. Not a whit of medical evidence to suggest Karen's death was anything but accidental."

Don shrugs. "Gideon's from Key West, Florida. He got in touch with the DA's office here looking for some background information on Emerson. I asked him to come out here. I thought it might be good if he talked to your parents. Good for them at least."

Hargreaves shakes his head again, turning to me. "Roy's in Key West?"

"Been there about a year now."

"What's he doing?"

"I'm not sure. Investments. Real estate. It isn't too clear exactly what he does. But he is getting married again soon."

A slight smile creases Hargreaves's smooth face. "How can I help you?"

"You did know Roy, didn't you?"

"Sure, I knew him. I introduced him to Karen. Don must have told you that."

I nod. "I'm curious about your relationship with Roy."

"We worked on a project together. I liked him. He was smart and had a talent for bringing people together and getting things off the ground."

"What was the project?"

"A development just outside town. It was meant to be a trading post with a variety of shops and a motel attached, along with a theme park where the kids could hang out. We were even going to have wild animals in pens. A bear or two, and buffalo, that kind of thing. For those people who didn't want to traipse through Yellowstone looking for them in the wild."

Apart from the animals, the very sort of thing that Key West now traffics in. The kind of insipid nonsense that has ruined a perfectly real town. Don sits with his hands folded over his belly, looking like a cowboy Buddha. Though he doesn't say anything, I can just imagine what he's thinking. Bears in a pen!

"Did Emerson invest in it?"

"Roy was the principal. He had the thing put together in record time. Met with officials to get the variances and paperwork needed. He did it all."

"Can I see the results?"

"Unfortunately, not. The place burned before it was half completed."

"Do tell," I say. "Roy held the insurance papers on it, I suppose."

Jim Hargreaves nods.

29

◇

Jim Hargreaves is right. There is nothing in any of this to accuse a man of murder, even arson, much less convict him of either. Still, I feel the urgent need to talk to Gaby, and this isn't going to be easy. Somehow I must convey enough of what I have learned to let her know that she should proceed cautiously with Emerson—but without having her feel that I am advising her to end that relationship or that I have taken it upon myself to interfere in her personal life. Not without more hard evidence.

It isn't going to be easy.

Jim Hargreaves regrets introducing his sister to Roy Emerson, he remarks. "Roy is a scoundrel. No doubt in my mind about that. A charming scoundrel, too. Maybe the worst kind. But I'll be damned if I am convinced that he's capable of murder."

"Arson?"

Hargreaves lifts his hands. "I don't know."

There seems to be nothing left to say. Don fiddles with the brim of his Stetson. "On what terms did you and Emerson end up?"

Jim seems to suppress a laugh. "My sister is dead, and he cost me nearly a hundred grand. How do you think we ended up?"

"Did the two of you talk before he left town?"

"No. As far as I know no one knew he was leaving. He just vanished one day."

"Didn't you think that was a little suspicious?"

"I don't think Roy Emerson had a lot of credibility left in Jackson Hole."

I nod, considering further questions. I have a check in my pocket, a case I am now being paid to investigate. Despite his feelings about Roy, Jim Hargreaves has made it clear that he would not approve this investigation. My chair squeaks against the tile when I move it to get up.

"I'm sorry I can't be of more help," Hargreaves says, standing.

I shrug, watching Don Cameron push his bulk up. The three of us shake hands, and Don and I leave. Outside, we stand on the boardwalk beneath the overhang above the porch for a moment.

"You don't like him, do you?" I ask Cameron.

"I don't have strong feelings about him one way or the other. Growing up, Jim and Karen were close. I think he tried to influence her away from the ranch."

"Why?"

"Hell, the same reason you'd influence anyone you loved away from that line of work. No future in it."

"And yet you'd go back to it in a heartbeat?"

"It's a way of life. Karen had it in her blood. The boys for some reason didn't. That shit about trading posts, theme parks, and bear pens. That's where the future is."

"But you already told me you thought Karen would have run the ranch."

Don begins walking back toward the Jeep. "I've heard rumors that the boys would like to have seen the place turned into a guest ranch."

"Meaning?"

"Meaning once Bob and Ruth were gone, the ranch would be managed for paying guests. Dudes, they used to call them. People who'd never been on a horse, rich folks who would be willing to pay a fortune for a couple weeks in the mountains."

"You don't approve?"

"I don't know what it's like in your part of the country, but out here no one much cares what anyone thinks beyond the immediate concern of making a buck as fast as they can and any way they can."

"I'd say that was true in Key West."

"Take folks like Roy Emerson. The guy comes in, contributes to ruining a place, and succeed or fail, he's off to the next place."

"Sounds familiar."

"My guess is they tried to persuade Karen to run the ranch on those conditions and she said no."

"What about Bob and Ruth?"

"If all three kids were behind it, I suppose the thinking was their parents would go along with it. Given their age and the circumstances."

"What happened?"

"Karen wouldn't do it."

As I weigh the consequences of this remark, a stagecoach goes by, pulled by four roan horses, their heads down and wearing blinders, while the driver, decked out in woolly chaps and a high-crowned Stetson, beseeches passengers.

"You talked to Karen about this?" I ask Don, watching the progress of the stagecoach.

"I told you. I'm guessing. But it's something to think about."

Back at Cameron's Jeep, I start to climb in until Don stops on my side and leans up against the Jeep's front fender. "Here's the deal," he says. I close the door. "I can take you over to the medical examiner and you can talk to him, question him about Karen's death."

"You've already done that."

"That's right. I've got his reports and I can tell you what he said. But it's your case now. I want to give you the option to ask your own questions."

I shrug. I do not doubt Cameron's ability. With the years that have passed since this was first investigated, I can't imagine I would be able to dig anything fresh from the M.E.

"Fine," Don says. For the first time a trace of a smile plays in his eyes. "You don't mind joining me at the bar, I could use a beer." He looks at his watch. "A mite early, but this has been a troubling day."

The bar is across the street from where the Jeep is parked. Off the beaten track. An old weathered joint without the chic. A scarred mahogany bar, wooden barstools, and a mirrored back bar the only accessories. The walls are filled with mounted trophy heads of deer, elk, and ante-lope—their tawny coats dusty and their big glassy eyes shining like gemstones.

"Don," the bartender greets him, and places a mug of draft beer on a mat in front of him before turning to me. "What can I get you?"

"Club soda."

He walks away, returning moments later with a tall glass of fizzy water. He chats with Don for a moment, then leaves to tend another customer.

"Well, you've gotten the picture," Don says after a short sip of beer.

"Such as it is."

"You see why I was anxious to get you out here. This couldn't have been done on the phone. Bob and Ruth aren't that kind of people. They needed to look you in the eye. You measured up. They like you."

"For whatever it's worth."

"If nothing more, you've got your expenses covered and been paid for some of your time."

"Now what I need is some hard evidence. Something more than conjecture."

"I know. I wish I had it to give. I don't. But there is more circumstantial stuff."

"Like what?"

Don takes another pull from the mug. Then, wiping foam from his mustache, says, "The other victim."

Even though he mentioned the drowning when we first spoke on the phone, a tingle passes across the back of my neck like a chill. "When was this?"

"Three years ago. More than a year after Karen's death."

"Where?"

"Over in Idaho. Sun Valley. Another resort town."

"Tell me again what happened."

"A woman drowned. She and Roy were engaged. They were alone, on a picnic at an isolated lake. She went swimming, the water was cold, she cramped up, and before he could get to her, she was gone. That was his story."

"You investigated?"

"I drove over there, about a day's drive from here. The woman had no close family. There was nothing in the inquest to suggest it happened other than Roy described it."

"Motive?"

Don shakes his head. "They had a joint bank account. Apparently the woman had inherited some money, substantial, but not a lot. Of course, it went to Roy."

Once again my mind races back to Gaby. Alone in her house. Remote. Telling me how bees mate, the queen leading the drones on a suicide mission. Then Roy comes into the picture.

30

◇

At nine o'clock mountain time, given the two-hour time difference between Jackson Hole and Key West, I begin calling Gaby. I do not expect her to be home from work yet, so it is no surprise when the answering machine clicks on, and I hang up. I have deliberately chosen not to call Gaby at work. Having no idea what I will say to her, if anything, about Roy. But, with a mixture of pleasant anticipation and anxiety, I look forward to one of our late-night calls.

Don is on his third beer when I leave the bar. It is after sunset, quickly growing dark, and along with the drop in temperature, the wind has come sweeping into the valley carrying the icy chill of winter. Don proposes driving across the pass into Idaho tomorrow and hiking up the Devil's Staircase. In this thin air, my breathing is labored enough without my having to undergo a rigorous mountain-climbing expedition. Besides, I can see little to be gained. We agree, however, to meet for breakfast in the morning and determine our next move then.

After leaving Don, I go to the café and eat a bowl of chili before returning to my room, where I am free from the knife-edged wind and raw, burning cold.

At nine-thirty, I try Gaby again. Still getting only the answering machine. Restless, I walk down to the lobby, where a fire burns in the fireplace and the TV is on. Plopping down in one of the easy chairs closest to the fire, I watch a mindless sitcom, along with the elderly receptionist, who smiles at the TV banter.

It is somehow comforting here, the sitcom a distraction that momentarily keeps the worry at bay. Perhaps that's what this kind of program is designed for.

Shortly after ten, when the news comes on, I go back to my room. It is now after midnight in Key West. Gaby is still not home. It is possible that she has gone out for a drink before driving back to Sugarloaf, or perhaps she has stayed in town with Roy. In any case, it is too late to call again tonight.

A book that I brought with me on the plane, but was too nervous to read, is on the beside table. Entitled *Marquesa,* it describes six weeks in the life of its author, Jeffrey Cardenas, alone on a houseboat in the backcountry, the uninhabited islands of the Marquesas west of Key West. The descriptions of warm water and sky and fish make me homesick. After a couple of hours reading, I fall asleep and dream of the sea.

When the dream turns to a nightmare, I awake and read the luminescent hands on my watch. It is six o'clock, still pitch black beyond the window, where the mountains loom. Gaby was in the dream, caught in some swift outgoing tide, the swirling currents carrying her seaward as she struggles to get back to shore, where I watch helplessly. But the watching face turns from mine to Roy's. Grinning that crooked grin.

After peeing, I rinse my face in water so cold it feels as if it is straight from the fridge. Then go back and sit on the edge of the bed and reach for the phone. It is after eight in Florida. I dial Gaby's number, once again getting the answering machine.

Shivering, I lie back down in bed and pull the heavy covers over my shoulders. I crave warmth. I lie staring up into the dark until just after seven, when a hint of light creeps in the window, light that is more like a shadow. Sliding one hand out from under the covers, I reach for the phone. Dial. Click. The familiar voice, the now relentless message.

I dial information to get the number for the Blue Moon. Then dial it on the off chance that someone is there, taking reservations or making preparations. Someone is. A woman answers.

"I'm not in town and I need to reach Gabriella," I say. "I've tried her at home several times and there's no answer. It's important."

"She's out of town." The woman's voice is young, bright. I can feel the warmth of the tropics in it.

"Do you know how I can reach her?"

"No. She's in the Bahamas."

The Bahamas. Did Gaby mention anything about going to the Bahamas? No, I am sure she didn't. "Is everything okay there?"

"Everything's just fine." I can practically see the smile on the face of the woman speaking to me as I huddle under my blankets.

"Know when she'll be back?"

"She stole away for a couple of days with her fiancé. I'm not really certain when she returns."

"Roy," I say.

"Yes."

"I see." For the first time I am suddenly alarmed. Perhaps it is the dream, but I am now afraid for Gaby's life. There is nothing I can do from here. And probably little that I can do there, but I know I have to go back to Key West. Today.

A dense fog hangs like a veil over the valley. So dense that I can see little more than ten feet in front of me when I walk to the café at seven-thirty, huddled in my canvas coat. It is wet and cold. Cars come out of the fog like apparitions, their windshield wipers on, their headlights like yellow cat's eyes.

At the café I find Don Cameron seated at the counter. He lifts a hand casually in greeting when I sit next to him.

"I've got reservations back to Florida today."

Don nods. "Something come up?"

I tell him.

"The Bahamas," he says, looking off into the distance. "Heard of it. Where is it?"

"A string of islands in the Atlantic not far off the coast of south Florida."

"Another resort, vacation place?"

"Yeah, exactly."

Don picks up his fork and mixes some egg with his hash browns. It is the same breakfast he ate yesterday, probably the one that he eats every day. Routine—an ordered life. Not, I realize, unlike my own life in Key West.

"When's your flight?"

"Ten o'clock."

Don checks his watch. "I'll drive you to the airport."

The fog has not lifted. After breakfast I walk back to the hotel, put my meager things together, and check out. At eight forty-five Don is out front in the Jeep and I begin my trip home. Driving slowly as we creep through the fog, Don says little until we get to the airport, when he wishes me luck. "I wish I could be there," he says. "I've got a stake in this."

We shake hands. "I'll keep you posted," I say.

31

◇

The Tetons are invisible, their majesty shrouded in fog as we take off. Is the menace they impose on nervous fliers more acute when the mountains are seen, or not seen? It quickly becomes a moot question. At a thousand feet we break through the fog, pushing the trailing clouds aside, like a submarine suddenly surfacing from the dark depths of the sea; and there, in all their resplendent glory, are the snowcapped peaks bathed in bright sunlight. My grip on the armrest loosens and I begin to breathe easier.

Unlike the journey out here, the flights back are uneventful, and I even manage to sleep a good part of the way. I am due to arrive back in Key West at ten o'clock tonight, and though it has been just three days since I left, it feels like weeks. I begin to make plans for my return. The sea beckons. I promise myself a swim first thing tomorrow morning. A kind of baptism.

And, hanging in the balance, is Gaby. Surely, someone in the Blue Moon will know exactly where she can be reached in the Bahamas, so that I can at least phone her. The woman whom I spoke to earlier this morning said that she was stealing a couple of days. Gaby may even be back by tomorrow. Unless—

I put the thought out of my mind.

After a delayed flight out of Orlando it is closer to midnight when I reach Key West. Stepping off the plane, I breathe in the familiar scent, the sea smell mixed with that of the cloying, but less familiar, aviation fuel. The air is damp, but warm, the costly canvas coat that had been such a comfort only a few hours ago, now a burden—uncomfortably irritating against my bare arm over which it hangs as I make my way into the terminal.

Taxicabs line the roadway in front of the terminal, and beyond toward the beach, I can see the shadows of the tall, stately palm trees, leaning leeward, their dark fronds stirring in the light late-night breeze. Swept along the boulevard by taxi, the windows down, jazz spilling out into the night from the radio, I am home.

When the cab stops on Duval Street, I am suddenly reminded of what I have returned to. The shambles of the *groceria* stands like a desecrated shrine, soot-blackened.

In three days, however, my own place has been transformed. Freshly painted, it is like new. The carpenter has removed his tools, cleaned up the mess, and, in a phrase, I am back in business.

The only message on the answering machine is from Frank Pappagallo. When it has played and the machine clicks off, I hear a scratching sound that seems to come from the kitchen. I walk back there, turn the light on, and listen. And hear it again, something scratching against the back door. Turning the porch light on, I open the door. Tom, my cat, is there, his front paw lifted. I have not seen him since the fire, but I left water and food dishes out and instructed the carpenter to fill them each day.

His coat is smudged, and Tom seems thinner, more unstable when he stands, yawns, and hobbles inside, purring once as he wends through my legs.

I dump the water that is in his bowl into the sink and refill it. Tom drinks when I set it on the floor. There is nothing in the refrigerator for him, but I put a few cans of cat food on the shelf before I left and see that they are still there, suggesting that this must be his first time home since the fire. Old and blind in one eye, he would have had a hard time fending for himself, but I assume that he has managed to find scraps in the neighborhood, maybe a lizard or two to keep him going.

He sniffs at the canned food I put down. Then settles on his haunches to eat, slowly and deliberately, his one good eye closed. Tom eats less than half of what I put out for him before sitting back, running a paw over his face, then looking up at me. I scratch him between the ears. Then follow him into the office, where he struggles to clamber inside the file drawer in my desk.

It is after one o'clock by the time I shower, make up my bed, and turn in, falling asleep under a crisp sheet with the overhead fan stirring the air, the cold of Wyoming now only a distant memory.

32

◇

Pop is the first person I see the next morning. He and his son, Orlando, are clearing the debris from the ruined store, wearing gloves as they pick up the burnt wood, piece by piece, and toss it into the back of a truck parked behind the *groceria*.

"Oh, you come back, Bud," Pop says when I walk over to where they are working.

Is there some coolness in Pop's tone of voice, or is it my imagination? He does not stop working.

"I got back late last night," I tell him.

"They finish your place. Everything is fine."

"Yes. What about you? What are you going to do?"

Pop pauses, a charred two-by-four in his hand. He stares at me. "We going to sell, Bud."

We look at each other, and everything in that look speaks volumes, more than words will convey. And with it, I seem to make my own decision. I will not linger here, to be built around, surrounded, becoming a kind of dinosaur frozen in time. I, too, will sell. Pop picks up the wood, cradling it in both hands, before giving me a final look, then flinging part of his life into the truck bed.

In the drugstore, half a dozen people sit at a

table, their faces painted. Some in half masks with feathers crowning their heads. I am reminded that it is almost Halloween, Fantasy Fest. And although the parade is still a couple of days away, the revelry seems to have begun.

Frank Pappagallo is at the counter, and I sit next to him.

"Bud, where the hell you been?" Frank asks.

"Out of town."

"Since when did you become a travelin' man?"

"It was work, Frank."

I put my order in with Mary the waitress as the revelers file out, dancing in a sort of conga line and blowing on paper noisemakers that curl away from their lips like snakes.

"Let the good times roll," Frank says.

"Pop tells me he's selling," I remark when they are gone.

"That's what I was calling to tell you."

"What kind of a price did he get?"

Frank looks away, his mouth arching downward. "Below market." He pauses a beat, then adds, "Way below. But he hasn't got much choice. What's he going to do, rebuild?"

Inwardly, I wince, but something in my expression must show because Frank says, "I'm sorry, Bud." The way he says it, I am unsure if he is apologizing for himself, or me.

"Have they linked anyone to the fire?"

Frank shakes his head. "They think it was some crack addicts. They found a Coke can with holes in it like they use to smoke that shit."

"I don't believe it."

"Why not?"

"One, my bedroom wall's ten yards from the *groceria.* I'm a light sleeper. I've been awakened before by kids smoking back there."

"Maybe you were sleeping hard, Bud."

"Two, that fire was too intense in a very short time. It had to be fueled by something more than a spark from a crack pipe."

"The investigators found some evidence of oily rags and a can of linseed oil in what had been a storage closet where Pop kept his cleaning supplies. They think that's what fueled it."

"Maybe," I reply, looking away.

"You still think this was deliberate, Bud? That someone burned Pop out to get him to sell? I don't think you're going to get too far with that anymore."

"We'll see."

"Bud, I wouldn't start a vendetta, pushing peoples' noses out of joint."

"You keep warning me about that, Frank. If it was just a couple of crack addicts, what are you afraid of?"

Frank shakes his head. "Oh, what the hell. Sometimes there's no reasoning with you, Bud."

When Mary puts my breakfast down, Frank returns to his paper and I eat in silence. "What do you hear about Gaby?" I ask when I am finished.

"Not a thing. Why?"

"Apparently, she's over in the Bahamas with Roy Emerson."

"So? She's taking a vacation. No crime in that, is there?"

I pick up my check. "I hope not."

"What's that supposed to mean?"

"Exactly what I said. I hope there isn't any crime."

"Sometimes, Bud, I just don't understand you."

"I wouldn't lie awake nights trying," I reply, standing up from the counter.

"Wait a minute, Bud. What about you?"

"What about me?"

"You come to any decisions on your place?"

"I have," I say. "I'm ready to sell."

Frank beams. "No kidding."

"I'm not kidding. The place is on the market. You're the first to know, Frank."

"You got a figure in mind?"

"As a matter of fact, I do."

"Well?"

"Market value plus whatever loss Pop was forced to take on his deal."

Frank's face drops.

"Handle it for me, Frank. I'm counting on you." Taking my check to the register, I pay, then give the crestfallen Frank Pappagallo a wave on the way out.

33

◇

After breakfast, I put on a pair of swim trunks and carry a towel and mask three blocks down to the beach at the end of Duval. The water is cool and clear as glass. Wading out to waist-deep water, I adjust the mask on my head, then plunge in, feeling the skin-tightening tingle of salt, bracing as I begin my mile-long swim. An hour later, my muscles loosened up after the days of cold and tension, I return home and stand under a long cool shower.

The rest of the morning I spend on the phone trying unsuccessfully to track down Gaby. She seems to have vanished; yes, to the Bahamas, but no one apparently knows where exactly in the Bahamas, or for how long she will be gone. Everyone I talk to agrees that it is very unlike Gaby, who is normally so punctilious, so methodical. "You could set your watch by her," one of her friends tells me. Very mysterious.

She seemed okay when she left, I am told. Nothing unusual about her. Happy. Glad to be getting off the rock for a while.

I pursue my questioning, trying not to sound an alarm, for it is certain that when she returns, Gaby will hear from a variety of people that I have been asking about her.

At noon I decide to call and leave a message on

her answering machine. The phone rings three times, during which I prepare my spiel, ready to deliver it when the machine clicks on. But it doesn't. Instead, the phone is answered on the fourth ring by a breathless Gaby. "Bud!" she says. "When did you get back?"

"Last night. Late. How about you?"

"This morning. Less than an hour ago, in fact."

"You didn't tell me you were going away."

"It was kind of spur-of-the-moment."

"Where'd you go?"

"Bimini."

"Good time?"

"The best."

"Just you and Roy?"

"*Hmm uh.* Bud, you've got your investigator's tone of voice. Is anything wrong?"

"Nope. Curious is all. Sort of unusual for you to take off like that, isn't it?"

"Not when you're getting married."

"What?"

"Are you going deaf, Bud? I said, not when you're getting married."

"I heard you. I was surprised. I didn't think you were going to do it this soon."

"Changed our minds. We didn't want a big to-do. So we just decided to elope and get it over with."

"Your idea?"

"Mostly Roy's, but I wasn't against it."

"Let me be the first to congratulate you."

Gaby laughs. "Thanks, Bud. Now tell me about your trip."

"I probably ought to wait on that," I say. "Is Roy moving into your place?"

"Because of his work we're going to keep the same arrangement for the time being. He'll spend weekends out here."

"So the marriage was just a piece of paper. A formality."

"Bud, that sounds terribly cold. What's wrong with you?"

"Are you happy?"

"Very."

"Can I still see you? I mean for dinner sometime. Just the two of us."

Gaby tries to laugh again, but it is not quite so carefree. "Of course you can, Bud. Anytime. Nothing's changed."

"How about this evening?"

Gaby hesitates. "I suppose. I hadn't really intended to go back to work until tomorrow."

"And Roy?"

"What about him?"

"He won't mind?"

"Bud, what's gotten into you? Is something wrong?"

"I need to talk to you."

"You can talk to me anytime. Nothing's changed between us just because I'm married."

"I'm glad to hear that."

"Would you like to go to the Blue Moon?"

"How about someplace off the beaten track? In your area maybe."

"All right. There are a couple of places nearby. Why don't you drive up around seven and we'll go together?"

"Perfect. I'll see you at seven."

Have I pushed too hard, sounding some alarm

in Gaby? I wonder. The trick is going to be to make her wary without completely warning her that she may be married to a murderer. I do not know how to do that. Her marriage to Roy has made the situation even more delicate now. And, if the past can be any indication of things to come, time will not be on our side. I must take some decisive action but without alienating Gaby.

After hanging up, I call Fred Pacey's office.

"Mr. Pacey's in a meeting right now," his secretary tells me. "Can I take a message?"

" 'May.' "

"What?"

" 'May I take a message.' "

"I'm sorry, I don't—"

"Forget about it. What time do you expect he will be free?"

"I really don't know." Whatever warmth her voice contained has evaporated.

"I'll check back later."

"He'll be going to lunch after his meeting ends, and I don't expect him back the rest of the day."

"Thanks. I'll catch up with him."

With the thousand-dollar check from Bob Hargreaves in my pocket, I bike down to the bank, which is directly across the street from Fred Pacey's office building. After depositing the check, I pick up a newspaper and stand at one of several counters for filling out deposit slips, one that is near a window and affords a view across the street.

Twenty minutes later, Fred Pacey comes out of his office. He is accompanied by Frank Pappagallo. And Roy Faulkner Emerson.

34

◇

Fortunately, the trio remains on foot, easy enough to follow. A crowd of tourists prowls the streets with blank expressions, gawking at the gift shops, refreshment stands, bars, and restaurants, and I quickly blend in amongst them.

A couple of blocks from his office, Pacey and his party turn into one of the restaurants, an outdoor joint where a deck has been built around the spreading limbs of an old banyan tree on the second floor. I watch from the sidewalk below as they are seated at one of the tables overlooking the street.

Across the street is a square where outdoor vendors sell jewelry and trinkets from their mobile carts. There are some park benches in the shade of another banyan tree. Also beneath it a Filipino guy, wearing a handmade hat woven from thin strips of palm fronds, sits on the padded bicycle seat attached to his pushcart containing cold drinks. He is working a crossword puzzle folded from the morning newspaper, occasionally touching the tip of his lead pencil against his tongue before writing in a word.

Crossing the street, I enter the square and approach him. "Elmore. How's business?"

Elmore looks up. He wears glasses with lenses a quarter of an inch thick, magnifying his already big brown eyes. He grins; his large teeth flashing in his pink gums are flat white, like old ivory piano keys. "Cain't complain, Bud. Always a buck to make round chere."

Elmore is from the Philippines, a World War II refugee. He has somehow made a living plying the tourist trade. "Selling iced tea today?"

"Sure, why not?" Elmore puts his paper on a shelf attached to his cart, weighing it down with a conch shell, and takes a paper cup with the Coca-Cola logo from a stack, fills it with shaved ice from one compartment; then taking out a gallon jug of tea from another compartment, he pours the tea into the cup. "Want some key lime, Bud?"

I nod, watching as he squeezes juice from half a lime into the tea. "How much, Elmore?"

"Three bits." Elmore learned his English from American GIs in the Philippines.

I give him a dollar and tell him to keep the change.

"Thanks, Bud. Maria got some hot bollos and conch fritters down the way."

Looking in the direction he points, I see Elmore's wife at another stand, and walk over there to get half a dozen of the wok-fried fritters before going to a bench in the shade of the banyan, where I can eat while still being able to observe Pacey having lunch with Frank and Roy on the restaurant deck in the distance.

The fritters are perfect: spicy, plenty of garlic, light on the inside with a crispy exterior. Probably not what Doc Russell would recommend, but otherwise I have been diligent about the diet. An occasional reward seems harmless enough. The iced tea tastes freshly brewed. A light breeze drifts through the heavy-branched tree as a young black kid begins working on a set of steel drums at the opposite end of the square.

Half an hour goes by as I watch tourists mill around, haggling with the vendors over the price of costume jewelry. Then, an hour after they went into the restaurant, Pacey and company depart, retracing their footsteps. Pacey goes back to the office, and Roy and Frank stand outside talking for a few minutes before going off in different directions.

Frank turns onto Duval Street, ambling along leisurely, pausing now and then to look into shop windows. Everywhere Halloween festoons the atmosphere. Cheap paper cutouts of hobgoblins and vampires dripping bloody teeth cavort together in windows streaming with fuzzy gauze-like cotton candy, while jack-o'-lanterns seem to pucker and wilt under the tropical climate.

"Clever, isn't it, Frank?" I ask. He has stopped in front of a department store window, staring at a witch on a broomstick attached to a hidden track in the ceiling and flying around the interior perimeter. Once every revolution a tinny cackle emits from a loudspeaker. "Who would have thought Key West would ever get this kind of big-city sophistication. I remember when the best we could do for a holiday was a skinny Santa Claus in a moth-eaten red suit in the Christmas parade."

"Earl Tidwell," Frank says, continuing to stare at the witch.

"What?"

"Earl Tidwell. He was always the Santa. After Webb Conners put on so much weight, they tried to get him one year, but Earl wouldn't stand for it. Tradition, he told the city. Tucked a pillow up under his suit and went on until he died. Probably the oldest Santa in the country."

"I didn't know that."

"Times change, Bud."

"Sure they do. How was your lunch?"

Frank looks startled for a moment, then laughs. "You get around, don't you, Bud?"

"Now and then. Tell me about Roy Emerson."

"What do you want to know?"

"What he's got going with Fred Pacey?"

"He's handling the details on the upper Duval development."

"My place?"

Frank nods.

"You told them about my offer?"

"Of course, Bud."

"What did Pacey say?"

"He wasn't happy."

"He wasn't happy. That's all?"

"He didn't say no."

"And he didn't say yes."

Frank glances back at the witch.

"Maybe I better stay awake nights from now on," I say.

35

◇

"How well do you know Roy?"

Wearing a linen jacket over a blouse whose collar is turned up around her neck, Gaby gazes at me across the table in the outdoor restaurant a couple of miles from her home. A quizzical expression centers on her face. "I'm not sure what you're getting at, Bud. How well does anyone know anyone?"

"What I mean is, his background, his past." I realize I am stumbling, on shaky ground here. "His people," I add.

"Bud Lowry, are you jealous?" Gaby lifts her wineglass, smiling. I can't help but notice the diamond that glints on her ring finger.

Forcing a smile of my own, I lift my glass, touching hers. "Curious."

"One of the things I love about you, Bud, is your protectiveness. You're so insulated. It's really—" She seems to search for a word.

"Quaint."

"Sort of."

"I never thought of myself in those terms."

"Well, you know what I mean. I talked to friends today who said you'd called them. Are you worried about me? What's going on, Bud?"

A waitress comes and takes our order, giving me a brief respite. A chance to regroup.

But Gaby doesn't give me the opportunity. She bores in. "You still don't like Roy, do you? You think I've made a mistake."

"He's involved with Fred Pacey and the development project in my block. Did you know that?"

Gaby nods. "So," she says with some finality, "that's it."

"I can't say I'm exactly happy about it."

Gaby is sympathetic. "I understand. I'm sure I'd feel the same way. But you've got to separate Roy my husband from Roy the guy whose work you don't like. Or maybe you don't have to, but I do."

"Sure. I wish it was that easy."

"It has to be that easy, Bud. Otherwise our relationship is compromised. Yours and mine. And I don't want that to happen. We've always been very close."

Almost like lovers, I think, we stare into one another's eyes. "I don't want that to happen, either," I say.

"Then you've got to give Roy and me a chance. If you've got to fight with him, fine. I will understand. But please leave me out of it." She picks up her glass and drinks.

"Just one personal question?"

"Of course."

"Are you investing in this deal?"

"Bud, you're incorrigible. No."

But she does shift in her seat, I notice, crossing her legs beneath the table. She squirms.

I change the subject. "Nice rock," I say, admiring the ring. "Looks expensive."

With her thumb Gaby pushes the ring around on her finger. "It is a family heirloom," she says. "It belonged to Roy's grandmother."

Heirloom! The sonofabitch hasn't even paid for her ring! He could have told Gaby anything. It may even have belonged to his first wife, Karen. I make a mental note to call and ask Bob Hargreaves what became of his daughter's engagement ring.

I lift my glass once again in a toast. "Good luck, Gaby."

"Thanks. What are you thinking about?"

"Nothing." But I can see that Gaby doesn't believe me. Someone else crossed my mind just now, another marriage.

"Bud, is everything okay?"

"Fine."

Our food arrives. For a moment it is like old times. Gaby savors each bite, delineating each flavor, while providing a running commentary. By her standards, it isn't that good. An overuse of fruit to add flavor to overcooked fish. My lamb with mint sauce fares better. Nothing unusual, but there's something to be said for tradition, Gaby says. Then for a time we eat in silence.

"What about the trip you took?" Gaby asks, over coffee. "Tell me about it?"

"A case I'm working on," I say. "I can't really talk about it."

"Not even where you were."

I shake my head. "The West Coast." Knowing she will think Florida's west coast, that I would never have ventured all the way to the other side of the country. And, of course, had it not been for her, I would not have.

"Sometimes I think that you're being deliberately mysterious."

"And sometimes I have to be."

"And I have the feeling that it has to do with Roy."

The waitress brings the check. Gaby and I both reach for it. "On me this time," I say.

"Well, does it?" she asks, relinquishing her hold on the check.

"Does what?"

"Have anything to do with Roy?"

I smile. "Suppose I told you Roy was a serial killer?"

Gaby laughs. "I wouldn't believe you."

"Then it wouldn't make sense to tell you, would it?"

"But it isn't that bad, so tell me the truth."

I shrug. "Come on, Gaby. Let's get out of here."

We both stand up. I sense her nervousness. Perhaps I have done the right thing, having at least cautioned her without putting her in a position of denial, of having to defend Roy. I don't know.

We have come in Gaby's car, and we drive back to her place in silence. A cloud seems to have fallen over us, both of us tense, as if we are unsure how to proceed. As for myself, I now know what I have to do. Gaby's survival may depend on how well I do it.

36

◇

Gaby has told me that Roy Emerson lives in a condominium on the beach, and at seven-thirty the next morning I park the Buick on a side street where I am able to see both driveways leading in and out of the building.

With its toneless gray bulk that is monstrously out of proportion with the neighborhood, the condo is an eyesore that no amount of landscaping can hide. The puttylike walls and small flat windows of each of the twin wings resemble nothing so much as those of a prison. And by blocking the tolerant easterly sea breezes from reaching those of us inland, it has, in a sense, made prisoners of us all.

A few minutes before eight I see Roy drive out in his sports car. Leaving the Buick where it is, I walk across the street to one of the two entrances, where the building directory is located. One R. Emerson is listed in apartment 308 G. Pushing the intercom button next to his name, I hear a beep, which goes unanswered.

Locked glass doors lead to the interior of the building, where there are two elevators. A young couple is just coming out of one elevator, and I stand at the door, smiling as they exit.

"Forgot my key," I say.

The guy holds the door, grinning, but without paying much attention to me as he keeps up a conversation with his companion. I ride the elevator up to the third floor and exit onto a long, depressing corridor with apartment doors on either side of it. Overhead spotlighting casts weird shadows as I advance along the corridor, which seems to go on for half a mile, my soft-soled shoes squeaking against the tiles.

At the far end is 308 G, the last door, in fact. Roy no doubt has an apartment with a sea view. Each door has a peephole, and there is no way my approach could have gone unmonitored if someone were on the other side of the door.

Further back down the hallway, a door opens and closes, and as I knock lightly on Roy's door, I glance back quickly to see a man beginning his long march to the elevators. After a few seconds I try the door, which is, as I was sure it would be, locked.

The only keyhole is in the doorknob, which means, luckily, that there is no deadbolt. Certainly, a considerable savings to the developer with the number of doors in this place.

Satisfied that I've got the information I came for, I turn and walk back to the elevators, sure that on my next visit I won't have any problem picking the lock.

Back home, I call Fred Pacey's office and am told that he is not expected in before ten. Do I want to leave a message?

No, I don't. I want a cup of coffee and to read the paper, which I didn't have time for this morning, so I head over by bike to the drugstore and make good on one wish, anyway.

By a quarter to ten I am at Fred Pacey's building, lingering outside, waiting for the great man himself. He does not disappoint. At five past ten he strolls around the corner, his brow knit, but that could just have been from the too tightly knotted tie at his throat.

"Morning, Fred."

Pacey looks up. He has the startled but resolute stare of a small animal that has been captured in the glare of headlights. His hair seems to have thinned more since we last met, and his face has the sallow, pasty complexion of someone who spends too much time under fluorescent lighting.

The last time we met was under unfavorable circumstances, and I can see in Pacey's eyes the dawning awareness that this is not a coincidental meeting; I spell trouble. He looks at his watch.

"I've got a busy morning, Bud. I'm already late for an appointment."

"I'm not going to take up much time," I say.

Pacey seems to hesitate, as if he is unsure whether to barge past me or listen to what I have to say. Curiosity wins out. "What is it, Bud?"

Smiling, I tell him. I tell him what I think of his planned destruction of my neighborhood. I tell him what I think of his attempt to capitalize on the misfortune of my friend Pop. I put a little touch of sarcasm in my voice when I pronounce "misfortune" so that there is no uncertainty in regard to my feelings about that event.

Passersby, tourists, pause, looking at us. Pacey turns a shade darker in the face, running a finger between his neck and collar, a grimace on his otherwise expressionless face. I give him the clincher.

"Twenty-four hours," I say. "To make a decision on my offer. After that the price goes up, or I may even withdraw the offer altogether."

Pacey squares his shoulders. "Is that it, Bud?"

"No." I lift the end of his tie, rubbing my thumb against the silk. "Nice. Expensive." Then let it drop. "Any accidents, the sort of misfortune that occurred to Pop—I rebuild." I get on my bike. "That's it, Fred. Have a nice day."

I am home less than an hour when the phone rings. It is Frank.

"Bud, what the hell are you doing?"

"Making a point."

"Fred is furious."

"Good. For a while I was afraid he had no emotions."

"I wouldn't push him."

"He pushed me and I'm pushing back. That's what it comes down to."

"He's got a lot of influence in this town."

"With arsonists?"

"Bud, you're on shaky ground there."

"I wonder where I might find Roy Emerson this time of day."

"What do you want with him?"

"I'd just feel a little more secure if I knew where he was."

37

◇

Roy doesn't have an office, Frank tells me. He works out of other people's offices. Or, Frank confides, when he can, out of his car.

"What do you mean 'out of his car'?"

Frank laughs. "Roy's one of those guys who likes to be on the move. Can't seem to sit still for long. Likes to do business on the road, working the cellular. He'll think nothing of driving eighty or a hundred miles up the Keys to take someone to lunch, or dinner."

"He must be doing business with people who've got a lot of time on their hands."

"When he's trying to nail down a contract, I guess it's impressive. Roy's smooth."

"So I hear. Are you impressed, Frank?"

"Bud, between you and me, I don't like the guy. Okay? There's something about him, and I can't tell you what it is, but I don't like him. But I'll tell you something else. I'm not going to cross him, either."

"Level with me, Frank. Do you think he started that fire?"

"No. Now, do you want to ask me do I think he could have had a hand in someone else starting it? I'd say yes, it's possible. But I'd only say that to you, Bud, and you repeat it, I'll deny it."

"What about Gabriella?"

"What about her?"

"She married him."

"Listen, Bud, I'm a lawyer. Not a shrink. What brings two people together is beyond me. You ask me, half the married people I know, it doesn't make sense. But that's their business. As a lawyer, all I've got to do is get them out of it when it's time. Not analyze it."

In the street outside, a car painted orange and black drives by, a huge carved pumpkin with flashing lights mounted on its roof. A ghost is driving. Frank warns me once again against pushing Fred Pacey.

"Frank, I want this settled. I gave him twenty-four hours, and I meant it."

Frank sighs. "Bud, take my advice. Do what the kids today say."

"What's that?"

"Chill."

"I don't like the cold."

Frank does not laugh. "If you sell, have you thought about what you're going to do? Where you'll live?"

"Maybe I'll just rent a place."

"As your lawyer, I wouldn't advise you to do that. You sell this place and don't invest it, the capital gains taxes will kill you. "

"So as my lawyer, what would you advise me to do?"

"Buy something."

"You got any leads?"

"As a matter of fact, while you were away, Bud, your place on William Street went on the market."

I feel a tightening in my chest. "My place?"

"The ancestral home. Where you grew up."

Images of my childhood play before me. "It's a big house," I say. It had been converted to a bed and breakfast a decade or so ago.

"Not that big. You could live in the downstairs, have your office there, and rent out the upstairs. Have some income out of it."

I have not been in the place in nearly twenty-five years, but my mind has often been haunted by memories of my life there with my father, Captain Billy, my mother, Phyllis, and my brother, Carl, all of whom are dead. "What are they asking?"

"I think you could get it for under five."

I know that he means $500,000. And I also know that my mother could never have imagined the place would be worth that kind of money only twenty-five years after her death. "Where am I going to get that kind of money, Frank?"

"Have you forgotten what you're asking for your place? You make a sizable down payment, with money left over to make whatever changes you need to make to get some rental income. You'll be in a quiet neighborhood, off Duval Street, sitting pretty. What do you think?"

I think it sounds crazy. "When can I look at it?" I ask.

"I could set something up this afternoon."

We agree on a time, and when we hang up, I call Gaby, reaching her at home.

"I apologize," I say when she answers.

"For?"

"I had no business questioning your judgment. I was out of line. I truly hope you'll be happy."

"Thanks, Bud. I confess I've been bothered by our conversation."

"Forget it. You're special, Gaby. Maybe I am jealous."

"Don't be. You know how I feel about you, Bud."

"Have you seen Roy?"

"No, but he'll be here this evening."

"I'd just as soon you didn't say anything to him about last night."

"I hadn't planned on it."

"Maybe we can get together again. I'll be better behaved."

"Of course, Bud. Anytime."

Before hanging up, I tell her about my plan to look at the old Lowry homestead.

"That's wonderful," Gaby says. "Do it. It would be a kind of homecoming."

I am not so sure. But for whatever reasons, I have agreed to at least look at the house, and I find that it has provoked a strange nervousness in me, the sort of feeling that comes with the thought of impending confrontation.

38

◇

At two o'clock I am on William Street, standing beneath the familiar royal poinciana tree, whose barren, sticklike branches poke through the tangle of electrical wires stretched between wooden poles along the street. At this time of year it is always difficult to imagine these brittle, flaky trees exploding in fiery orange blossoms each spring, but in my childhood I awaited their arrival with the keen awareness that the first stab of color heralded the end of school and the approaching summer.

The exterior of the frame house is gray with green trim and shutters, the wide front porch bedecked with white wrought-iron porch furniture. It is inviting, welcoming. Everything clean, cool, and protected in the shade of the sheltering palm trees that grow on either side of the old poinciana.

"Looks pretty good, doesn't it, Bud?"

Soundlessly, catching me by surprise, Frank has come up beside me.

"A little more gussied up than it ever was when I was growing up here."

"You'll be able to tone it down once you're living in it."

"You seem confident I'm going to buy it."

"It makes sense," Frank says. "Come on. I've got the key."

I follow Frank up the sidewalk and watch as he unlocks the door to a place I have not been inside in nearly twenty-five years, since my mother's death.

The layout remains essentially unchanged from the way I remember it. Two front bedrooms off either side of the long hallway, with a stairway leading to the second floor, where there are two more bedrooms and a bath. In the back is the large kitchen and screened-in porch looking out over the deck under the shade of the thick, green leaves of a giant sapodilla tree.

Frank leads me through as if he's conducting a tour. "My idea," he says, "is one of the front bedrooms you could use, the other you'd turn into your office. Upstairs you put in a kitchenette and you've got a ready-made rental apartment. The place isn't that big, but it gives you some space, and everything is in good condition. That way it will generate income that should pay for whatever modest mortgage you have to carry."

Frank seems to have it all figured out. It's true. The hardwood floors have been kept up, everything is painted and clean. As a kid the place did seem much bigger. Now it is just a house, and I am happy not to be overwhelmed with the ghosts of my past.

"Well, what do you think?" Frank asks. We are standing in the kitchen. Everything is in place, but it is clear no one is living here. The cabinets are empty. There is nothing in the fridge.

"Why is it on the market?"

"Two guys operated it as a guesthouse. One of them died of AIDS a few months ago. His partner kept the business going for a while, but he just didn't have the enthusiasm for operating the place alone. He gave it up a month ago and left town."

An all too familiar story.

"To get a quick turnover, he's ready to make the price attractive."

"And what would that be?"

"I checked at the realty company. Four twenty-five."

I scoff. "Captain Billy bought the place for less than a thousand dollars."

"Sure. And twenty-five years ago you could hardly give one of these places away."

I try to remember what my brother and I sold the place for after Phyllis died. Maybe a hundred thousand.

"What I'm saying," Frank says, "is you're making an investment here. You sell your place, and put the money in this. You can't lose."

"If I get the price I'm asking for my place."

"I talked to Fred before I came over here. He's going to make an offer."

"I made the offer. All he's got to do is accept it. I made that plain."

"Okay. Okay." Frank looks skyward, exasperated. "Just hear what he has to say. I don't know what he's going to do. He didn't tell me."

Bob Hargreaves flashes across my mind, he and his wife Ruth, still living in the house his grandfather had homesteaded.

"I'll keep it in mind," I tell Frank.

He nods, but appears unconvinced. "I'm looking out for your best interests. This would be a good deal for you, Bud."

"I said I'll think about it."

Frank shrugs, and we leave the house, Frank locking the door. After telling him I will be in touch, I get on my bike and head home.

The space I have been living in the past thirty years seems spartan after revisiting the house where I grew up. Maybe Frank is right; it would make sense, but I wonder if I could adjust. If I am prepared to handle the intrusion of the past at this time in my life.

As I consider it all, the phone rings. It is Roy Emerson. From the background noise I can tell that he is on his cellular phone, in his car. "Bud, this is Roy. Gaby's husband."

I can hear what sounds like a smirk in his voice.

"I think we should talk," he continues. "Float some ideas around."

"What kind of ideas?"

Roy laughs. "The only kind that matter. Numbers."

"And when would you like to float these numbers?"

"How about tomorrow morning? I'll be up at Gaby's tonight, but I could drive in and pick you up at ten. Maybe have lunch up the Keys."

That would be fine, I tell him. And perhaps, after the work I intend to do tonight, we'll even have something more interesting to talk about than numbers.

39

◇

The building where Roy lives is more imposing and sinister in the dark than it is in daylight. At eight-thirty I park in the dimly lit lot. Wearing a dark sport jacket and an old straw hat I found in my closet, I walk up to the glass entry door where I was allowed in this morning. It is quiet, no one around. As a precaution, I punch in Roy's number and, as expected, get no answer.

When a car drives into the parking lot, I walk away from the building, listening as a man's footsteps walk across the drive and up to the entrance. Hearing the door click, I turn and walk back, lingering in the shadows of shrubbery where I can watch the door. If I can get in the condo as someone is leaving rather than entering, I figure my chances of being seen and remembered will be reduced in the event something goes amiss.

It's the dinner hour for people who live in fancy condos on the water, the time, I've calculated, when there should be the least movement in and out. Fifteen minutes pass before anyone comes out.

As two women leave the elevator together, I walk toward the door, fumbling for my keys, timing it so that I get there just as they open the door.

It goes as smoothly as the earlier rehearsal. The women seem to pay no attention to me. Smiling, I hold the door for them, then go in and take the waiting elevator. On the ride up I take from my jacket pocket the two lock picks I've brought with me, palming them as the elevator door opens on the third floor. A middle-aged guy is waiting. He steps back to let me out. We speak, and as he enters the elevator, I begin the long march down the corridor.

Although the lock on Roy's door is as easy to pick as I anticipated it would be, twice I am forced to step aside and hide in a narrow alcove beside the fire extinguisher when I hear the elevator or people entering or exiting their apartments.

Finally, when the corridor is clear the second time, I go back to Roy's door and, with just the right pressure, feel the tumblers fall into place as the knob turns in my hand.

Stepping inside and closing the door behind me, I stand for several seconds letting my eyes adjust to the dark. A hallway gives onto a kitchen and, beyond that, the living room. A quick walkthrough reveals a two-bedroom, one-bath apartment. Everything is furnished in the standard, homogenous furnishings one would expect in a luxury rental unit. A sofa, a glass-topped coffee table, a couple of matching leather chairs, and a dining room with a bamboo-and-glass table and four bamboo chairs covered in some sort of tropical print. The kitchen has all the modern conveniences. Dishwasher, garbage disposal, and a freezer with an ice dispenser. In the fridge, I find a bottle of V-8 juice, a half-empty container of milk, three eggs, and an unopened package of cheddar cheese. Everything is neatly ordered, in its place, as if no one lives here or, more probably, I think, Roy is the type to have a maid come in on a routine basis.

In the living room two long, narrow, fixed windows, incapable of being opened, look out over the beach. Between them a door opens onto a small balcony. Along an adjacent wall is a new desk, designed, however, to look as though it were an antique. A small laptop computer is positioned in the center of the desk. Beside it is a telephone and answering machine, its red message light blinking insistently. I close the drapes over the windows, then switch on the brass desk lamp with its green shade and sit down behind the desk.

A few papers cover the desk's surface. Glancing at them, I see that one is an American Express bill, the others mostly advertising circulars and catalogs. I pick up the AmEx bill. The itemized list of charges suggests a spree in Miami in the past month. Restaurant charges, each meal totaling more than a hundred dollars. Nearly three hundred in charges at Bloomingdale's and over five hundred in a jewelry store in Coral Gables. All told, Roy has racked up more than two thousand dollars in expenses for the previous month on Am Ex, most of them from Miami, incurred in a matter of days.

Before turning to the answering machine, I jot down in my pocket notepad the names of the establishments Roy has frequented in Miami, as well as the dates of his consumption and purchases.

The answering machine looks like a quality, high-priced instrument, with automatic speed-dial and a variety of other buttons, along with a message screen and some features that mean nothing to me. I press the message button, confident that whatever is on the machine will not be erased.

A beep and Fred Pacey's voice comes on, asking Roy to call him first thing in the morning.

Another beep. And the sound of a receiver hanging up. Beep. "Hi, honey," a woman's voice says. Young. But not Gaby's. "Listen, my plans got changed. I'm going to be in all evening. So call me whenever you get this and let's talk. I'm bored." There is a flirtatious laugh before she hangs up. A beep followed by three beeps, and the machine clicks off.

For a while I sit staring at the phone. Roy has a mother who is alive, no other relatives that I know of, but this was not a mother's voice. Or a sister's. It had the unmistakably intimate tone of a lover, a girlfriend.

Opening the desk drawers, I search for an address book. Roy is extremely neat, organized. Everything labeled, put together in some order. Carefully trying not to disturb any of it, I examine the various bits and pieces of paper. Unable to find an address book, I walk into the bedroom and look on a bedside table, where there is another phone. No book. Nothing in the drawer of the table.

In the closet, Roy's clothes hang neatly, shirts together on one side, a few suits with nothing in their pockets, several pairs of shoes lined up and a couple pairs of cowboy boots, polished. I return to the desk in the living room.

A few first names, some initials have been penned next to the speed-dial buttons on the phone. Except for Gaby's name, the others mean nothing to me. The other names are men's. And there are a half-dozen listings with initials only. I pick up the phone, press the button next to an initial, listening to a ring that goes unanswered.

After disconnecting, I press a second button, and a man answers on the third ring. I hang up, then try a third button. Four rings and I am about to hang up when a woman answers.

"Hi, Roy. That was quick. I really didn't expect to hear from you tonight. Hang on a sec. I just got out of the shower. I'm standing here dripping wet."

I stand there mesmerized. It is the same voice I heard on the answering machine. She must have caller ID, which means when she next talks to Roy, he will know someone has been in the apartment. I hang up and wonder what I should do. I can call back with some lame excuse, but I am damned if I can think of one that would prevent her from saying anything to Roy. I am pondering that when the phone rings. I stare at it. A little light has come on the message screen with the name Page Anderson and a phone number.

The answering machine takes the call, and Page says, "Roy, what's going on? Are you playing games with me? You just called. Pick up the phone. Come on, honey. Don't do this. Roy . . . Roy? Come on, pick up the phone. I know you're there. . . . All right. You'll never know what you missed." That flirtatious laughter. Then, click. She hangs up.

40

◇

Page Anderson. After calling information in a couple of places in the 305 area code, I find her listed in Coral Gables. A Miami residential district. It is now ten past nine. I have been in Roy's apartment less than an hour, but in that time I seem to have uncovered an interesting little side piece to his life story. Perhaps there is a perfectly reasonable explanation of it; nothing more than an old family friend. And perhaps, as we used to say, the moon is made of green cheese.

I consider my options. Whether to call Page again and confront her with the truth, that Roy Emerson is a married man, or to confront Roy. Either way I need to quiz her, to find out what his exact relationship with her is, and I cannot risk revealing my identity. Roy is soon going to know that someone called Page from his apartment, and that should no doubt sound an alarm with him. I decide to call her tonight from a pay phone, even though there is no reason for Roy to connect me to the break-in.

Before leaving, I turn off the light, open the drapes, then go through the apartment to be sure nothing has been disturbed. As I look over the desk once more and check my pockets to see that

I've got the tools that I came with and my notepad, my hand closes on a book of matches, the sort of thing I routinely pick up. But these are from the café in Jackson Hole. On impulse, I drop them on the floor by the corner of the desk.

Before cracking the front door and looking out, I listen for sounds of anyone in the corridor. No one seems to be around. I lock the door before closing it and head toward the elevator.

There is a pay phone on the corner of the park near the beach, only a few blocks from here. I drive there, park the Buick beneath some Australian pine trees, and sit for a moment dreaming up something to say. Finally, I walk to the phone and dial Page Anderson. She picks up on the second ring, a hint of curiosity in her voice.

"Is Roy there?" I ask.

There is a brief hesitation. "Who's calling?"

"Don." I repeat Page's phone number, telling her that Roy had given it to me.

"Oh. Well, he isn't here."

"Do you expect him?"

"Actually, he's out of town. I don't expect him before next week, no." Something in her voice makes me think that she is happy that Roy has given someone her number.

"Sorry to bother you, Mrs. Emerson."

Page laughs. "We're not actually married."

"Oh, I seem to remember Roy telling me he was getting married. I assumed—"

"In June."

"What?"

"We're getting married in June."

"I guess that was it. Well, congratulations."

"Thanks. I'll be happy to take a message and have him call you."

"I'm just passing through and thought I would call. I'm going to be traveling for a while and unreachable."

"And your name again."

"Yes, of course. Don. He'll know who it is."

"Well, I'll certainly tell him you called. Is there any message?"

"Oh, no. We knew each other out West. He'll know what it's about."

"All right."

"Nice talking to you. And congratulations again."

I hang up.

The sulfuric stench of rotting seaweed drifts across the road from the beach. An odor that carries the toxic quality of gas that has suddenly been released from its stoppered container, the kind of smell that would send a chemistry class full of kids into fitful laughter. The unmistakable reek of something dead and decomposing. All from a weed aimlessly adrift on the surface of the sea, tugged and pulled by the wind, by currents and the tide, some of it eventually piling up onto a shoreline, and the beauty and the mystery is that it should pile up here, spreading its noxious aroma along a beach that is crowded with the condos and private homes of the rich.

Beautifully mysterious, and ironic. How a guy like Roy Faulkner Emerson should have to live surrounded by a stench that fits him to a T.

41

◇

Roy shows up the next morning at five minutes before ten. He is wearing jeans, a crisp white shirt, a pair of soft leather moccasins on his feet. His face is freshly shaved, and in the breeze stirred by the overhead fan, I get a whiff of the lingering scent of cloves. The crooked smile creases the lines around his mouth together, but there is something more in his face now. A certain tension that I have not seen in him before.

"Well, Bud, you ready to go for a ride?"

"I'm not much of a traveling man."

"Oh? That's not what I hear." Roy smirks. And for a second I think he has heard about my trip to Jackson Hole. It is conceivable that he still has contacts there. If so, then he may well have put two and two together and come up with an answer to the mysterious intruder in his condo last night. I am relieved when he says, "Gaby tells me you've been away on a trip."

"Work," I reply. As if that one word can dull whatever pleasure some people might get from travel.

"So how about it? I know a good seafood place up the Keys. We leave now, we can have lunch there and I'll get you back by two o'clock."

I shrug. "Work," I repeat. "I don't have time."

For a moment I am surprised when Roy appears to be sincerely disappointed. Hurt. "Anything interesting?"

"I don't discuss my cases."

"Just curious. I've often wondered how you guys do what you do."

"Why? You looking for another career?"

Roy grins. "As long as we're not going anyplace, mind if I sit?"

I motion to the chair in front of my desk and Roy sits down. I take a seat behind the desk. "This is the way it begins, right? A client comes in, sits down, and tells you his problem. You ask a few questions, then go out and solve the problem."

"Something like that."

"That must make you feel pretty good. Solving people's problems."

"Sometimes."

"I mean, for example. Let's say I got somebody bugging me. I want to find out who it is, what they want, and get them off my back. Now, in theory, I come to you, and you take care of it for me."

"In theory."

"And to do that you might have to snoop around some, am I right?"

I nod, feeling another twitch of discomfort.

"Would you break into somebody's house? I mean if I had hired you and you felt it was necessary to solve my problem?"

Clearing my throat, I say, "I'd rather not break the law."

"Of course. But in the interests of your client?"

"Sometimes there is a fine line, and sometimes

you are forced to step over it." I concentrate on staring Roy in the eye.

Roy does not blink. Finally, he grins. "Isn't that just a poke in the eye with a sharp stick."

"What's that?"

"Legal beagles. Always ready to break the law to make the law."

"What are you getting at, Roy?"

"Somebody broke into my place last night."

"What's that got to do with me?"

"I think it was a shamus."

"Why would he want to break into your place?"

"Because somebody was paying him to snoop."

"I see." I feel my scalp begin to tingle. "That's what this is all about. Have you got something to hide?"

Roy looks slightly amused. "Everybody's got something to hide. Don't you?"

I think about it. All the past trials and tribulations with my difficult family, the marriages, the years of heavy drinking. Yeah, along the way there have been awkward and embarrassing episodes, things that I would just as soon let molder away in my own interior attic, but I have never killed anyone; nor have I committed bigamy. "Sure," I say to Roy, "but nothing I can't live with if it got out in the open."

"If it gets out in the open, that's one thing. If it's pried out that's another."

I force a smile. "What skeletons have you got hanging in your closet, Roy?"

Roy does not return the smile. "Papers. Business stuff. It gets into the wrong hands and I'm dead."

"So, what you're saying is that you're a victim of corporate espionage? Somebody's spying on you for business purposes. Is that it?"

"What I'm saying is that somebody broke in my place last night."

"They take anything?"

"I don't know yet."

"You call the police?"

Roy scoffs. "More legal beagles."

"So what do you want me to do?"

"Nothing. I'm just telling you, since you're in the same slimy line of work."

"What are you going to do?"

"Don't worry. I can handle it myself."

Two thoughts cross my mind, causing relief and concern at the same time. One, Roy does not suspect me. And two, I should call Don Cameron as soon as Roy leaves.

42

◇

Roy's face contorts once more, and that devil-may-care grin returns. I try to picture him on the mountain trail with Karen Hargreaves on the last day of her life and wonder what expression he wore just before she took the tumble.

Roy spreads his hands, looking up at the ceiling. "Amazing. A place like this, anywhere else in the world and you couldn't give it away. A shack."

"Location, location, location." I repeat Frank Pappagallo's mantra.

"Exactly." Roy leans forward. "But you're still asking too much. Now, let's talk turkey."

"Turkey?"

"Why I'm here. Let's get an agreement."

"I gave Fred Pacey my price. I think I made it clear. He didn't tell you?"

"He told me. Now, can we talk?"

"I hope I don't stutter. It's a take-it-or-leave-it kind of deal."

"Not in real estate; it doesn't work like that. There's always room for some negotiation."

"And arson."

"For the sake of our relationship I'll pretend I didn't hear that."

"You're pretending not to hear a lot of things, Roy. There's nothing to negotiate."

Roy picks up the leather satchel that is beside his chair. "You got a minute, I'd like to show you something."

"A minute's just about all I've got."

Roy pulls out some papers from the satchel and spreads them on the desk. "Here are the plans. I thought you might like to have a look at them."

I look over the sketches of the mall that's planned for here. Little blue lines in the shape of buildings with numbers, dimensions, some palm trees and a fountain drawn in. Except for the precision, they could be a child's drawings. "Okay. What am I supposed to say?"

"You know what these represent?"

"Buildings. Sure, I see them."

"Yeah, but the establishments themselves. The names are down there in fine print. Let me show you." Roy stands up and leans over the desk. Taking a pen from his shirt pocket, he points out some of what's to be built here. "We've got commitments from these outfits. They're on board. See that one? Bazoombas."

"Bazoombas?"

"Bazoombas. You know, the chain outfit. Bar, women in skimpy costumes." Roy makes a motion with his hands, holding them in front of his chest. "It's going in next door. The little grocery store that burned."

"Classy."

"You like it? Open till two or three in the morning. Tends to draw the young crowd. Spring-break types. Now, here's one. A store that's going to sell motorcycle paraphernalia, with a coffee bar and a café inside. It's been real popular in New York and on the West Coast. We look for it to draw a biker crowd, along with the wannabes, of course. And then there's the usual assortment of clothing stores and one upscale restaurant. All in all, we expect to have pretty much around-the-clock traffic through here. Like it?"

"Maybe it will be good for my business."

"Maybe. But somehow I don't think the people who come through here will be looking for shamuses."

"You never know. It sounds like the kind of place that could generate a high crime rate."

"Don't be a fool, Bud. You know as well as I do life is going to be pretty miserable if you're trying to live here."

"Life can be that way sometimes. You take the good with the bad."

"But not if you don't have to. We're offering a tidy sum so you only have to take the good."

"Yeah, but it isn't my sum."

"So we're back to that." Roy begins to fold up the drawings.

I nod. "We're back to that."

"You won't even think about five hundred thousand dollars?"

"I'll think about it. I'll think about it a lot. But you can come back here a hundred times with plans for an airport and a zoo, and I'll tell you the same thing. I told Fred Pacey—"

"Spare me, Bud. You don't need to keep repeating yourself."

"Apparently, I do. You're not getting the message."

Roy crams the papers in his satchel. "Don't be a fool, Bud."

"You're repeating yourself."

Roy's grin flickers, turning into a twitch before he walks out the door.

I'm left sitting alone thinking about $500,000. After the down payment on the family home on William Street, I'd still have a pretty nest egg. But I would have to live with the notion that I'd been robbed. And Pop had been burned out. Neither of those notions are acceptable.

It is ten-thirty, eight-thirty in Jackson Hole. I get myself a ginger ale and look up Don Cameron's office number.

43

◇

Am I wrong about Roy? I wonder as I dial the Wyoming number. Am I simply pursuing another man's obsession? Anything's possible, I realize, but because of Gaby I cannot retreat.

Don's voice comes across the line, the slow western drawl like the sound of the wind along a dry river bed. I can picture him in his office, the Stetson pushed back on his head, the thick droopy mustache covering his mouth, and his booted feet propped up on the corner of the desk.

Without mentioning this morning's encounter with Roy, I bring him up to date on Roy's other involvements. When I am finished, Don whistles softly and says, "Well, that squares."

"You think he's feathering his nest?"

"What else? What do you know about Page Anderson?"

"Not a thing. That's next on the agenda."

"Ten will get you twenty she's got no problem with cash flow."

"The thought has crossed my mind. Maybe you can give me a hand."

"Sure. What do you need?"

I tell him about the book of matches from the café in Jackson Hole that I planted in Roy's apartment and the call to Page I made identifying myself as Don. No last name.

That bit of information doesn't seem to bother him. "So assuming she's told Roy, he thinks I'm in Florida tailing him."

"That's exactly what he thinks. Does he know you?"

"We never had the pleasure. But he certainly knows *of* me."

"And why you would be tailing him?"

"Of course."

"And maybe a little surprised that after all these years you have tracked him down again."

"I would think so."

"Good. Why not give Anderson an anonymous call from your office. Bring her up to date on Roy's marital status."

"Why anonymous?"

"I've already talked to her, so she probably would pick up on the difference in our voices."

"Why don't you call her then?"

"For one thing, she's got caller ID. Maybe that doesn't reach across state lines, but even if it does, a call from your office will add some weight to it. For another, I'd rather have Roy believing you were in Jackson Hole."

"Kind of a scattershot tactic, isn't it, Gideon?"

"Kind of."

"Doesn't it put the two women in some jeopardy?"

"I've thought about that," I tell him. "In fact, give it a day before you make the call. And give her Gabriella's phone number."

"Sure."

After giving him Gaby's number, I ask about the Hargreaves.

"Getting older," Don says. "Just like the rest of us."

"Well, pay my respects."

"I'll do that. And take it easy. Sounds like you're close to having a tiger by the tail. Be careful you don't get bit."

"I'll do that, Don." Then I hang up.

Don, of course, is right. I am putting Gaby at risk. And possibly Page Anderson. It isn't going to be easy, but I know I have to tell Gaby, have to convince her that the man she is married to, besides being a two-timer, may also be a murderer about ready to strike again. And I need to enlist her help in catching him.

After digging out the Miami phone book, I look up Hoke Moseley, a retired cop I know who has gone into private practice.

"What's doing?" I ask when he answers the phone.

"Just sitting around in a blue funk waiting on you to call, Gideon. How's by you?"

"I don't want to waste your time with my complaints."

Hoke laughs. "Time, I've got."

"I'd rather take it up getting a little job done."

"How little?"

"I need some background information on someone in your area. A short bio will do."

"Does someone have a name?"

"Page Anderson. She lives in Coral Gables." I give him the address and telephone number.

"You're making it too easy. I thought I was

going to have to work. When do you need it? Yesterday?"

"That would have been nice. But today will do."

"Okay. So I do get to work. I'll be in touch."

44

◇

The club is crowded with costumed revelers when I show up to play at nine o'clock. Ronnie greets me with a mile-wide grin, the kind that says the tip jar is overflowing. "Going to the parade tomorrow night?" she asks.

"How can I miss it? I've got a front-row seat."

Ronnie winks and hurries off to fill drink orders. The noise is a steady crescendo of voices and laughter as more and more people file into the dimly lit, smoke-filled room. I mount the stage to the piano and strike a couple of chords that quickly become lost in the bedlam.

Tomorrow night's parade down Duval Street is the culmination of several days of public partying, a time of mayhem and silliness, when strangers can let down their inhibitions for a night without any clear excuse other than the one of tradition, which fifteen years of celebrating Halloween in this fashion has produced. The town seems to be full, expectant. Upbeat. Next week the city will return to its senses as business groups begin to add up the revenue. And, at the same time various religious and conservative elements will continue to challenge the weeklong debauchery, urging the city to restrain the more flagrant and outrageous libertarians at next year's festival.

Tinseltown is this year's festival theme. I recognize a few attempts at creating Hollywood characters, but for the most part the costumes are generic, feathers and masks. And a lot of body paint.

A few people gather around the piano, clapping and singing, as I pound out a chorus of "When the Saints Go Marching In." Always a crowd pleaser. The circle around the piano grows. "I want to be in that number," someone croons in counterpoint. "Wait your turn," another voice shouts, drawing a laugh. Everyone begins to clap.

I wind up with a vibrant two-handed trill that would have made Jerry Lee Lewis proud, and people begin to shout out requests. For an hour I play old standards, mostly show tunes that encourage a kind of rowdy singalong as well as tips that begin to fill the oversize balloon brandy snifter that rests on the baby grand.

The crowd seems expansive, expectant. An easy gig. For an hour and a half I play nonstop before taking my first break. After a pit stop, I carry a glass of seltzer out on the balcony to brace myself with some fresh air.

The night hums, tight as a string on a bass fiddle. Pedestrians prowl Duval Street like fat in search of a sizzle. A car horn honks; someone shouts. Laughter erupts from the street, carried upward on the scented breeze—a mixture of exhaust fumes, sweat, and beer.

Back inside, the crowd has grown, fanned out. The mood has changed, and no amount of trickery will induce them back to the piano again. A woman wearing body paint and little else comes in with an entourage. Her small breasts, painted red, white, and blue in concentric circles have become like wheels, each nipple a hub to which a small flashing light has somehow been attached.

She is surrounded by guys in some sort of cavalry uniform, denim blue shirts with double button fronts, tight khaki trousers tucked into calf-high, lace-up boots. And Stetsons. They form a phalanx, escorting her to the bar, where Ronnie takes their drink orders. The cavalry looks on proudly, as if they are on a mission.

It is steadily downhill from then until my gig ends at two in the morning. Drinks are spilled. A fight breaks out between one of the cavalrymen and a civilian who stares too long at the painted lady. A bouncer comes and separates them before anyone is hurt, tossing the civilian out, while allowing the cavalryman to remain. A married couple dressed in space suits get into an argument at the bar.

By the end of the night the costumes seem to have wilted. The mood has gone as flat as a week-old open container of Coke. What was once excitement has now turned to rancor and irritation. I walk over to the bar, where Ronnie appears frazzled.

"Jesus!" she says. "Is it worth it?"

"Just a dress rehearsal for tomorrow."

She shakes her head. "No, this is the big night. Tomorrow they tank up early and are out of here by parade time. Except for the stragglers. When are you back here?"

"Next weekend."

"Lucky you. Take it easy, Gideon."

"You too, Ronnie."

Carrying a plastic cup of seltzer, I go out and walk down Duval. People are still prowling, but the debris of the night lies in the gutter, the trash cans full of discarded beverage containers, a slightly sickening sour smell hanging over the street. In a doorway a young guy plays the saxophone, stumbling over some early Coltrane, bobbing his horn when I toss a fiver into his open instrument case.

At home there is a message on the machine from Hoke Moseley. He has the information I requested, and I can call him before eleven or after seven tomorrow morning. This morning.

After a long cool shower, I hit the sack and fall into a dreamless sleep.

45

◇

It is bright and sunny the next morning, too bright and too sunny. I can still taste last night's residue of secondhand smoke and booze. Between that and less than five hours sleep, I feel as if I have crawled out of a Mexican cantina after a night of mariachi music and cheap tequila. Mouthwash doesn't help. The only hope is coffee, which I'm forbidden.

A few minutes before eight I sit down at my desk and phone Hoke in Miami.

"Brother, Gideon," he says, "age has its rewards. We don't need so much sleep."

"I need it. I just can't get it."

"Soon enough, my friend. Soon enough." Hoke laughs.

"You've got something for me on the Page Anderson woman?"

"I do. She's thirty-five years old, widowed once, and has no sign of financial problems. And did I mention? Easy on the eyes as well. Any help?"

"It fits a pattern. Where does the money come from?"

"She married well. Page started out in the entertainment business. Worked the dinner-theater circuit around south Florida for a few years, but her career never took off. When she was pushing thirty, she made the club scene as a singer under the name Page Paradise. Ever heard of her?"

"Nope."

"That was the problem. Which was where her husband entered. Bob Anderson. A big shot in the tire business. You've probably seen his ads on TV."

"I don't have a TV."

"Oh. Well, he did a song-and-dance routine. Kind of corny, but I guess it sells tires. Page even made a few ads with him."

"What happened to him?"

"Cancer. Leukemia. Took him in less than a year from the time he was diagnosed."

"How long ago?"

"About two years."

"And what's Page been doing in that time?"

"About a year ago she made an effort to revive her career, but she'd been away from it too long and there wasn't much to revive in the first place. Besides, with what she got from the tire mogul she doesn't need a career. She's got a house in the Gables, and when she needs money, all she's got to do is clip a coupon."

"Doesn't sound like much of a life."

"Which is maybe why she wants to get married again."

"The only problem with that is the fella she's picked out is already married."

Hoke remains silent for a moment. "So that's what this is about. I've been wondering."

"That's what it's about."

"Who are you working for?"

"A family out of state. This has happened before with not-so-pretty consequences."

"I see. Well, if there's anything more I can do, I'll just be sitting around on the porch watching the sun go down."

"Thanks, Hoke. What do I owe you?"

"A C-note will do."

"Done. I'll put a check in the mail today."

"And keep me posted."

"Sure thing."

After hanging up, I write a check out to Hoke, put it in an envelope, and drop it in the mailbox on the way to breakfast at the drugstore.

The information Hoke has provided is interesting but about what I had expected. At least I've got a take on Page Paradise Anderson, and something to think about. Like what she will do when she gets a call from Don Cameron this morning.

It is close to ten o'clock when I get back home and do what chores need doing around the house. At ten-thirty, just as I'm about ready to go out again, Frank Pappagallo shows up.

"Bud, for heaven's sake, why won't you listen to reason?"

Frank has on a straw hat, imitation Panama with a black band and the brim turned down all around. With his large nose and sallow complexion he looks ridiculous.

"I'm always willing to listen to reason. She just doesn't speak much anymore."

Frank sidles into the office. "Pacey's furious.

He's threatening to withdraw his offer, to build around you."

I snicker. "I know. Surrounded by big bazoombas and Harleys. Life in the fast lane."

"Come on, Bud. I'm trying to do you a favor. What's a hundred grand?"

"I'll tell you what it is. It's a price tag. It means you can be bought. I won't be bought by a lowlife like Fred Pacey, no matter what I have to live with."

Frank lifts the hat by the brim and scratches his head with the same hand. Then puts the hat back on again. "What's it going to get you, Bud?"

"To sleep at night."

"All right." Frank sidles back to the door in the same herky-jerky way he came in. "Don't blame me if this blows up in your face."

I don't like the expression. "Cut the crap, Frank. If this blows up in my face, I'll hold Pacey, *and you,* responsible. You've known me too long for that. I won't be bought and I can't be pushed."

We stand eyeing each other, waiting. Finally, Frank sees there is no advantage to it and goes out the door in disgust.

I stay at my desk wondering if my pride has got the best of me. After half an hour of that, I say to hell with it, get the keys to the Buick, and leave the house.

46

◇

On my way out of Key West I think about stopping at Gaby's. Sooner or later she is going to hear something. From Page, or Roy. Or both of them. And she is going to blame me. By not stopping I am postponing the inevitable, but I will see her tonight for sure at the private party she is giving at the Blue Moon. The inevitable can wait a few hours.

Instead, I drive. With nowhere to go and no reason to get there, I head up the Keys, thinking of Roy, who so much likes to do business out of his car while on the road. Usually, I detest this sort of aimless driving but it does have certain benefits. Drifting and dreaming. The radio on, the music turned low; a warm, deliciously dry breeze floating in on a late October morning. A perfect time for reflection.

The traffic coming into Key West is a steady crawl of cars, vans, and buses. Judging from the expressions that I am able to catch a glimpse of now and then, it is a rowdy crowd on the way to a party.

Along the walkways of the old bridges, a few fishermen stand leaning over the rails, waiting for something to bite. The water is calm, about the color of a green tomato just on the vine. Off in the distance I can see a few flatboats, the guides standing like scarecrows on their platforms built over the outboard engines, from whence they slowly pole their way across the shallows. Some commercial boats are out, too, working their traplines. The unholy alliance of industry and tourism, all right here along the highway, competing for a buck.

Coming into one of the many indistinguishable hamlets that dot the roadside through the Keys, I pass a service station and a convenience store before turning into and parking the Buick in the dusty lot of a shack that bills itself The Long Spoon Café.

Two wooden booths and half a dozen rickety tables are empty inside the screened-in porch. I perch on one of the counter stools and order iced tea from a waitress with stringy gray hair and an expressionless face that is as wrinkled as a dried prune.

"Anything else?" she asks, putting the glass of tea, some of which slops onto the counter, in front of me.

"How's the fish sandwich?"

"Fresh."

"The only way I like it. Any particular fish or just whatever happens to be biting?"

"Today it's snapper, and don't ask what kind of snapper, because I don't know."

"I wouldn't dream of it. I'll take one."

"Fried or grilled?"

"Next you're going to offer me the wine list." That gets nothing from her. "Fried," I say.

The waitress makes a couple of ticks on her bill, tears it from the pad, and slides it under a bell in a hole in the wall that connects to the kitchen. Then comes back and puts down a napkin, anchoring it with a knife and fork.

"Kind of quiet for this time of day, isn't it?" I ask, continuing my quest for conversation.

She eyes me through narrow, dark slits. "What time of day is it?"

I look at my watch. "Lunchtime."

"Early," she says, swiping at the spilled liquid with a rag that looks like it has been used to clean oil sticks.

I just shrug rather than press the issue. The waitress moves away. I hear the sizzle of my fresh fish as it hits the fat in the kitchen. Five minutes later the waitress puts a platter in front of me with the fish on Cuban bread and some potato chips.

"You ain't a tourist, are you?" she asks. The eyes have opened a crack.

"Nope. Born and raised about twenty-five miles down the road from here."

"I thought so. Your accent." I sense that I have somehow paid my dues into this club. And wonder, like Groucho Marx, if I really want to be a member here.

"Key West?" she asks.

"Yeah. Maybe here you consider anyone down there a tourist, though."

"I lived in Key Weird a few years. It was all right. Until it got to be overrun."

"Don't let the chamber of commerce hear you. They regard that kind of talk as subversive."

"Screw the chamber of commerce. Tourists stop

and take a look in here, they usually turn around and go straight back to their cars."

I let that pass, since I have no difficulty believing her.

"How's the sandwich?"

"Any fresher and I'd have to thump it with a stick."

A smile almost adds another crease to the crone's face. Instead, she turns to the coffee urn, empties out the sludge, and rinses the pot before making a fresh batch. Then she disappears.

I finish my sandwich as a couple of fishermen come in, their T-shirts stained with dried blood and what looks like fish entrails. The waitress comes out of nowhere and, without speaking, draws two drafts into chilled mugs, putting them in front of the two men. Then walks over to me.

"Anything else?"

I lift out my wallet and put a ten-dollar bill on the counter. "How'd they come up with the name for this place?"

The waitress snaps the ten between her fingers, carries it over to the register, rings up the sale, and brings back my change. "Check out the sign next to the door on your way out."

Leaving a couple bucks on the counter, I pocket the rest of the change and walk to the door. The sign next to it is old, scarred, and stained. "If you dine with the devil," it reads, "bring a long spoon."

47

◇

Surprisingly, there are no messages on the answering machine when I return home late in the afternoon. I have been expecting to hear something from Gaby, or at least Don Cameron, but silence is loudest perhaps just before the clamor.

Sitting down at the desk, I put in a call to Don. He does not answer, neither at the office nor his home. Putting my feet up on the desk, I stare out the window.

Duval Street has been closed off, and a glut of pedestrians in costumes fills the street, a kind of warm-up act to the grand parade that is scheduled to start in less than two hours.

From a dime store I have purchased a black half-mask, the kind made famous by the Lone Ranger so many decades ago. It will do little to conceal my identity, but it does fulfill the requirement in Gaby's invitation.

Half an hour before the parade is to begin, I shower and shave and put on a clean pair of khakis with a freshly laundered white shirt. Then, as I stand before the bathroom mirror feeling somewhat foolish, I pull on the black mask, surprised by the change it renders. I, at least, barely recognize the portly gentleman who stands half-masked before me.

It is dark when I go out to join the throng. Multitudes have crowded in on this narrow piece of asphalt—estimates from those who keep tabs on such things are that more than fifty thousand people will be on Duval tonight, a street that is less than a mile long. That seems like a staggering number, since it represents almost twice the normal population of this island.

Walking in the street toward the Blue Moon, I am quickly lost among the fray. The mostly elderly, early-bird observers craving front-row seats have brought their folding lawn chairs and are seated curbside, sipping drinks from their portable coolers, talking with their neighbors, and watching the spectacle with what appears to be an uncertain mixture of bemusement and outrage.

A guy in a Richard Nixon mask and a long raincoat prowls the edge of the street, waving one hand over his head in the familiar Nixon cliché before suddenly opening his raincoat to reveal a rubber phallus hanging down below his knees.

Various Disney creations scamper by: the mouse and the duck and the three little pigs. Little Red Riding Hood is pursued by the Big Bad Wolf, who is also in a raincoat, which he pops open on occasion to reveal equipment similar to Nixon's. Guys on stilts and bare-breasted women in body paint wiggle and dance. Cowboys and Indians and an array of movie characters dance by to shouts from the crowd. Tinseltown has come to Key West.

By the time I reach the Blue Moon, I am sweating. Beyond the lighted glass windows of the restaurant, the invitation-only crowd has gathered inside, all in considerably more elaborate costumes than the one I am wearing. Opening the door, I step into the dizzying, heady aroma of the party.

"Bud, I would have recognized you anywhere."

There is something familiar in the exaggerated, southern-accented voice, but at first I don't recognize it. It is not Gaby's. The woman is dressed in a Victorian gown, a wig with long, curly ringlets and a mask, and I assume she is meant to be Scarlett O'Hara. Clark Gable as Rhett Butler stands beside her.

"All I can say is, I don't give a damn," I say.

There are squeals of laughter from Scarlett, and a polite smile from Rhett as I make my way to the bar, where Humphrey Bogart in a white dinner jacket is dispensing drinks.

"What'll it be, Bud?" Bogart asks in a stagey voice, around the edge of a cigarette.

"Shirley Temple," I say, having no idea who the guy is behind the mask.

"She's around somewhere." Bogart laughs. He mixes my drink, hands it to me, then drawls, "Play it again, Sam."

Next to the bar a woman in a tuxedo, her short hair slicked back, begins singing "Strangers in the Night," doing not a bad imitation of Frank Sinatra.

Gaby has cleared out the tables and a few couples dance on the waxed hardwood floors. In one corner a buffet has been set up with some trays of hors d'oeuvres, kept filled by the kitchen staff, whose faces have been painted in black and white with elf caps covering their heads.

Among the revelers, I look for someone I recognize, but finding no one, carry my drink to a corner near the window where I can stand and keep an eye both on the street and the proceedings inside.

"What do you think, Bud? You like it?"

The voice is Frank Pappagallo's. The costume is Carmen Miranda. My lawyer is in blackface and drag, a basket of fruit perched precariously on his head. I stare at him with incredulity.

"It was my wife's idea," Frank says, a little apologetically it seems.

"Nice, Frank. You going to eat the fruit when you get home?"

Frank laughs, the bodice of his south-of-the-border-style dress jiggling with the water-filled balloons that provide his cleavage. " 'Eat the fruit.' That's rich, Bud. Maybe before the night's over. Great party, isn't it?"

"Beautiful."

Frank wanders away. I peer out the window. The cavalry, or whatever they are meant to be, some of whom were in the club last night, are marching by and tossing beads to the crowd. Many of them are older guys, rather stout, red-faced, sweating profusely in their uniforms. I watch them, wondering where they have come from, and do a double take just as they pass out of my line of sight. One of them looks a lot like Don Cameron.

"Like to dance, Bud?" Scarlett O'Hara taps my shoulder.

The female version of Sinatra is belting out "You'd Be So Nice to Come Home To" as I follow

Scarlett onto the floor. We do a little two-step shuffle, and there is something familiar in the feel of her body, the way she moves to my touch.

"You really didn't recognize me, did you, Bud?"

She has dropped the phony southern accent, and now I hear the voice of my first wife, Peggy Baker Lowry Maloney.

"Jesus, Peg," I say. "You're the last person I expected to see here, and in that getup."

Peggy smiles. "Jake and I don't get out much. We thought it would be a hoot."

Jake Maloney is Peggy's current husband. "Rhett?" I ask.

"Isn't he good-looking?"

"Better than Gable himself," I say, feeling Peggy swell with pride.

"Everything all right with you?" Peggy asks as the song ends.

"Just fine," I say.

Peggy smiles and toddles off to join her husband, whom I can see watching us from the bar.

"Bud, could I see you a minute?"

It is Gaby. She is wearing the hat and white veil with the fine mesh that hides her features, the one she wears to tend her bees. Her voice has a peremptory quality, and I realize I am being summoned like a lamb to the slaughter as I follow her across the crowded room to her tiny office off the kitchen.

48

◇

Gaby's office is cramped, with barely enough room for the two of us to stand. There is a small desk, its surface covered with restaurant trade magazines, receipts and order forms, and business ledgers. Some filing cabinets take up the remainder of the floor space. All the intricacies of running a successful restaurant tucked in a cubbyhole. Gaby stands behind the desk, leaving the white veil, which resembles chain mail, to shroud her face. This is going to be difficult, perhaps easier done behind masks, I think.

"Just one question," Gaby says. "Why?"

From beyond the door, the sounds of laughter, kitchen staff, and the "voice" of Frank Sinatra blend and quaver.

"I was trying to protect you."

"Protect me?" Gaby's voice breaks slightly. "Do I look like a woman who needs protection, Bud? After all the years you've known me. Please. I'm not some waif, dependent on men, who breaks into tears whenever I've been hurt. I thought you knew me better than that, Bud."

"I do. You aren't that kind of woman. But what you are is in love. Maybe that's blinded you."

Gaby slowly shakes her head. "I don't think that's for you to decide, Bud."

"I was in the middle of an investigation. I still am. Looking for evidence, some proof of a crime."

"And did you get it?"

"Nothing that I could bring to you that would have changed your mind. I tried making certain suggestions, remember? You accused me of being jealous."

"Well, aren't you?"

"Not at this point."

Gaby shifts uneasily on her feet. "Who is this woman in Miami?"

"Page Anderson?"

"Yes. She called me. It wasn't pretty. Did you put her up to it?"

"No. I stumbled across her by accident."

"She's coming down here, looking for Roy, she says."

"Where is Roy?"

"No idea. I haven't seen him since last night."

"Does he know about this?"

"You mean what I now know?"

I nod.

"He should. I called and left a message asking for an explanation. I haven't heard from him."

The air in the room is close. There are food smells, and the slightly musty odor of paper. Still, I can smell Gaby's scent, the subtle and familiar cologne that she wears.

"It may be worse than another woman."

"What are you talking about?"

"Roy may also be a murderer."

There is a visible shift in her center of gravity. Gaby's shoulders slump, her head tilts forward. She rests her fists on top of her desk as if to support herself. When she speaks, her voice is distant. "Bud, why don't you just tell me everything."

I do. Telling her about my trip to Jackson Hole, and the Hargreaves family. While describing the cloud of suspicion Roy is under out there, "Sinatra" is belting out an upbeat version of "Fly Me to the Moon." When I finish, Gaby slumps down in the straight-back chair behind the desk. She picks up a letter opener, twisting it in her hands.

"Bud, this is unforgivable."

"I'm sorry, Gaby. I didn't know any of this until I went out there. I didn't know you were going to get married as quickly as you did."

"No, you still don't seem to get it. We're not kids, Bud. We've got past lives. All of us. And you of all people, I would think, should understand that. When we were in the Bahamas, Roy told me about his life in Wyoming. What's unforgivable is that you would take it upon yourself to meddle to the extent that you have."

Gaby lifts the veil from her face, folding it back over the top of her pith helmet, which she pushes back on her head. An angry welt appears where the band of the helmet rested against her forehead. Her face is flushed, her eyes like dead coals.

"I'd like to talk to Roy."

Gaby shrugs. "I don't think that would be advisable."

"Do you know where he is?"

"No, I don't. I think you should go now, Bud."

Gaby stares at me; the look is clearly accusatory.

"I don't think you should go home tonight," I tell her.

Gaby continues to stare at me. "Stop being my daddy, Bud. It doesn't suit you."

"Gaby—"

"Leave me. Please. I want some time alone."

I hesitate. Gaby puts the letter opener down.

Opening the door, I step outside and get the force of the party in full swing. "Sinatra" is singing "Black Magic." Much of the crowd is gathered in front of the windows, and the parade has started. I head over to the nearly empty bar and order a club soda. Bogart has disappeared, and one of the jokers from the kitchen staff has replaced him behind the bar.

"Gaby knows how to throw a party, doesn't she, Bud?"

Frank has come up beside me. One of the water-filled balloons has burst, and the front of his dress is damp. The fruit arrangement on top of his head has begun to work itself loose, and one banana hangs like a yellow horn just above his left ear, while a bunch of red grapes spills over his forehead like curls of hair.

"You need to go to the ladies' room and freshen up," I tell him.

Frank smiles, trying unsuccessfully to prop the grapes up.

"Have you seen Roy?"

"No. I've been looking for him, though. I was expecting to see him here."

"Maybe he doesn't recognize you in drag."

"Cut it out, Bud."

"Sorry, Frank." I finish my soda and see Gaby come out of her office and head into the kitchen, her head covered again by the veil. "I'll see you later," I say to Frank. "Keep your bazoombas up."

49

◇

Making my way back to the kitchen, I look for
Gaby, who is nowhere in sight. When I stop one of
the costumed staff to ask if she has seen Gaby, she
says, "I think she just went out the back." Then
she scurries away, carrying a plate of prosciutto
wrapped around wedges of melon.

The back door gives off on a sidewalk leading
to a parking lot. The smell of sweat and beer
braces the humid, deathly still air. Walking back
to the parking lot, I find Gaby's empty car. No one
is around, so I walk back to Duval Street, where a
Budweiser truck has stalled in front of the Blue
Moon, the float it is pulling filled with half-naked
women, their flesh a milky sheen under the klieg
lights mounted on balconies along the street. The
women's hands are raised in a fixed wave, like
those of royalty, their red lips curled in ghoulishly
frozen smiles. From loudspeakers on the float
comes a tinny-sounding rock tune, the jarring
lyrics impossible to make out in the pandemo-
nium of the crowd.

I try to work my way up the street, but it is like
swimming against an opposing current, impossible to measure much in the way of progress.

The club is only a block away, and what would

normally be a three-minute walk takes me more than ten minutes as I fight through the dense, roiling mob. After taking the elevator up, I hurry over to where Ronnie is tending bar, a few castaways having their plastic go-cups filled.

"Have you seen Gaby?"

Ronnie looks at me blankly.

"From the Blue Moon."

"Oh, her. No, I haven't."

"She might have been wearing a funny hat with a veil covering her face."

Ronnie's face brightens. "Yeah, just a few minutes ago. I served her a drink and she went out. You must have just crossed on the elevators."

"Was she alone?"

Ronnie nods.

I walk out onto the balcony overlooking the street. There is a crowd here, too, although, despite providing a bird's-eye view of the street, it does not seem like the best vantage point from which to watch a parade.

For two or three blocks in both directions, I scan the crowd, looking for Gaby. Amidst such a mob there seems little chance of spotting one individual.

Because of their numbers and blue uniforms, a few members of the cavalry outfit stand out in the crowd, reminding me that earlier I thought I saw Don Cameron among them. Which came as a complete surprise. What would he be doing here, I wonder?

From the window of the Blue Moon the only fleeting glimpse I had was of someone about Cameron's build wearing a Stetson similar to the

one Don always wore and with the same droopy
mustache. On the other hand, most of these guys
are wearing similar hats, and many of them probably have mustaches. And if it was Cameron, why
had he not told me he was coming here?

If Cameron has flown all this way, then he is
here, I am sure, on his own agenda that has to do
with Roy, and not to march in a parade. The possibility that Don, in his quietly eccentric manner, is
some kind of avenging angel does not escape me.

The parade stutters along, the music of several
bands bouncing into the night air. Many of the
floats are little more than commercial boosterism,
a few ragged palm fronds stacked across a truck
bed, some coconuts and bunting, advertising a
local bar. A few of the floats, however, are elaborate.

A giant gorilla, affixed atop a scaled version of
Key West's lighthouse, holds a screaming, partially clad woman, the gorilla's red eyes oscillat-
ing in their sockets. A tropical version of King
Kong.

On the side streets beyond Duval it is dark,
without traffic, as if the rest of the town has been
abandoned for a few hours. And for half an hour I
stand there transfixed as the parade moves along
in its herky-jerky fashion, like a filmstrip being
slowly pulled by hand through a lighted projector.

Finally, reluctantly, I ride the elevator down
and rejoin the fray, plunging back into the crowd
to look for Gaby. It is quickly apparent that it is
unreasonable to think that I will find her this way.

By the time I have pushed and clawed my way
through the sweating throng, had drinks spilled

on me, been cursed and spat on, the parade has reached its end, an intolerable cacophony of sound erupting as the mob begins to overrun the street.

I find myself pressed against one of the stray blue shirts, who is drunk, holding on to the waist of a young lady in a black cat suit. I ask him if he knows Don Cameron.

"Who?" The black cat puts both her arms around the soldier, and purrs.

"Don Cameron."

"Never heard of him."

"Would you know everyone in this outfit?"

"Hell, no. We come from all over the country. I don't know most of them."

He grins, takes a swig of his drink, and stumbles off with his feline friend.

It is useless to fight the crowd. I go along with its surge and flow, swept uptown in the direction from which I have come, sure that none of the downtown bars would attract Gaby. A few minutes later I come on another of the blue shirts and ask him about Cameron.

"Sure, he's around."

"Don Cameron from Jackson Hole?"

"Yeah, that's the one."

"Do you know where I can find him?"

"Nope. He was with us until a few blocks back, where I saw him drop out. He met up with a woman, I think."

What woman? I wonder. It doesn't sound like Don. Someone he knew? Somehow, I manage to dislodge myself from the crowd and cut over to a side street where King Kong on his lighthouse

stands silenced, the eyes deadened, dark orbs.
There is no sign of the screaming woman he had
clutched in his fist.

Finally, I return to the Blue Moon, where the
party goes on. When I ask around about Gaby, no
one has seen her. Frank is no longer in the crowd,
either. Scarlett O'Hara, aka Peggy Maloney, my ex-
wife, is standing at the bar with her husband
Rhett Butler, aka Jake Maloney. I push my way
through the tangle of bodies toward them.

"Peggy."

"Oh, hi, Bud. Did you see the parade? Wasn't it
the best?"

So typically Peggy, childlike in her enthusiasm.
I agree that it was spectacular. "Have you seen
Gaby?"

Peggy looks at Jake. "Didn't we see her a while
ago?"

Jake shrugs. "I think she was with Bogie,"
Peggy says, turning back to me.

"Bogie?"

"You know, the bartender."

Yes, of course. That Bogie. "How long ago?"

"Oh, Bud, I don't remember. Maybe half an
hour ago. Why? Is something wrong?"

Her question falls on my retreating back as I
turn away and head for the kitchen. The staff are
congregated back there, beginning the clean-up
process. Still in their black-and-white harlequin
paint, a couple of them look up when I come in.
"The bartender," I say. "Does anyone know who
he was?"

Everyone looks around, shaking their heads.
Someone points to a woman who is just coming in

carrying an empty serving tray. I ask her. She says she thinks he was a stand-in. The regular bartender had called in sick at the last minute.

"But you don't know who the replacement was?"

No, she says, she has no idea. Gaby would probably know, but she has gone.

And I am left with the inescapable fear that Gaby is in danger. Whatever doubt may have crossed my mind earlier has been erased. I am willing to bet that behind the Bogie costume lurks a killer. Roy Emerson.

50

◇

Gaby's car is still in the parking lot behind the Blue Moon, its doors locked. Looking around the small lot, which is restricted during the day to area business parking only, I can see no sign of Roy's car. There is no reason why he would have parked here, but the fact that Gaby's car is here, his isn't, and Gaby was last seen leaving with the masked bartender leaves me with an uneasy feeling.

The crowd noise is spreading from Duval to the side streets as the party begins to break up. Foot traffic is beginning to disperse, and the sound of cars zooming off into the night fills the air, along with the squeal and roar from thousands of people trying to keep the party alive. A certain helplessness overcomes me when I realize that I have no idea where to begin to look for Gaby. If she has gone off with Roy, I don't even know if it was voluntary.

I can wait here at her car, but if she doesn't show up, I'm wasting valuable time. The only sensible thing I can think to do is to go home and get the Buick and drive up the Keys to see if she's there. After another five minutes of hanging around and turning the limited options over in my mind, I set off for home.

It is after midnight, and as I approach my place,

I am surprised to see Pop on the sidewalk in front of the shell of the old *groceria.*

"What are you doing down here, Pop?"

"We watched the parade." He seems to get older and smaller each time I see him; his dark eyes still have that haunted look.

"Where's the family?" I ask. There's still a mix of costumed people wandering up and down the street, some of them drinking from beer cans loosely concealed in small paper bags.

"They went home. I wasn't ready to go yet."

"It still hurts, doesn't it, Pop?"

He nods. The lights from the used-car lot across the street spill over us, but the dark gap where Pop's place used to be is a shadowy frame with a few burnt timbers still poking up from the ground, like dead tree limbs that have been scarred by lightning.

"I need to ask you something that's been on my mind for a while now, Pop." I stare into his eyes while he looks off into the distance.

"Sure, Bud."

"Do you blame me?"

He remains motionless, seeming to stare at something that is beyond my vision. I feel a cool trickle of sweat run down the base of my spine. Finally, Pop shrugs his shoulders. "Nobody to blame, Bud."

Something in his voice is off, though.

"Sooner or later they get you. There's no place for the little guy in this country."

Though his voice contains a quality of sadness, I know Pop is simply stating a fact, something he believes, and not feeling sorry for himself.

"It's a struggle, Pop. Always has been, always will be."

Pop nods. *"La lucha."*

"What's that?"

"Same thing. The struggle. So what you going to do, Bud?"

"Sell. If I can get my price."

"Be careful, Bud."

"Yeah, I will."

I offer Pop my hand. We shake, and I can feel his thin, bony fingers, the flesh smooth as a washed stone in a creek. "And don't worry, Pop," I say. "This is for both of us."

Pop looks at me questioningly, and I feel his eyes on me as I turn and go into the house.

Sitting down at my desk, I pick up the phone and dial Gaby's number. No answer. After looking up Roy's number, I dial it. Again, nothing. I sit back and contemplate driving up to Gaby's. I am still sitting ten minutes later when I hear footsteps on the porch and someone knocks on the door.

It is nearly one o'clock. I walk over to the door and look through the slats in the blind. Don Cameron stands on the porch, his blue twill shirt darkened with sweat stains.

"Surprise," he grumbles when I open the door.

"Not quite. I thought I saw you in the parade tonight."

"I figured you would avoid that. Too much tourism."

"If I hadn't been working, I probably would have. Kind of unlike you to come all this way just for a parade, isn't it?"

"Working too. Bob Hargreaves asked me to come. Man, it's hot here."

"Can't they find a tropical uniform for you

guys? You look like you're dressed for a reenact-
ment of Custer's last stand."

Don shrugs, standing under the overhead fan
while he mops the sweat from his brow with a
blue bandanna.

"So you told Bob Hargreaves about Roy, and he
sent you down here?"

Don nods. "Just in case."

"Just in case I couldn't handle the situation."

"No, nothing like that." Don glances around the
room. "For Bob, even for me, it's personal. You
know that. I wanted to be here. Bob would have
come himself if he was in better shape."

"You planning on confronting Roy?"

"I don't know. From what you described on the
phone, I'd say he was going to make a move. It
sounds like he's been cornered."

"Maybe."

"Where is he?"

"I wish I knew."

"And his wife?"

"I was with her earlier. I don't know where she
is now, and she's still defending Roy."

"That's not a good sign."

"I was getting ready to drive up to her place."

"You want company?"

I shake my head. "I'd rather you stake out Roy's
place in town. Just in case he shows up there.
Have you got a rental car?"

Don nods.

"You can follow me and I'll show you where he
lives."

51

$\diamond$

Driving up the Keys, I try to think of something more I might have said to Gaby, some approach I could have taken that would have been more convincing. As it is, I now no longer know what kind of a reception to expect when I encounter her.

Traffic is light, and half an hour later I pull into Gaby's drive. It is well after two o'clock in the morning. The place is dark. My headlights don't pick out any vehicles parked in the carport below the house. I shut off the lights and the ignition and sit for a moment in the darkness. There are no sounds coming from inside the house.

In fact, the surrounding silence is deafening. The nearest house to Gaby's is a quarter of a mile away. She is tucked back here in a wooded hammock several miles from the highway. Each crackle of a dry thatch palm leaf brushing against another, the scuttle of lizards through the thick underbrush, and the whine of a mosquito now and then as it cruises in my open window, resonate like thunder over the silence. Unless she is in bed, sleeping soundly, it seems certain that if Gaby is inside, she will have heard my car when I drove up.

There are no streetlights back here, and stars

are strewn across the sky like confetti. I open the car door and step out, the gravel drive crunching under my weight, and close the door quietly. A gentle rhythmic sighing, almost like breathing or a rusty hinge creaking against its holding pin, causes me to pause and listen. It is a sound so faint that it is hardly noticeable. Because there is no wind, it seems unlikely that the sound could be caused by a door swinging on its hinges.

Cautiously, I climb the steps, wishing I were carrying a gun. The creaking remains constant. On the landing at the top of the stairs I can look in the screen door, but everything is in darkness, with only the ghostly dim shadows of the furnishings visible.

A mosquito lands on my neck, and I slap at it, a sound that seems as loud as a rifle shot in my ear.

"Gaby," I call, my voice barely above a whisper.

There is no answer. I try the screen door. It is unlatched. Stepping inside and moving slowly into the room, I listen as the rhythmic creaking grows louder.

Walking into the main room of the house, I get a whiff of Gaby's perfume and, standing stock-still in nearly total darkness, reach out, my fingers fumbling along the wall where the overhead light switch should be.

There is a sudden flutter, something churning the air next to my face, and I flick the light on to see a giant black moth, the size of a bat, settling on the wall near the cornice just below the ceiling.

No one is in the room. Everything is in place. One of the overhead paddle fans, running on slow speed, makes the rhythmic bump and whine that I have been hearing. "Gaby?" I walk through the house, turning on lights and calling her name, but there is no one here, and nothing to indicate that anything is amiss.

When I return to the living room and look up at the moth, it looks like a dark stain on the wall—silent, motionless. Disturbing. After turning out the lights, I return to my car and sit there, uncertain what to do next.

There is nothing to do except wait. It seems only reasonable to believe that sooner or later Gaby will come home. Even though there's been nothing reasonable about this entire evening. It would be easy enough just to drive back to town, I think, go home and go to bed, which is what I would like to do. And, if it was anyone besides Gaby, that's exactly what I would do. Maybe I am feeling a little guilt because of her. Maybe I have handled this badly. Whatever, I have a hunch that what remains of the night isn't going to find me in my bed. About that at least, I'm not wrong.

Since I don't want her to see my car, I start the Buick and head back over to the main road, where earlier I passed a small marina that had a parking area with a couple of cars that had been left there. I pull in and cut the motor. She will have to pass by here on her way home.

A couple of residential streets lead off the main road along canals with houses built on either side of their banks. A quiet, peaceful little suburban setting. I can't see any lights, and there is no traffic along the road, and except for the fuzzy night sounds, it is still. Scrunching down in the seat, I put my head back against the cushion and close my eyes.

The sound of a distant car motor stirs me, and when I sit up and look at the clock on the dash, I see that it is almost five o'clock. I've got a kink in my neck, and my eyes feel heavy with sleep. The car is coming fast from the direction of the highway, and seconds later when it zooms by me, I see that it is Gaby's car, and in the brief seconds it takes to pass me, I think I see her reflection in the dash lights, but it is too dark to tell if there is anyone else in the car with her.

I wait, listening as the car slows down, and am about to start the Buick when another car goes by at a high rate of speed. Roy's car. I let another couple of minutes go by, then drive down to the turnoff to Gaby's and park along the road before setting out on foot on the less than a quarter of a mile to Gaby's.

When I get within sight of the house, I see both cars parked side by side outside the carport. A couple of lights are on in the house, one in the kitchen and another upstairs in one of the bedrooms. Standing near one of the parked cars, I can see only into the kitchen, beyond the front porch. I hear a toilet flush, and a pump comes on somewhere in the direction of the carport.

After a while Roy Emerson walks into the kitchen. He is wearing the white dinner jacket that he had on when he was tending bar in the Blue Moon. The Bogart mask is gone, and his black bow tie is unclipped, though still around his neck.

I watch as he opens the refrigerator and takes

out a carton of eggs and begins breaking several of them into a glass bowl. Moments later the smell of bacon frying wafts across the sullen night air, followed by the scent of freshly brewed coffee.

Just then Gaby comes into the kitchen. She has changed clothes. She seems to be wearing a robe. She stands, leaning against the counter, watching Roy cook breakfast. There is something about her, something in her look that I can't put my finger on. Until she moves again. And says something I can't hear to Roy. He looks at her with dark, narrow eyes, his lip curled.

Gaby staggers slightly against the counter, then leans slowly into it. From the tilt of her head to the attempt at precision in each movement she makes, I recognize that she has had too much to drink.

52

◇

I continue to watch as Roy uncorks a bottle of white wine, pouring some into a glass, which he hands to Gaby. She stares at him. It is hard to read anything in her expression. She could be staring right through him, for all I know. I have no difficulty, however, reading the chilling smile on Roy's face as he walks up beside her, puts his arm around her shoulders, then picks up his own glass in his free hand and holds it toward her in a toast.

Gaby just stands there, leaning against the counter, staring at nothing. At least nothing that I can see. Then, slowly, she lifts the glass, seems to look at it for a moment before turning to Roy, and tosses the contents in his face.

Roy lifts his hand from her shoulder and wipes his face. He doesn't do anything about the grin. Gaby just stands there looking at him, and although her lips move, I can't hear what she says. Suddenly, Roy grabs her around the waist and pulls her against him, forcing his mouth over hers. Gaby shrinks back, her hands pressed against his shoulders, before slowly giving in to the kiss.

As they kiss, Roy runs one hand through her dark, tangled hair. Then he steps back, grinning down at her. Gaby holds on to his arms, weaving slightly. Roy pours more wine, and now Gaby clinks glasses with him.

As they drink, it begins to seem likely to me that this fight has been going on most of the night—what was left of the night, anyway, after Gaby left the Blue Moon this evening. I can imagine that they found an out-of-the-way bar where they sat and had a real scrap, the kind someone who has been put through what Gaby has been put through might provoke. All of the venom she'd stored up and would not release when I told her about Roy would have bubbled over once she was alone with him. In addition, there was the emotional toll she had suffered.

All of it fueled by alcohol, of course. And, Roy, I can picture, would have remained his usual cool, unshakable self, denying everything, always with a ready explanation. At closing time, still angry, Gaby would have insisted on coming home alone. Roy, the dutiful husband, would have followed.

If that is the way it happened, then what I have witnessed here is the culmination of that fight. They should be ready to go to bed and sleep it off, wake up later today to a clean slate.

Instead, I watch as Roy crooks a finger on the inside lapel of Gaby's robe, pulls the cloth open, and pours what's left of his wine down her front.

I can't see the expression in Gaby's eyes, but I do see her shudder. I wait for some other reaction from her, but it doesn't come. Instead, Roy pulls the robe open, exposing Gaby's breasts, and runs his hand across them. Then bends to take one of her nipples in his mouth. Gaby's head arches backward.

A gray dawn is beginning to push back the darkness, and I want to go home. There is something spiteful, even vindictive, in the way Roy takes her, reaching for her under the folds of her robe, standing, Gaby's back pressed against the counter, her hands flung upward as if she is warding off blows until Roy collapses against her.

Later, Roy finishes cooking breakfast, and they sit now at the kitchen counter, eating. Gaby is still unsteady, eats little, nursing another glass of wine, while Roy packs it away as though it were his last meal.

By the time they have finished, there is enough light in the sky to make concealment impossible, and I am forced to move away, further back up the road and into some shrubbery that conceals not only me but also my view of Gaby and Roy.

I want to see the lights go out and the house to go quiet and know that they have gone to bed. Then I can linger around here for a while longer before walking back to my car and driving home to do the same. Tonight or tomorrow I can meet with Don Cameron and tell him I'm finished with Roy Emerson. If Bob Hargreaves wants any more service, he can get someone else to provide it. And I'll happily give him back his money, or some of it, to be done with this caper.

It has already cost me in nonnegotiable matters, and I'm no longer willing to pay further for someone else's obsession.

On the other hand, maybe I am just tired, bone tired, and I'll think more clearly after several hours sleep and a decent meal. Maybe—but I don't think so.

In any case, I'm not given the opportunity. Fifteen minutes later, when I think everything has settled down, the screen door bangs and I see Roy, wearing a pair of swim trunks, come down the stairs, leading Gaby by the hand. She stumbles on one of the steps, and Roy keeps her from falling, then puts an arm around her waist as they walk down the dock toward the water.

I hear a splash, and moments later a shriek that could have come only from Gaby.

53

◇

The first orange arc of the sun has penetrated the horizon as I run to the end of the dock. Shallow, even with the tide in, the surrounding water is luminous. Turtle grass shimmers like burnished silver just below the surface. A school of snapper hangs off the pilings, noses into the gently flowing current. For miles around it is soundless, a calm more suited to a pond than the fringe of the Gulf of Mexico.

A hundred yards out, at the edge of the channel, the pewter-colored water suddenly turns inky blue, demarcating deeper water. There I see Roy, his head bobbing like a cork. But no sign of Gaby.

"Roy!"

He turns toward my voice just as Gaby's face breaks the surface, one hand clutching at him, the other struggling to tread water, a tiny maelstrom in the midst of the calm.

Kicking off my shoes and stripping down to my boxer shorts, I jump down from the dock and begin to swim toward them. Roy looks benign, a puppy caught chewing on his master's shoe. For a second he seems uncertain what to do, whether to flee or stay. Then, as I swim toward them, he cradles Gaby in the crook of his arm and begins side-stroking toward me.

I can hear Gaby sputtering, trying to cough up water.

"Current got her," Roy says, gasping for breath. "Help me get her back to the dock."

Once back in water shallow enough to stand in, we float Gaby between us, Roy holding her head out of the water, while her legs and arms dangle lifelessly from her naked body. She is alive, her skin cool—the cough less persistent now.

"Lucky you came along," Roy says as we get near the dock. "Don't know if I could have gotten her out of the water by myself."

Roy stands on the concrete supports and hoists himself up onto the dock while I hold Gaby. Then, as I lift her out of the water, Roy leans down and grabs her by the underarms, and together we heave and push her up onto the dock.

"You know any CPR?" Roy asks when I climb out of the water and bend down, pressing a finger against Gaby's throat to check her pulse.

"Yeah, but you'd better go call and get someone out here fast."

Roy hesitates. "By the way, what are you doing out here at this time of day?"

"Go on, man, if you want her to live."

We stare at one another for a second before Roy starts down the dock and I bend over and press my lips to Gaby's.

Her pulse is strong, and as I breathe into her, pushing against her diaphragm, a trickle of water comes out her mouth. Her eyes open, flickering, as a spasm of coughing racks her body. She turns her head and vomits. Then lies flat, looking up at me. "Bud, is that you?"

"Yes," I say. "You're going to be okay."

"Where's Roy?"

"He's gone to get some help."

She shakes her head. "I don't want to see him." She tries to sit up, suddenly aware of her nakedness.

Picking up my shirt from the dock, I put it on her. Gaby coughs again, then sits holding her face in her hands as I pull on my khakis.

When she looks up, her eyes have cleared; there is a look of awareness on her face, as if she has just come home from a long journey, a look of recognition.

"What happened out there?" I ask.

Gaby pushes her hair back, then looks at me. "He tried to kill me."

I don't say anything.

"I'm sorry," Gaby says.

"You don't have anything to be sorry about."

"For blaming you."

"Forget it."

"I'm a fool, Bud."

"Just take it easy, Gaby."

"I tried to put my life on hold. I thought I was doing the right thing."

"Don't do this now." I sit down beside her and put my arm around her.

She stares out at the sea. "I've been so self-involved, determined to get everything in order."

"Gaby—"

"Let me finish, Bud. I couldn't see through Roy because I was in such a hurry. It was time. Time to get married. Time to raise a family."

I hear footsteps coming back down the dock.

"I thought I was doing the right thing, and when it was too late, I couldn't admit that I'd made a mistake."

"What mistake?" Roy asks.

Gaby and I both turn toward him. He is holding a gun, a little snub-nosed .38, not really pointing it at anyone, but that doesn't seem to provide any comfort.

"You, darling," Gaby says.

54

◇

"It's all over, Roy," I say. "Your days as a Romeo are finished. Don Cameron flew in from Jackson Hole the other day. We know about Karen Hargreaves and the woman out in Idaho you drowned."

Standing there in his swim trunks, Roy, his eyes hooded, looks from me to Gaby, and back to me. The thin curl of his lip slips for just a moment, then returns. "You like the sound of your own voice, dickus, or is this just some cheap theatrics?"

"Take your pick, Roy. Either way, the jig's up. The end of the road."

"We'll see about that." He raises the gun. "By the time the sharks get finished with you, there won't be enough of you left to put under a microscope."

"I wouldn't count on it. Looks like it's going to be a pretty day. Lots of boat traffic. Gunshots out here on the water will be heard for miles. Our bodies could be spotted and picked up before you get off the key."

Roy seems to consider that. "You've got a point. Let's go up to the house."

"Sure. You could kill us there, then torch the

place. That's more your style, isn't it? Just like the grocery store you burned down in Key West."

"You're lucky I didn't get your shack."

"If Pacey didn't rein you in, you probably would have."

"Fred Pacey's a wimp. I controlled that project. He didn't have anything to do with it."

"He didn't approve the arson?"

"He thought it was his luck. Guys with money like that can afford to believe in luck. I've got to make my own. All of your detecting, you should know that."

"Just like in Jackson Hole? The trading post development you burned."

Roy grins now. "Okay, dickus, you've proved you're good at your job. Let's go and see how well you die."

Gaby and I stand up. She squeezes my hand as we start walking up the dock toward her house.

When we have walked beyond the mangrove shoreline into the wetland clearing leading to the house, Gaby stops. "Roy," she says, "don't do this. You can walk out of here. No one's got anything on you. I'm not going to press charges. Don't dig yourself in any deeper than you already are."

"Too late, Gabe. You should have thought of that when you hired Sam Spade here to dig into my past."

Gaby takes a couple of steps toward Roy.

"Stay back," Roy barks.

"Come on, Roy," I say. "You don't murder women in cold blood. You set up *accidents*. So there's never any hard evidence against you."

"I can make an exception."

"Gaby's right. Why start now?"

"Just turn around and keep walking."

"Roy, listen to me." Gaby takes a couple more steps in his direction, close enough now that she could reach out and touch him. But she just stands there.

"Forget it, Gabe."

Gaby looks back at me. I shrug.

On either side of the narrow dock are wetlands, hard caprock poking through the ground, and miniature wildflowers that look like weeds growing out of the caprock amidst the driftwood that sprouts like bleached bones. Nearby, Gaby's beehives are stacked two high on wooden bottom boards.

As Gaby turns toward me, she trips on a warped gray plank in the dock that has sprung loose from the piling, sticking up a couple of inches from the rest of the dock.

Roy instinctively bends toward her, lowering the gun as he does, a two-second distraction that allows me to hurl my body at him in a flying tackle, taking both of us down hard against the dock.

Roy manages to hang on to the gun, and I feel the butt of it hammer against my shoulder blade. Getting one knee planted on the dock, I throw my left hand up to grab Roy's wrist before he can hammer me again. I'm reaching for his neck with my right hand when he swings his knee up, clipping me good in the kidneys, then twists sideways as I try to hang on to his gun hand.

Working with twenty-five extra years and as many extra pounds, I realize I'm no match for Roy without getting the gun away from him.

I don't see Gaby, who has either jumped or been pushed off the dock in the tumult. Right now I don't see anything except the blue steel of Roy's snub-nosed .38. Sweat drips down my hairline.

I've still got a clamp on Roy's wrist, reaching up with my right hand to try to get another hold. Roy manages to struggle to his feet, pulling me against the rough plank boards as I feel my grip begin to loosen.

Suddenly, Roy jerks his gun hand free, and all I can do is grab a leg, upending him as the gun roars, the shot skying as Roy falls.

Lunging forward, I get my knee in his chest this time and both hands around his right arm, twisting it backward against the edge of the dock until Roy is forced to drop the gun, which clatters down against caprock.

I hear myself wheezing and gasping for air as I cock my fist and attempt to throw a punch into the side of Roy's face. He bucks and dodges; the punch lands a glancing blow off the side of his head as we both tumble over the side of the dock.

I feel the scrape of the hard Florida landscape against bare skin, prickly scrabble biting into my sweat-soaked body. Roy jumps to his feet and flings himself toward where the gun lies, while I struggle to my feet, propelled upward now only by adrenaline, seeing Roy poised over the .38, grasping it by the barrel, as I throw a punch, feeling my fist hit against his rib cage. Roy falls to the side against a piling. I rush him, pinioning his arms beneath mine, too tired now to do anything except hold on, like a boxer on the ropes.

We dance back, and as we do, I see Gaby floating in the distance, a kind of mirage, surrounded by a cloud of yellow and black, walking toward us, something hanging from her hand, enveloped in a scent of thick, flowery sweetness.

Roy seems to have seen her, too. He surges violently against me, ripping one arm free as Gaby begins to run and swing whatever it is she is carrying, swinging it back and forth, like it was something sacred, part of a ritual.

As Roy attempts to break free, I hang on, waiting until the cloud that surrounds Gaby swarms toward us. Bees. Thousands of them. Drifting over us like a toxic cloud. Settling on our bare skin, their welcome stings like pin pricks from a doctor's needle.

55

◇

At the house, Gaby picks up the phone and punches in some numbers. After a while she hangs up without speaking to anyone. I watch as she takes some ice from the freezer and brings it over to where I'm sitting, touching the ice to the red welts that have begun to swell where I've been stung. The cold is soothing.

From the deck we can see Roy on the ground where he fell, a few bees still hovering over his body.

"Charley, the doctor who came the last time, isn't home," Gaby says, rubbing the ice on my skin without looking at me. "I'm going to call 911 now, but it will take them a while to get here. There's nothing anyone can do for Roy. I should have had some epinephrine on hand, but I don't. Roy refused to get a prescription. 'Lightning doesn't strike the same place twice,' he told me." Gaby looks at me. "He was wrong, wasn't he?"

The look in Gaby's eyes is decisive, determined. "Sure, he was," I say.

"I'm going to get dressed, then go down to the dock and get the gun and toss it in the sea. Then, I'll put that hive back together and wait for the medics. When they get here, I'll be the grieving widow."

"Okay," I say. "But you may have to explain some of the bruises on Roy's body."

"He fell off the dock when he was stung."

"You don't have to do this, you know. It was self-defense."

"I have some pride, Bud. If you don't mind, I'd like to hang on to what's left of it." Gaby stands up. "The bees swarmed suddenly, unpredictably. We were in the wrong place at the wrong time."

"Sure."

"Just keep putting ice on those stings. Tomorrow they'll be itchy. You'll be okay. We both will."

I watch her from the back deck of the house as she goes about the tasks she designated. Twenty minutes later when the medics show up and put Roy's body on the stretcher, I go inside and make a phone call.

"Frank, Roy's dead. He was stung by bees."

"What happened?"

I relate Gaby's version. "I thought you ought to let Fred Pacey know."

"I'll do that," Frank replies.

"You might also want to tell him that Roy confessed to starting the fire at Pop's place."

"Bud—"

"Listen to me carefully, Frank. He said Fred doesn't know anything about it. And, I'm not going to make an issue of this unless I'm forced to. I want my price for the property and I want a hundred grand up front. Simple as that."

"I'll tell him, Bud."

The rest of the day Gaby tends to my wounds. There is no further mention of Roy. In the afternoon, I fall asleep on the couch for a couple of hours, and when I wake, it is to the smell of steak being grilled.

"Feeling any better?" Gaby asks when I join her in the kitchen.

"Hungry."

"I guessed you might be. I slept some, too, and woke up ravenous."

When we sit down at the table to eat, Gaby announces that she is going to take some time away from work. "I'm going to make some changes in the way I live."

"Good," I say.

"I've been thinking that I may need a chaperone."

I look at her. Her eyes are still set and determined, but the corners of her mouth have begun to relax a little.

"You going to take applications for the job?"

"I don't think so. There's only one person I know well enough to trust my life to. Are you interested?"

"Maybe." I study her eyes, which look into mine with a cool detachment. "I've got a question."

Gaby nods. "Only one?"

"For now. How did you know I wasn't allergic to bees?"

Gaby's expression doesn't change. "I didn't," she says. "I took a chance. It's rare; I don't know what the odds are of it happening like that. Once in—" She lifts her hands.

"In a blue moon?"

"Something like that." Gaby smiles.

Pocket Books and
John Leslie
present

The Gideon Lowry Mysteries

LOVE FOR SALE
❏ 51126-2/$6.50

BLUE MOON
❏ 53515-3/$6.50

Available from Pocket Books

FREUD AND THE POST-FREUDIANS

FREUD
AND THE POST-FREUDIANS

J. A. C. BROWN

CASSELL · LONDON

CASSELL & COMPANY LTD

35 Red Lion Square · London WC 1

and at

MELBOURNE · SYDNEY · TORONTO · CAPE TOWN

JOHANNESBURG · AUCKLAND

———

© J. A. C. Brown 1961

Originally published by Penguin Books in 1961

This edition first published 1963

Printed in Czechoslovakia

CONTENTS

Editorial Foreword

IT was often asked why the Pelican Psychology Series did not contain a volume on the psychology of Sigmund Freud, since Freud is admitted on all hands to be the dominating figure in psychology of the present century.

An account of the good and sufficient reasons for the delay in publishing such a work would make tedious reading, and would be only of academic interest now that, in other volumes, the deficiency has been remedied. The delay has had some compensating advantages.

Freud's psychology during his life was a living and developing system. Then and since it has been the point of departure for a number of variant and 'deviant' doctrines. It is perhaps only now just becoming possible to see Freudian psychology in perspective. Looking back Freud is on the horizon. Little is gained by trying to place Freud's system against the background of the antecedent, by way of tracing Freud's psychology from its antecedent. The transition from Pre-Freudian to Freudian psychology is as abrupt as any transition in the history of the subject. This must have been a very difficult book to write, and no one writing such a book could hope to please all professional readers, some of whom demand unqualified adherence to the doctrines of Freud as Freud himself has stated them; others of whom press remorselessly for validation by rigorous scientific methods. It is no doubt a very good thing that there should be these two points of view. It is a good thing that some should say: 'Before we start to "interpret" or amend let us first be clear as to what Freud actually said.' It is a good thing that there should be others who say: 'Take Freud's doctrines one by one and ask, had he good scientific reasons for what he said?'

But neither of these 'professional' points of view is the best for presenting Freud to the intelligent general reader, who wishes to have first of all a broad general account of the work of Freud himself and of those most influenced by Freud, a broad introduction which might well become for some the beginning of close and continuous study, especially study of the texts of Freud himself and those of his successors.

This book provides (i) a simple and clear statement of some basic concepts of psychoanalytic theory, (ii) a brief account of Freud's theory and its development in the forty-odd years of his own creative work, (iii) a survey of the contribution of Freud's contemporaries and immediate followers, (iv) a synoptic view of the later variations and deviations of others who have been influenced by Freud. Few people can be so well qualified to write such an introduction as is the author of this book. Dr Brown has himself been sufficiently closely associated with Freudian psychology in its stricter interpretation to be a reliable exponent of Freudian doctrines. He has knowledge and sympathy sufficiently wide to do justice to the doctrine of the most important deviants and eclectics. He has in addition a qualification rather rare among analytical writers—familiarity with 'academic psychology'—having indeed written a text book on this subject.

C. A. MACE

CHAPTER I

Basic Concepts of Psychoanalysis

THE word 'psychoanalysis', strictly speaking, refers solely to the theories of Freud and the method of psychotherapy and investigation based thereon. This was recognized by Alfred Adler who, on breaking with Freud, gave his school the name of 'Individual Psychology' and by C. G. Jung who used the title 'Analytical Psychology' in similar circumstances. Although the former was the least individually-orientated and the latter the least analytic of the earlier schools, their originators at any rate recognized that their thought was not Freudian and hence not psychoanalytic. But in more recent times, and particularly in the United States, the word has been used to describe loosely all those schools of thought which took their origin from the work of Freud, however much they diverge from it now, and the theories of Fromm, Horney, Sullivan, and others are classified as 'Neo-Freudian' in spite of the fact that they really bear very little resemblance to the original. However, since Neo-Freudians exist, they will be so described here, but the term 'psychoanalytic' will be reserved for orthodox views only and 'analytic' as an innocuous generic term to cover all those psychotherapeutic methods which by any stretch of the imagination can be said to make use of investigation and explanation rather than suggestion. It is convenient, too, to regard the total body of Freudian thought as falling into roughly three categories: its basic psychological concepts which are the subject of the present chapter; the theories based on clinical observations and described in terms of this conceptual scheme which are very briefly discussed in the following one; and the essentially philosophical conclusions on such subjects as the nature of society and civilization, war and religion, which Freud drew from his own thought and experience. Whether or not such a division is logically justifiable it is undoubtedly empirically useful in any consideration of his influence on scientific thought; for many would accept his general approach to psychological problems who would not be uncritical of his theories, and others would accept both without taking very seriously his metaphysical conclusions. It would probably be true to say that it was Freud's method of approaching psychological problems, rather than any specific observations or theories, which revolutionized psychology and transformed it from an academic and wholly static discipline making use of terms borrowed from physics and philosophy into a science, rooted in biology but spreading outwards into sociology, describing behaviour in dynamic and goal-directed terms. Academic psychology had been content to observe and describe behaviour; Freud saw the need to explain it. But he did much more than this because—again almost irrespective of theoretical details—he changed the whole tenor of human thought so that even those who most violently denounce his views attack them in Freudian clichés and with arguments which would have been incomprehensible had he never existed. Like Copernicus and Darwin, the men with whom he compared himself. Freud revolutionized our way of looking at ourselves, and like them he may well come to be regarded rather as a moulder of thought than as a mere discoverer of facts. Copernicus demolished the official theory of a geocentric universe by dragging from oblivion the ancient heliocentric theory of the Pythagoreans and giving new reasons (some of them extremely unsound) for accepting it. Darwin took the equally ancient theory of evolution, and by the addition of his own observations on natural selection as its possible mechanism made it seem entirely credible—although few modern biologists would consider natural selection as conceived by its originator a sufficient explanation in itself of the undoubted fact of biological evolution. Yet inadequate, unsound, or downright wrong as some of their reasons may have been, we have regarded the world in a totally different light since we discovered our insignificant position in relation to the rest of the universe and our biological continuity with other living things, and it is not unreasonable to suggest that the transformation was completed by Freud, whose work implied that man's godlike intellect was, as H. G. Wells expressed it, 'no more designed for discovering the truth than a pig's snout'! The fact is that each of these men happened to live at a time when the current of opinion was changing as traditional beliefs disintegrated, and their work heralded or helped to hasten this change because it was in accord with new trends of thought. Freud's own researches were based on certain hypotheses not in themselves entirely original but novel and fruitful when re-interpreted and brought together in a coherent scheme, and perhaps these will form as good an introduction as any to his theories.

The principle of causality is not, of course, strictly speaking a scientific law but rather a necessary assumption without which no science would be possible. But Freud was the first to apply it to the study of personality in the form of a literal and uncompromising psychic determinism which accepted no mental happenings as 'accidental'. His predecessors in psychology had thought of behaviour as determined by such factors as rational motives, instincts, or the purely mechanical association of ideas by contiguity in space or time of the entities they symbolized or by their similarity. They did not doubt that all events were caused, but distinguished between those for which one or more clear-cut causes were known or could be readily postulated, and chance or random events which were the result of many separate and apparently trivial causes which it would be fruitless or impossible to analyse. It was accepted that most psychological happenings were of this nature and therefore could only be discussed in broad descriptive terms rather than analysed in detail in any particular case. Freud took issue with this older interpretation of psychological determinism. In his early studies of hysterical patients he had been able to show that the apparently irrational symptoms which had puzzled physicians for centuries were meaningful when seen in terms of painful memories which had been repressed into the unconscious and were striving to find expression. There appeared to be a logical continuity in the mental life of the individual, and therefore symptoms were not mysterious incursions from without but rather exaggerated expressions of processes common to everyone which revealed the specific stresses of the patient who developed them. They were not fortuitous in the classical sense, and the causes could be uncovered by analysis. The same reasoning was applied to other seemingly random or irrational events, to the mistakes of everyday life, dreams, slips of the tongue, and the apparent coincidences which in some individuals appeared to repeat themselves throughout a lifetime. Naturally, neither Freud nor any of his followers ever denied the existence of events which were accidental in the original meaning of the word – that is to say, occurrences brought about by intrusions from other systems which had nothing to do with the personality of the individual who experienced them. A slate falling from a roof and injuring a man's head is clearly of this nature, and a woman who finds that she has married a drunkard may simply be unlucky or careless; but if a physically healthy man of normal intelligence repeatedly becomes involved in road accidents or if the unlucky woman marries three alcoholics in succession we should certainly be entitled to consider the possibility that their personality rather than their environment is to blame. This phenomenon, described by Freudians as the repetition compulsion, is met with most frequently clinically (as in the latter case) in the choice of a mate where the same personality type is selected each time, the relationship being invariably a sadomasochistic one. Similarly, no Freudian would be disposed to deny that one may be more likely to dream when sleeping in an uncomfortable or a strange bed after a heavy meal, or that the figures in the dream and the events depicted may reflect one's recent experiences, but he would deny that these extraneous factors in any way explain the inner significance of the dream, which interpretation, it is asserted, can show to be determined by purely personal issues in the individual's emotional life. The Freudian concept of psychic determinism does not postulate a simple one-to-one relationship of cause and effect in all mental events, and it is recognized that a single event may be *overdetermined*, being the final common path of many forces, whether constitutional, developmental or environmental. According to this view the personality is most clearly revealed when the intellect is exercising least control, and it follows that a patient's dreams, his behaviour when under the influence of drugs or alcohol, the odd *lapsus linguae*, the events he unaccountably forgets, tell more about him than his socially-controlled behaviour. Therefore the patient who is always emotionally controlled, who rarely dreams, and is unable to give himself up to the stream of uncontrolled ideas in free association sets a difficult problem for the analyst.

The part played by the unconscious is another basic postulate of

Freudian theory, although so far as the mere recognition of unconscious mental processes is concerned it was by no means original.
Indeed once it is accepted that mental events are caused and that
personality has continuity it is necessary to assume something of
the sort in order to explain the discontinuity of manifest behaviour
—and in fact all schools of psychology do so without invariably
making use of the same terminology. Alfred Adler, for example,
rarely mentions the unconscious, but since an Adlerian analysis is
devoted to making the patient aware of his life style and fictive aims
(i.e. his real but neurotic aims as revealed by his actual behaviour
as contrasted with what he consciously believes to be his aims) it is
clearly implied that the former were unconscious prior to treatment. The psychologist's concept of 'attitude' has a similar meaning, and even Behaviourism in its use of the conditioned reflex
demonstrates that the subject of the experiment is responding
not to the immediate stimulus as such but automatically—that is,
in one sense of the word, unconsciously—to its past associations.
Such a mechanism is naturally advantageous in simple situations
where it ensures a rapid response, saves nervous energy, and is
likely to lead to a satisfactory result; for if the ringing of a bell immediately preceded the giving of food on many occasions in the
past there is no reason why it should not continue to do so in the
future, and expectant salivation is not inappropriate. But relatively
simple situations confronting dogs or human beings are very different from complex human situations, and a man who responds
indiscriminately towards all authority as he did towards the original authority of a hated father is likely to find himself in difficulties.
Much of the Freudian theory of neurosis can be explained in terms
of conditioned reflexes which have replaced the sort of discrimina-
tory behaviour necessary to the higher mental functions (the terms
'fixate' or 'fixate by conditioning' have this significance), and conversely we may think of the conditioned reflex in terms of unconscious associations although not necessarily repressed ones in the
Freudian sense. The fact that not all psychologists use the word
does not mean that they do not think in terms which imply the concept. This makes it all the more odd that one of the first criticisms
levelled against Freud was the absurdly academic one that to speak
of the 'unconscious mind' was a contradiction in terms, since 'mind'

is by definition that which is conscious. In fact he originated neither the term nor the concept but learned them in the sixth form of his school in Vienna, where he was taught the psychology of Herbart at about the same time that William James in America was popularizing the word 'subconscious' and showing the importance of this type of motivation in mental life. Freud was a very great man, but it is preposterous to assume with the uncritical that all his basic concepts were entirely original or with the very erudite that they originated from such exalted sources as Plato, Spinoza, Nietzsche, and Schopenhauer. On the contrary, they were based on ideas which in one form or another happened to be in the air at the time he was developing his theories and amongst psychiatrists, psychologists, and physicians rather than amongst philosophers, whose works he is unlikely to have studied during those early years. Certainly he was not acquainted with the works of either Nietzsche or Schopenhauer until quite late in life, and all that need be assumed in the way of influences is that Freud, like most scientists of his time, was a rationalist and materialist with a great admiration for Darwin, whence came his evolutionary and biological approach; that he learned the Herbartian doctrine of the unconscious at school and later became a physician specializing in neurology but, finding that many of his patients were suffering from psychological rather than organic complaints, went to Paris, where he saw that hypnosis could both produce and remove hysterical symptoms and was told by Charcot that 'sex is always at the bottom of the trouble'; that, finally, on his return to Vienna he found Breuer using hypnosis in a new way but, not being a particularly good hypnotist himself, was driven to achieve the same results by other means. As a result of these experiences Freud's picture of the unconscious differed considerably from that of his predecessors in that he pictured it as a dynamic force rather than as a mere waste-paper basket of ideas and memories which had fallen below the threshold of awareness because they were relatively unimportant and lacked the mental energy to force their way into consciousness. He was able to show that precisely the opposite was the case, that the unconscious plays a predominant part in mental life, since it takes its energy from the instinctual drives, and its contents are kept out of awareness not because

6

they lack significance but because they may be so significant as to constitute what is felt as a threat to the ego. When this occurs they are actively repressed and can find expression only by devious methods, as in symptoms, certain character traits, and the other phenomena mentioned above which represent compromise solutions to a conflict between primitive drives seeking an outlet and learned ego and superego behaviour patterns which must inhibit them as unrealistic, contrary to the individual's own values or what he regards as the expectations of others. Repression is itself an unconscious process, and in their disguised form the true nature of the drives remains unknown to their possessor after their transformation by the ego defences. More broadly, Freud described a Pleasure Principle which urged the organism toward drive gratification but was opposed by the Reality Principle; this rather unfortunate terminology complicates rather than simplifies his valuable concept of a tendency towards constancy of psychic phenomena analogous to that equilibrium in the physiological sphere later described by Cannon as 'homeostasis'. Just as a reduction in blood sugar is speedily made good by the breakdown of glycogen in the liver into glucose, or a high salt intake is followed by increased fluid loss to carry the excess away, so drives which upset the psychic equilibrium tend towards tension-reducing gratification; but in this case the learning of detour behaviour by the ego may inhibit their immediate and direct satisfaction in the interest of the more general well-being of the organism as a social animal. Neurotic symptoms in this view are unstable compromise attempts at drive gratification when this has been inhibited by learned responses as incompatible with other dominant personality trends. For example, a phobia which manifests itself as a fear of knives, or the character trait of exaggerated distaste for any form of aggressive manifestation, may conceal deep-seated destructive wishes, and the obsessive fear of being sexually assaulted may conceal a desire. Such compromise solutions are ultimately both unrealistic and uncomfortable, but they serve the immediate function of keeping the individual's self-esteem intact in situations which he, being the person he is, interprets as dangerous, whilst enabling him to remain absorbed with primitive desires which are reinterpreted in terms of fear or disgust. Hence the not uncommon picture of the avowedly pacific person who hates all forms of cruelty and brutality (even to the extent of finding them where others do not) and yet is known by his closer associates to be quarrelsome and unhealthily obsessed with newspaper reports of sadism; or the puritan who, hating pornography, nevertheless regards it as his duty to study all the potentially pornographic works in his local library. At a more superficial level, the writer's cramp of a clerical worker conceals the distaste for his job which, in view of family or other responsibilities or his picture of himself as a highly conscientious man, he refuses to recognize, and the soldier's battle-neurosis hides his inadmissible fear of action. Symptoms are a means of preventing what has been repressed—probably sexualized hostility and its associated anxiety and guilt—from upsetting the rest of the personality, and there is therefore a sense in which it is true to say that the neurotic has a wish to fall ill. This tendency to exercise control over the self, over circumstances, or over the behaviour of others by making a weakness appear as strength or using it as a weapon was regarded by Adler as lying at the root of all neurosis, but Freud, while recognizing the importance and universality of such 'secondary gains', did not accept that they were other than attempts to deal with personality problems which had arisen from more deep-seated conflicts.

The above examples illustrate a third Freudian postulate: that all behaviour is motivated and goal-directed. His early work on hysteria had shown that symptoms could be understood in terms of psychic determinism and also that they had a purposiveness of their own. The patient with hysteria had forgotten events which it suited him to forget because they were painful or would appear discreditable to the conscious self, and at that time the symptoms were regarded as fulfilling a wish. Since the memories recovered under hypnosis or by free association seemed to concern sexual occurrences in early childhood intolerable to the adult mind they were said to be censored and therefore capable of expression only in the disguised form of the symptom. This explanation, for reasons to be discussed later, proved to be unacceptable as originally presented, but it was the first step in the direction of modern dynamic psychology and in marked contrast to the views current towards the end of last century. Breuer, Freud's colleague at this time, had become aware of the importance of the unconscious and in fact anticipated Freud with his observation in the early case of Anna O. that the hysterical paralysis of an arm was directly related to a forgotten event and disappeared when the event was recalled under hypnosis. But to him the choice of symptom was fortuitous, the result of the mere coincidence that the patient's arm had been in an uncomfortable position while she was in a suggestible state (it had 'gone to sleep' while Anna sat somnolent by her father's death-bed). Freud saw the need to explain why a specific memory had been repressed and why its forgetting should have pathological consequences; Breuer did not. On the contrary he seems to have supposed with Janet and others that the mind of the hysteric is abnormally suggestible and constitutionally lacking in the ability to remain integrated and that because of this it is prone under stress to fragmentation into independently-acting systems. Charcot expressed the conventional view when he stated that hysteria was a form of hereditary degeneration with a physiological basis, and Freud himself attached some significance to this notion; but whereas other psychiatrists based their approach to mental disorders on the search for such general laws governing the appearance of mental phenomena, he looked for their aim. In the course of time his early wish-fulfilment theory gave way to the satisfaction of libidinal and instinctual needs and finally to goal-directedness.

These views were criticized on many grounds, particularly when Freud began to apply his findings to other neuroses than hysteria and to the behaviour of normal people. It was argued that theories based on the investigation of abnormal individuals, belonging moreover to a small and extremely atypical social group, could not be indiscriminately used outside the field from which they were derived. However he continued to do so with the result that the argument is now little used and all psychiatrists, whatever else they may feel about psychoanalysis, are at one in agreeing that neurotic and normal behaviour differ in degree rather than kind. The modern Neo-Freudian schools, while not disagreeing with this conclusion, have raised the question of cultural influences in determining what is to be regarded as normal or abnormal, pointing out that what Europeans consider to be indubitably abnormal may elsewhere lie at the very root of a culture's social structure, and that our own characteristic sources of conflict are not necessarily universal. This does not affect Freud's main contention, which is that, in Groddeck's phrase, 'we are lived by our unconscious' and it is the function of reason to channel this energy into modes of expression in accord with the demands of society and objective reality, both of which may vary from one time and place to another. But nobody in any society lives his life by rationally planning every single act or emotion, since normal, as well as abnormal, goals are largely unconsciously determined and the essence of normality is that his unconscious goals and conscious aims should be in harmony with each other and appropriate to the situations in which he finds himself. Freud has also been taken to task for his tendency to refer to the unconscious as if it were a fixed geographical location with boundaries impregnable save to special methods of investigation and containing material which could only manifest itself in disguised form. Adler, as we have seen, made little use of the concept in its original form, although unconscious motivation is certainly implicit in his psychology, and Wilhelm Stekel preferred to think in terms of 'scotomata' or blind spots which he seems to have regarded as almost wilfully kept out of awareness in the interests of the patient's self-esteem. But whether Freud was simply speaking metaphorically in order to clarify the relationships of complex mental events or whether he had not completely freed himself from the tendency to reification typical of the older mechanistic and largely descriptive psychology, it is certain that the ultimate effect of his work has been to cause psychologists to think in terms of processes rather than separate mental entities or locations. Similarly, although psychoanalysis is usually – and quite correctly – described as an instinct psychology, it was perhaps Freud more than anyone else who destroyed the old concept of human instincts as automatic and unlearned responses to specific stimuli like those of other animals, replacing it with the concept of a relatively undifferentiated energy capable of almost infinite variation through experience. Indeed, Freud did not use the term 'Instinkt', which in English signifies instinct as defined above, but the word 'Trieb', mistranslated as 'instinct' but more correctly defined as 'drive', which is used by most psychologists today. As

Fenichel points out, it is characteristic of *Triebe* that they are changed in aim and object under influences stemming from the environment, and Freud was at one time of the opinion that they might originate under the same influence. This concern of psychoanalysis with the how and why of human behaviour and the fact that present symptoms appeared to be connected with past events inevitably led to a search for origins which necessitated the replacement of a cross-sectional view of the patient's present reactions by a longitudinal one which presented the problem historically and developmentally. The faculties or ideas of the older psychology had supposedly initiated behaviour by way of the brain which, isolated in its ivory tower (on both the literal and figurative senses), was the seat of the mind. Thus to those who were not complete materialists it seemed not unreasonable to believe that in disease it was really the brain that was disordered and that the mind functioned badly because its instrument was damaged or inadequate, whereas to those who were the problem was even simpler. In the final analysis, to most dualists and all materialists, mind disease and brain disease were virtually synonymous. Freud was a materialist who used psychological terminology – his 'mythology' as he called it – to describe processes that in his view would one day be described in physico-chemical terms so far as their bodily component was concerned; yet since these interacted with an environment the most significant part of which was other human beings he saw the system as a whole as basically an interpersonal one, because personality with its physiological roots arises in the course of living and relating oneself to others. Personality traits are not simply *there* to be academically described, because initially there are no traits but only potentialities which develop with the individual's attempts to adapt himself to the situations he meets throughout life. It had always been accepted that in a general way the child is father to the man, but Freud insisted on the overwhelming importance of infancy and early childhood as the period during which the undifferentiated psyche of the newly-born child is moulded and takes on the directions it will later follow.

These four postulates: psychic determinism, the role of the unconscious, the goal-directed nature of behaviour, and the developmental or historical approach, have been accepted in one form or another by all the analytic schools and probably by most of those psychologists – they are by no means so numerous as the uninitiated might expect – who concern themselves with the study of personality. But there are two further and related postulates fundamental to orthodox Freudian theory which, especially in recent times, have produced profound disagreement in many quarters and notably in the United States: its biological orientation and the libido theory. It is basically over this issue that the major division has occurred between what may be described as the libido school of Freud and his followers and the non-libido schools of Adler, Horney, Fromm, Sullivan, and others, who may almost be said to have built up their theories specifically against these concepts. The detailed discussion of these differences must be left until later, but speaking generally the practical issue is whether personality is based on biological drives mainly sexual in nature which, rooted in the body with its unalterable hereditary constitution, pass inexorably through certain stages of development during the first five years and then cease to develop but continue to influence behaviour throughout life, or whether, as the Neo-Freudians believe, it is a social product using biological energy but modifying it as circumstances demand, strongly influenced but not narrowly determined by constitutional or developmental factors which are less important on the whole than cultural ones, and possessing needs which arise as much from the individual's society as from his biology. Nobody denies that biological factors are important or that all mental energy must ultimately be rooted in the body, but what is denied by the non-libido schools is that all behaviour is directed towards the satisfaction of biological needs in the straightforward way suggested by Freud. If, for example, one accepts for the sake of argument the orthodox thesis that hoarding or collecting is a trait associated with a particular stage of libido development, the anal retentive phase, it seems absurd in the view of Neo-Freudians and many others that one should be further expected to believe that this is a complete and adequate explanation of collecting in general. The first thesis, they say in effect, may be feasible but the second is preposterous. Experience suggests that for every stamp collector who is satisfying his libidinous needs at the anal level there are dozens who collect because it is profitable to do so, because their friends collect too, or simply because they were given a stamp album as a present when they were wondering what hobby to adopt. Furthermore, as Fromm points out, there are historical periods, such as the rise of capitalism towards the end of the eighteenth century, when anal traits of acquisitiveness, punctuality, regularity, cleanliness, and meticulous attention to detail predominated and became the ethos of a whole society, which translated them into virtues. This must be difficult to explain on a purely biological hypothesis according to some critics, who take it to imply either that changing patterns of child-rearing brought about the Industrial Revolution, which is manifestly nonsense, or that the changing economic structure brought about a new personality type, which would be tantamount to admitting that the biological factor is not primary and social factors are. In fact the conflict is an unreal one, since all those who hold the biological view have to point out is that in a changing economic system the process of natural selection picked out automatically those who were best fitted to run it, weeded out the rest, and continued unconsciously to perpetuate by child-rearing methods the successful type. But it is perhaps fair to allege that Freudians, more by inference than by anything they actually say, seem to give the impression that, for example, playing a musical instrument or having an interest in mathematics (counting = playing with the fingers to obtain satisfaction) are *nothing but* masturbatory equivalents just as whatever is hoarded or collected is *nothing but* symbolic faeces. To the historian or social scientist such observations are to be judged not as either true or untrue but as totally irrelevant, and many psychologists would agree with Allport that attitudes or traits may develop a functional autonomy of their own and subsequently derive their energy from quite different sources than a narrowly reductive analysis of their primal origin might suggest. Freud's view of human nature as interpreted by his critics is that of Hobbes and Darwin, which depicts society as a mass of isolated individuals whose most natural emotion is hostility, pushing and jostling each other in the name of the survival of the fittest, but willing under certain circumstances to band together for self-protection. Their ivory towers conceal the inner stinking cave by the entrance of which they ruthlessly trade physical needs or personal relationships for private gain, returning to the innermost recesses to enjoy them without interference – and this, after all, is not surprising, since they ceased to develop emotionally at the age of five and any trait presented in later life is mere camouflage to conceal what goes on within. Outside the tower are displayed their paintings, their collections of *objets d'art*, their musical skill and wit, or their scientific curiosity, when the psychoanalyst knows perfectly well that inside they are smearing the walls with ordure or enjoying 'retention pleasure', satisfying their autoerotism, or preparing to bite and rend any source of frustration. The scientifically-inclined do indeed pay some attention to the world around them, but more particularly to that part of it where they can witness the intimate goings-on between parents or other adults and in attempting to take possession of this secret and forbidden knowledge can subsequently persuade themselves and others that their sexual curiosity was really a disinterested search for truth with the whole universe as its object. More objectively expressed, Freud believed in the person as a social atom requiring community only as a means to the satisfaction of his needs; in a primary hostility so strong that only sheer necessity or common hatred directed elsewhere could join people in love; in a certain biological inevitability of hereditary constitution, anatomy, and development, which strictly limits human possibilities; in an inner private existence which, although in part the result of early personal relationships, seems in later life to make only indirect contact with external reality (i.e. the causes of behaviour stem from biological and infantile sources rather than from subsequent or contemporary ones – Róheim, indeed, denies that 'environmental influences' exist); and finally in civilization as the result of thwarted libidinous impulses which have been deflected to symbolic ends. Freud's biologism led him to a conviction that the source of man's trouble lies deep within himself and is not simply the result of adverse social or material conditions. But these biological justifications of original sin and predestination appeal primarily to old tradition-bound societies and as such are violently rejected by new or post-revolutionary ones committed to the contrary hypothesis that men are naturally good, are born free and equal with almost infinite potentialities, and that therefore

whatever troubles they suffer must be due to social or environmental factors rather than to individual ones. Stemming from
John Locke and Rousseau, this belief passed to the United States
by way of Jeffersonian democracy and to the Soviet Union by way
of Marx, whose dictatorship of the proletariat was, of course, to
be succeeded by a Rousseauesque classless society; it is therefore not surprising to find that both these countries shared in the
birth of Behaviourism (which rejects 'original sin' in the form of
innate ideas) or that America is almost uniquely the birthplace of
social psychology. For although all schools of psychology dealing
with the total personality claim to be wholly scientific and to have
based their theories solely on hard facts and the results of experi-
ments or dispassionate observation, this is not in fact true, since
they inevitably begin with a belief about man's essential nature
which forms the implicit frame of reference into which their facts
and the results of their observations are fitted rather than the reverse, as they would have us believe. Thus J. B. Watson, the father
of American Behaviourism, who was so sceptical that he denied the
existence of mind, hereditary mental traits, and instinct, was nevertheless prepared to make the astounding claim that he could
take any normal child and with proper training and environment
make it into 'any type of specialist I might select – doctor, lawyer,
artist, merchant-chief and, yes, even beggar-man and thief, regardless of his talents, penchants, tendencies, abilities, vocations,
and race of his ancestors', not because he had discovered it, much
less proved it to be possible in practice, but simply because this is
the logical consequence of believing that men are born free and
equal and that all their troubles are essentially environmental ones.
Freud's aristocratic distaste for the rabble, which, like Voltaire,
he believed should be ruled for its own good by the intelligent, his
fatalism, and his conviction of the non-perfectibility of man being
in conflict with these self-evident truths, the Neo-Freudian Americans solved the problem to their own satisfaction by turning him
upside-down and transforming him into a supporter of Jeffersonian democracy. They did not *discover* that sin was socially derived
or that aggressiveness is not innate – nor, working along totally
different lines, did Watson – because nobody has done so and
it is difficult to see how anyone ever could. Neither had Freud

proved the contrary, since practically speaking there is no difference between the proposition that hostility is innate and the proposition that it is not but that it is a natural response to frustration. There are no means of proving scientifically that men are 'naturally' either good or bad, that their relationship with society is 'naturally' this or that, and that when things go wrong one or the other is to blame, because these are not scientific propositions but articles of faith and the hypercritical may doubt whether they have any meaning at all. Frustration is and always will be universal, so hostility whether innate or not is also universal, and since the individual man only becomes a human being within society the antithesis between the two is unreal. Behind this rather futile philosophizing, however, there is a real issue, the issue of whether in practice human problems are best approached as individual or as social ones. The American approach is characteristically sociological and the Neo-Freudians although dealing with individuals by analytic methods tend to regard the patient's conflicts as a microcosm of social ones; in Europe, on the contrary, the approach is not only predominantly biological but, under the influence of Melanie Klein and others, increasingly so. Scientific theories as someone has pointed out are not statements of irrevocable and absolute truth but useful devices for understanding, and since we understand in terms of what we know they are inevitably influenced by the scientist's social background. Equally inevitably, psychological theories are more culture-bound than most. What really matters is that they should provide a satisfactory explanation of known facts and lead us to discover new ones. How far the various analytic schools have done so is the concern of later chapters, but in the following one Freudian theory is considered in greater detail as it developed historically, with a view to clarifying the issues separating them.

CHAPTER 2

The Theories of Freud: a General Survey

SIGMUND FREUD was born in 1856 in a small town in Moravia, now Czechoslovakia, but then a part of the Austro-Hungarian Empire. He studied medicine in Vienna, which became his home until 1938 when the Nazi annexation of Austria sent him into exile in London, where he died in 1939. Primarily interested in the physiology of the nervous system (he was co-discoverer with Karl Koller of the local anaesthetic effects of cocaine), Freud went to Paris in 1885 to study under Charcot, who was experimenting with the use of hypnosis in cases of hysteria, and on his return to Vienna began himself to make use of this method. It was, however, only occasionally successful, since not all patients could be hypnotized and, even when they were, relief by no means always followed. One of his colleagues, Dr Josef Breuer, had also been using hypnosis, but instead of making a direct attack on the symptoms Breuer encouraged patients to discuss their emotional problems while in the hypnotic state – a process which was described as catharsis or purging, since it seemed to work by relieving the patient of pent-up emotions. *Studies in Hysteria* by Freud and Breuer was published in 1893, but shortly afterwards Breuer ceased to collaborate, leaving Freud to carry on his studies alone. For the reasons already mentioned, he soon gave up the practice of hypnosis and began to use another technique which was to become fundamental to the psychoanalytic approach, that of free association. Patients were asked to relax on a couch and say whatever came into their minds, however absurd, unpleasant, or obscene it might appear by everyday standards. When this was done it appeared that powerful emotional drives swept the uncontrolled thoughts in the direction of the psychic conflict as logs floating on the surface of a great river are whirled about by the currents beneath the surface of the water.

During their period of collaboration, Breuer and Freud had concluded that when a specific memory association for each symptom had been found, painful emotions were drained off as if a psychic abscess had been opened and the purulent matter within evacuated. A strange characteristic of these forgotten and painful memories noted by Freud was the frequency with which they were found to relate to traumatic sexual experiences in childhood. He therefore came to the conclusion that hysteria was produced when the patient had been the passive victim of sexual seduction by an adult in childhood, while another type of psychic illness, the obsessional neurosis, was the result of active participation in such childhood seductions. The latter supposition was based on Freud's observation that obsessional neuroses seemed to be invariably associated with a strong sense of guilt. It was in fact these disturbing discoveries that led Breuer to break off his association with Freud in 1894. Concerning Breuer's action Freud later wrote: 'When I began more and more resolutely to put forward the significance of sexuality in the aetiology of the neuroses, [Breuer] was the first to show that reaction of distaste and repudiation which was later to become so familiar to me, but which at that time I had not yet learnt to recognize as my inevitable fate' (*Collected Papers*, Vol. 1). From this period until 1900, Freud developed theories of unconscious motivation, repression (the process of making an experience unconscious), resistance (the way in which it is kept unconscious), transference (the emotional relationship between analyst and patient), and the causation of the neuroses.

The concept of the unconscious plays an important part in the works of the psychologist Herbart, studied by Freud at school, in the writings of Carl Gustav Carus, Court Physician to the King of Saxony (1848), and, twenty years later, in Eduard von Hartmann's *Philosophy of the Unconscious* – not to mention the philosophies of Schopenhauer and Spinoza. But, to quote Professor J. C. Flugel's *A Hundred Years of Psychology:* 'Freud's theories [contrasted with those of Herbart] had the immense advantage of being based on years of laborious and systematic investigation of individual cases.... With Herbart the opposition [of ideas] seems to be on the whole an intellectual one: with Freud it depends upon an opposition in the field of desire; certain desires are incompatible with other dominant tendencies of the personality, and for this reason are banished to the unconscious.' The concepts of free

association, the unconscious, repression, resistance, and transference developed at this time were to remain an integral part of
orthodox Freudian theory, but the 'psychic abscess' hypothesis
of the causation of neurosis and the theory that anxiety is always
a purely physiological response to sexual frustration were largely
rejected.

Between 1900 and 1910 Freud began to develop new theories
concerning the origins of neurosis. As we have seen, it was at first
supposed that neuroses were due to the repressed memories of
actual events of sexual seductions in childhood which had created
a sort of psychic abscess that could only be cured by release or
'abreaction' of the associated emotions. The memory had been
repressed into the unconscious because, in the words of Flugel
already quoted, it was 'incompatible with other dominant tendencies of the personality'. It also seems to have been supposed that
when a memory became unconscious it was completely shut off
and could have no further influence upon the personality as a
whole unless it were excited by some subsequent event. Neurosis
at this time was clearly regarded as a local disturbance rather than
as a reaction of the total personality. But in the years between 1900
and 1910 Freud had to change his mind concerning these supposed
sexual seductions of childhood when he discovered that, in many
cases at least, no such seduction appeared to have occurred, and
from the accounts of relatives it seemed clear that the patient was
either lying or imagining an event which had never happened. At
first, this seemed to strike a final blow at Freud's theory, but with
characteristic tenacity he began to seek out a new formulation of
his beliefs. He had already noted that not only symptoms but also
dreams and slips of the tongue are unconsciously motivated, that
in the mental world as in the physical nothing happens without a
cause, and he felt himself entitled to assume that there must be
some adequate reason why so many of his patients imagined themselves to have been the object of sexual seduction by a parent. From
his observations that fears are frequently the expression of unconscious desires, that a conscious fear is often the expression of
an unconscious wish, Freud was led to formulate two further
hypotheses which were later to be incorporated in psychoanalytic
theory: the hypotheses of infantile sexuality and the Oedipus

complex. The new theory, so far as it may be described here, can be summarized as follows:

There were, it was postulated, two great vital drives—the drive for self-preservation and the drive towards procreation (i.e. the preservation of the species). The former presented no great difficulty to the individual since it was not ordinarily thwarted for any prolonged period of time. The latter, however, to which Freud gave the name of libido or sexual energy, was frequently blocked from overt expression by the repressing forces of civilization. Originally Freud, when he used the word 'sex', meant it to be understood in the ordinary everyday sense, but about this time he decided to use it in a much wider connotation to apply to any pleasurable sensation relating to the body functions, and also, through the concept of sublimation, to such feelings as tenderness, pleasure in work, and friendship. In other words, he used the word to refer to what would ordinarily be described as 'desire'. The reason Freud gave for defining sex in this unusual way was the obvious fact that adult sexual strivings are not necessarily exclusively directed towards persons of the opposite sex—in the perversions they may be directed towards persons of the same sex, towards the individual himself, towards animals, or even towards inanimate objects. Nor, for that matter, is genital union necessarily the object of sexual behaviour; for the mouth and anus may also be involved. Lastly, in the behaviour of infants actions are observable which resemble those of adult perverts (e.g. interest in urination and defaecation, thumb-sucking, or showing the naked body and taking pleasure in observing others naked). Since it was assumed that the self-preservative instinct was not often thwarted Freud directed all his attention to the study of the libido. Noting that the three orifices of the body—the mouth, anus, and genitals— were particularly associated with libidinous satisfactions, he postulated that interest in them developed in a definite chronological sequence from the moment of birth onwards. To the new-born child the mouth is the primary organ of pleasure for it is through the mouth that he makes contact with his first object of desire, the mother's breast. When the breast is withdrawn or not available he gains a substitute, if inferior, satisfaction by sucking his thumb or some other object. That interest in the mouth region is never entirely superseded is seen by the pleasure taken by adults in eating, smoking, kissing, and the more overtly sexual acts connected with the mouth. The early oral (passive) phase of this stage of development may be in evidence immediately after birth and before the infant has experienced the breast, since sucking movements have been observed prior to actual suckling. However the most primitive stage of libidinal investment is conceived of as a diffused spread of libido or drive energy throughout the whole body, internally and on the skin surface, which increasingly becomes focused in the mouth area, at first manifesting itself passively and then actively and aggressively with the eruption of the first teeth at the age of about six months. This later oral phase was described by Karl Abraham, to whom much of the libido theory is due. Abraham had been an embryologist before taking up psychoanalytic work, and it was natural for him to think in terms of maturational processes which caused libidinal development to take place in an orderly sequence of stages each with its typical zone and aim. The oral phase is overlapped and succeeded by the anal phase, characterized by an aim to expel aggressively and the later aim to retain which presumably coincides with the ability to control the anal sphincter developing towards the end of the first year. Pregenital sexuality as a stage of development closes about the end of the third year when with the early genital or phallic phase interest begins to centre on the penis—the word 'phallic' was used by Freud to indicate that the sexual object is not the genitals as such but the phallus, because this stage in his view 'knows only one sort of genital, the male'. In contrast to the autoerotic pregenital phases phallic satisfaction requires an external object. The latent period from the fifth to the tenth year is latent in the sense that only quantitative changes in the libido occur, and the term does not mean as some have supposed that sexual manifestations do not occur but simply that there are no qualitative developments. At the end of latency there may occur a reinforcement of pregenital drives when the child becomes more untidy and rebellious, but this is succeeded at puberty with the glandular changes which herald the arrival of adult genitality.

The libido theory is complex and has many aspects other than those concerning development described above. These are best expressed in the following brief but fairly comprehensive summary:

(1) Libido is best conceived as drive energy, the principal components of which are sexual (in the broad sense defined above), but Freud never subscribed to the view that no other instincts existed or that 'everything is sex'. Component instincts such as scoptophilia, the desire to look, and motility are described, and it was made quite clear that the sexual instinct was singled out because it was regarded as the most important one and, subject to repression, 'the one we know most about'. The term 'life force' is too metaphysical to apply to a concept which is a purely biological one.

(2) In its economic aspects, libido in an individual is regarded as a closed energy system regulated by the physical law of conservation of energy, so that libido withdrawn from one area must inevitably produce effects elsewhere. Hence the psychoanalyst's conviction that any symptom removed by suggestion (i.e. without release of the energy maintaining it) will make its appearance in some other form; e.g. cessation of smoking may be replaced by over-eating, cessation of habitual masturbation or intercourse by anxiety. In his theory of wit Freud saw laughter as an explosion of energy previously employed to repress antisocial feelings which for the moment society is prepared to permit in partially disguised form. Jokes about God or mothers-in-law under the disguise of 'just for fun' lift the repression from sadistic feelings embodying real hate or irreverence which are temporarily permitted expression in an implied playful contest. This realization is embodied in G. K. Chesterton's insight that we only laugh at serious things which would ordinarily produce sympathy, grief, fear, or awe, although obviously this applies to only one form of humour.

(3) Libido passes through the stages of maturation already described, each of which is biologically determined, is centred on a specific erotogenic zone (mouth, anus, penis), and has a specific aim of gratification (sucking, incorporating and biting, retention and aggressive expulsion, penetration). Adult genital sexuality represents a fusion of pregenital with genital drives, and a sexual perversion is said to be present only when pregenital drives in the

adult become primary and supersede the genital one as goal. But although the stages of libido development are biologically determined, it is recognized that their development is influenced by the reaction of significant figures to the child's behaviour while it is passing through them; the effects of upbringing, the parental attitudes to early bowel training and masturbation or prohibitions generally, have an immediate influence upon the relative emphasis or frustration of the particular zones and their aims, as also does the early or later timing of their application. The immediate effect, however, is of less significance than the delayed results of maturation and learning on the adult personality in terms of fixation, regression, object relationships, symptom formation, and character. The timing of maturation and learning is important because the same act on the part of the mother will produce different effects at different times in the child's life (phase specificity), and the interaction between events experienced at various stages of development must also be taken into account. Naturally, quantitative variations in the constitutional strength of a drive or in the strength of stimulation and the length of time it is applied have an important influence on the final result.

Character formation will be discussed later, when the appropriate stage in the development of Freud's thought is reached. All that need be said at this point is that Freudian theory conceives of the genesis of character in terms of pregenital drives which, under the influence of social pressures, have changed their aim or object or been otherwise modified by learning in the course of upbringing. For example, the anal character mentioned briefly in the last chapter may possess such traits as stubbornness, independence, or possessiveness derived from the retentive pleasure of the child who in face of parental entreaties responds in effect: 'What I have I keep.' Faeces come to be associated with possessions and particularly with money—otherwise, the Freudians not unreasonably ask, why should we use such phrases as 'stinking with money', 'filthy lucre', 'throwing money down the drain', and even 'rolling in the stuff', which all clearly equate money with faeces? Or why the concern over punctuality and cleanliness sometimes carried to pathological degrees if it is not to be regarded as a reaction against ʀprimitive wish for dirt and disorder? During the oral stage the infant is becoming aware of others and begins to assume relationships with them; during the anal stage he learns to relinquish immediate instinctual gratification in order to please or at any rate influence others. In Freudian theory then, it is accepted that the ease or difficulty experienced by the child in passing through the pregenital phases has a fundamental influence upon its later attitudes as an adult towards such basic forms of behaviour as giving and taking, defiance or submission, love or hate, and towards such sentiments as stinginess or generosity, optimism or pessimism, interest or indifference about others. Conflicts or difficulties experienced at one or other of these stages may lead to fixation of libido at this point or later troubles cause a regression to it.

The phallic phase, as we have seen, begins about the end of the third year when the boy's interest becomes centred upon his penis, and this interest soon gives rise to a feeling of sexual attraction towards the mother associated with feelings of jealousy or resentment directed against the father, who has thus become the boy's rival in his mother's affections. This of course is the well-known Oedipus complex, named after the king in Sophocles's play *Oedipus Rex* who killed his father and married his mother—without knowledge of their identity in either case—and thereby brought a plague to Thebes. The Oedipus complex finally comes to an end about the fourth or fifth year, primarily because of the boy's fears that his illicit desires might be punished by the father with castration (the castration complex), and is succeeded by the latency period, during which sexuality becomes virtually dormant or at any rate ceases to show any further qualitative developments and remains so right up to the period of puberty. In the case of the little girl the state of affairs is rather more complex, and Freud never seems to have been quite clear on this point. For both boys and girls the first object of attachment is necessarily the mother, and it is believed that after the oral and anal phases both have a primarily phallic orientation. The girl becomes interested in her clitoris as the biological equivalent of the boy's penis, but since this organ appears obviously inferior to the masculine one she develops an envious desire to be like the boy. This is described by Freud as 'penis envy', and it is postulated that the girl's attachment to her father which now takes place—the Electra complex, from a Greek myth in which Electra connives at the death of her mother Clytemnestra who had murdered her father Agamemnon—only occurs when she has renounced the hope of masculinity and reconciled herself to castration as an accepted fact. In Freud's interpretation the masculine Oedipus complex is *resolved* by the castration complex and is given up because of castration anxiety, while the feminine complex is *brought about* by the castration complex, when out of disappointment over the lack of a penis the girl turns her love towards the father and rejects the mother. The fact that the girl thinks 'I have been punished' while the boy fears 'I may be punished' is believed to have important consequences for their later development. But in both sexes the Oedipus complex comes as the climax of infantile sexuality and an overcoming of the strivings of this period with the attainment of adult sexuality is necessary for normality, whereas an unconscious clinging to Oedipus tendencies is typical of the neurotic mind.

Concerning the aetiology of the neuroses, Freud now (i.e. prior to 1910) believed that each type of neurosis was the result of a regression of libido which had been dammed up by a frustrating environment and therefore flowed back to an earlier stage at which during the course of development it had been partially fixated. Mental development never takes place completely according to plan, and characteristics of earlier levels persist inevitably alongside or behind the new one; disturbances are due not only to total arrest of development but also to the retaining of more traces of earlier stages than is normal. Frustration may bring about regression to a stage that was more successfully experienced in the past, one at which a large amount of libido remains fixated, and in each neurosis there is assumed to be a specific point of fixation such that the hysteric is said to have regressed to the phallic level, the obsessional to the anal. At this period Freud divided the personality into layers according to their degree of consciousness: the perceptual conscious contains present awareness, the preconscious or foreconscious that which, although unconscious now, is capable of recall, and the unconscious that which cannot be brought into awareness because it is actively repressed.

Following his break with Breuer in 1894 and right up to the beginning of the present century Freud was working alone. Yet it was during these years that much of his most important work was done, notably the publication of *The Interpretation of Dreams* in 1900 and of *The Psychopathology of Everyday Life* in the following year—not to mention the discovery of the basic principles of the psychoanalytic method already discussed. He was a slow and conscientious investigator, frequently presenting his observations to a somewhat indifferent public several years after they had been made, but in 1902 the whole complexion of things was changed when a group of Viennese physicians joined with him in a seminar for the study of psychoanalysis. Within a comparatively short time psychoanalysis had become a movement of world-wide proportions, in spite of the almost universal fury, resentment, and disgust which now surrounded the name of Freud in his supposed assault upon the innocence of childhood and his 'pansexualism'— a fury which raged unabated up to 1914, when the world had other matters to think about. Even amongst his own followers who at this time included such men as Abraham and Ferenczi, Bleuler, Jung, and Adler, there were those who had their reservations and felt that his persistent emphasis upon the sexual roots of neurosis to the exclusion of other factors was unsatisfactory. Adler began seriously to differ with Freud and broke with the movement in 1910 to found a system based on the thesis that human behaviour can be explained in terms of a struggle for power in order to overcome feelings of mental or physical inferiority, and this system, whatever its status today, carried three implications which proved to be of the greatest possible importance to psychoanalysis and were finally in one form or another adopted by it: that neurosis was a disorder of the total personality, that the ego played a large part in its genesis, and that non-sexual factors could also lead to conflict. Jung also differed from Freud over the sexual aetiology of the neuroses, but his theory took an entirely divergent course in which it has on the whole had very little influence either upon scientists or upon other analytic schools; he left the original group in 1913. Freud himself in the years during and after the war began to study the ego and to develop a theory of the whole personality; he saw too that the terrifying dreams of battle-shocked soldiers could hardly be explained in terms of sexual symbolism or wish-fulfilment and that aggression, as well as sex, might be an important instinct subject to repression and therefore liable to lead to neurosis. These considerations led him from 1920 onwards to develop a new theoretical framework for psychoanalysis. The theory of the Life and Death instincts, of repetition compulsion, and the division of the personality into ego, superego, and id, together with a new theory of the nature of anxiety, date from this time.

According to the fully-developed hypothesis there are two basic instincts, a Life instinct or Eros, and a Death instinct or Thanatos which has been named 'mortido' or 'destrudo' by some later writers. The Life instinct comprises the old concept of libido and part of the self-preservation drive. The Death instinct, however, is something new in the thought of Freud—it is quite separate from libido and represents, in fact, an innate destructiveness and aggression directed primarily against the self. While the Life instinct is creative, the Death instinct is a force which is constantly working towards death and ultimately towards a return to the original inorganic state of complete freedom from tension or striving. The repetition compulsion which showed itself in the battle-dreams of soldiers in the form of repeated dreams of the same traumatic incident was assumed to be related to the tendency of the Death instinct to return to earlier states (although psychiatrists in general have believed that such dreams have precisely the opposite function of compelling the mind to assimilate an experience which it had found temporarily intolerable in order to bring about integration). Since inwardly-directed aggression from whatever source is dangerous to the individual there arises a constant necessity to deal with it in such a manner as to make it less destructive to him, and this may be done in one of two ways: by erotizing it, that is to say by combining it with libido, in which case it may take the form of sadism or masochism (sexual perversions in which sex and aggression are combined), or by directing it outwards in aggression against others. Some aggression, too, plays a part in supporting the dictates of a harsh conscience or superego. On the basis of this theory Freud supposed that war might be understood as a nation's attempt at psychological self-preservation, since if it did not direct its aggression outwards it would finally destroy itself with internal feuds. Suicide is a failure to preserve the self by these means, and many lesser forms of self-damage from unconsciously motivated accidents, self-inflicted diseases, addictions, and failures, to the more dramatic but not infrequent crimes committed with the unconscious intent of being found out, can be attributed to inwardly-directed mortido. Almost alone amongst his pronouncements this conception raised a storm of protest amongst Freud's orthodox supporters, much of it couched in the language of moral disapproval. But it is probably wiser to accept Fenichel's more reasoned criticism that Freud had confused two entirely separate concepts: the first, that aggression is innate in man and its dynamics are as described, based as they are on clinical findings; the second, that because all men die and all behaviour is striving they must also be striving for death. The latter concept is a bad philosophical one which seems to argue that *because* instincts strive for gratification or reduction of tension and death is the ultimate tensionless state this must needs be their final aim, and *because* aggression can become directed against the self as demonstrated clinically *therefore* aggression and the Death instinct are one and the same. Freud's thesis in the ultimate analysis is a metaphysical one, and the present position amongst most psychoanalysts is an acceptance of his account of aggression and its vicissitudes with, on the whole, very little reference to either Life or Death instincts.

This theory first made its appearance in *Beyond the Pleasure Principle* published in 1922, and almost at the same time there appeared *The Ego and the Id*, which presented the following picture of the total personality. The new-born child is a seething mass of impulses or instinctual drives entirely lacking in any directing or guiding consciousness, and because of its impersonal nature this primitive mass is described as the 'id', Freud's Latinized version of Groddeck's 'das Es', the It. But since the child must come to terms with external reality a part of this primeval conglomeration sooner or later becomes separated off and differentiated as the 'ego' or self, the prime function of which is to test reality in order that the organism's reactions shall be in terms of what is, rather than uncoordinated responses or those aiming at direct and immediate satisfaction. At a still later stage of development there arises out of the need to face society's moral prohibitions the 'superego' loosely equated with 'conscience' although both more and less than this word implies. Whereas at an earlier period the child had accepted the moral dictates of its parents, their attitudes, opinions, and judgements, in the sense that it submitted more or less willingly to external authority, it now, by a process of identification, takes them within itself. In the words of Franz Alexander: 'Parental attitudes are taken over by the personality, one part of which (i.e. the superego) assumes the same attitude towards the rest as the parents did previously toward the child' (*Fundamentals of Psychoanalysis*). The superego is only in part conscious—a fact which explains the frequently-observed phenomenon that an individual may feel profound guilt after carrying out some action which his reason tells him is not at all immoral. Freud believed that in the boy the superego arose from the ashes of the Oedipus complex and the sense of guilt once based upon fear of punishment or rejection by the parents became, by the incorporation of parental standards within the mind itself, a self-imposed burden. Since the castration complex in the boy was supposed to be the most powerful factor in bringing the Oedipus stage to an end and thus forming the superego, and since, as we have already seen, the little girl must accept 'castration' as an unpleasant fact, already a *fait accompli*, little girls can never (or so the Freudians say) develop a strong superego. Hence arises the unfortunate fact of woman's weak moral nature, demonstrated, as everyone knows, by the action of Eve, who at one stroke lost us our birthright and brought about the need for psychoanalysts.

The individual's character-structure was now seen as the resultant of a three-cornered struggle between the external world, the id, and the superego. The primitive impulses of the id, including the residues of pregenital drives, are dealt with so as to make them compatible with external reality and the moral strivings of the superego. This is done in several ways, and therefore adult character traits may be the result of (a) an aim-inhibited or sublimated expression of pregenital libidinal drives, (b) a reaction-formation against such drives, or (c) a residue of pregenital drives. Thus the striving for power or indeed any form of self-assertion is seen as an expression of aim-inhibited sadism, any kind of affection as an expression of aim-inhibited sex, and painting or sculpture as a sublimation of anal erotism. In all these cases the ego has formed a channel rather than a dam for the libido which is directed on the whole along socially-approved lines. Sublimations are characterized (a) by the relatively smooth flow of pregenital drives towards alternative goals, and (b) by the choice of goals being acceptable to society. So whether we attribute incendiary tendencies and pyromania to sadistic-destructive drives or to urethral erotism seeking satisfaction by pouring water on fires, we are entitled to conclude that the man with such tendencies who becomes a good and efficient member of a fire-brigade is sublimating them, whereas one who starts fires and joins the fire-brigade in order to be able to put them out is not on the whole proving successful in his sublimations. Nor, since only pregenital drives are sublimated, can we speak of this mechanism with reference to a childless woman who takes pleasure in looking after the children of others, since in this case the aim of the drive is not pregenital, nor has it been changed. It is an example of substitution rather than sublimation. Reaction-formation is a mechanism in which the forbidden drive is firmly repressed and the libido dammed-up with the appearance of contrary tendencies which both maintain the repression and present the ego to society in a favourable light. The resulting tendencies of exaggerated puritanism or gentleness are not successful adjustments partly because of the lack of self-knowledge they imply, partly because of the wasted mental energy used for maintaining repression, but mostly because on their own terms they are unsuccessful and even the layman is able to perceive the prurience underlying the 'purity' and the sadism beneath this type of 'gentleness'. One of the aims of psychoanalysis so far as character is concerned is the transformation of such reactive traits into genuine sublimations. Freud's view of personality development implies a conception of learning in which emphasis is laid upon the influence of memories on the perception of contemporary stimuli so that *all* present perception is influenced by past perception and, as he wrote, ' . . . inner perceptions of ideational and emotional processes are projected outwardly and are used to shape the outer world, whereas they ought to remain in the inner world'. This process had been recognized by Herbart, who, describing it as 'apperception', supplied the following definition: 'The process by which new experiences are assimilated to and transformed by the residuum of past experience of any individual to form a new whole.' But the existence of apperception in the more strictly Freudian sense has two important implications, the first being that the world as experienced here and now consists of perceptions of reality which have been transformed by past experiences and interpreted in the light of these even although they remain unconscious, the second that the earlier an apperception the greater its controlling effect on the present. It is unnecessary to make a mystery of the psychoanalyst's emphasis on the period of infancy or to suppose that it requires the direct influence without intervening stages of a particular childhood event upon present behaviour, for all that need be accepted is that a diffuse awareness, for example at the mother's breast, of sensations with an ordinarily pleasurable feeling-tone or on the other hand of a generally unpleasant and frustrating one will influence the way events are experienced at the next pregenital stage and so on through the course of development. How much development is affected will depend on the primacy in time of an experience, its frequency, and its strength on each occasion.

Freud's biological approach tended in the course of time to become more sociologically orientated. Originally he had conceived of psychic energy as resembling a 'fluid electric current' which when dammed up and thus deflected from its normal outlets flowed into other organs manifesting itself in the form of neurotic symptoms. In hysteria the intolerable idea was associated with a certain amount of excitation which could only find release in some form of bodily expression, whereas in the case of obsessions and phobias the excitation had been detached from its original idea and attached to other ideas 'suited to it but not intolerable'. In these conditions there was an attempt to control anxiety by separating it from its real cause and deflecting it elsewhere, but in anxiety neurosis Freud saw '. . . a quantum of anxiety in a free-floating condition which in any state of expectation controls the selection of ideas and is ever ready to attach itself to any suitable ideational content'. Many neuroses were accepted as being due to hereditary defects or to unsatisfactory sexual practices which brought about excitation without relieving it. Coitus interruptus, prolonged abstinence, or relative abstinence in those used to more frequent satisfaction, were believed to release libido which in the absence of outlets became transformed into anxiety, because when an affect is repressed its fate is '... to be converted into anxiety no matter what quality of affect it would otherwise have been had it run its normal course'. This was Freud's explanation of anxiety prior to the First World War, and as it stands is in conformity with clinical observations or indeed with everyday ones, since everyone has noticed that strong emotions or desires held in check do in fact lead to tension, and psychiatrists recognize the existence of 'actual neuroses' brought about by the sexual causes mentioned and relieved by a change of sexual habits. However, this account is a purely descriptive one which provides no sort of causal explanation of the origin or meaning of anxiety, and the later theory pointed out that, while both anxiety and fear are reactions in face of a dangerous situation, fear is a response to a known and external danger, anxiety to an internal and unknown one. The source of danger in anxiety is instinctual when powerful and forbidden desires threaten to overwhelm the ego and endanger the individual's relations with others. In childhood forbidden acts are likely to lead to retribution (e.g. the symbolic punishment of castration) or loss of love on the part of the mother, but in adult life what is feared is social ostracism or rejection by society. Thus there is a hierarchy of sources of anxiety: loss of the original union with the mother at birth, loss of the breast at the oral period and of the penis at the phallic period, loss of the approval of the superego (social and moral approval of significant figures) in the latency period, and of society in adult life. Separation from the mother is the prototype of all subsequent anxieties up to and including the fear of death or the fear of loss of the love of God. Kierkegaard, who died a few months before Freud was born, had seen anxiety not only as inevitable but almost a duty in face of man's awareness of his separation from God brought about by his just strivings for absolute freedom and individuation, and emphasis on the will to be free and the inevitable separation-anxiety which accompanies it plays a considerable part in the theories of Rank and Erich Fromm to whom, as to Freud, separation-anxiety begins with the mother. With Kierkegaard it began with God, but otherwise the theologian who saw the connexion between individualism, separation, and anxiety had a good deal in common with the analysts. In his second theory of anxiety Freud showed that anxiety arises not in the unconscious following repression but in the ego itself which, perceiving the danger, creates the repression. 'We may now', he writes, 'take the view that the ego is the real locus of anxiety, and reject the earlier conception that the cathectic energy of the repressed impulse automatically becomes converted into anxiety' (*Inhibition, Symptom, and Anxiety*, 1927).

Finally it is necessary to say something about the actual process of psychoanalysis as carried out by orthodox practitioners, although of course this is naturally subject to modification by individual analysts. The psychoanalyst may be a layman but is ordinarily a physician and in Britain is also likely to have obtained the post-graduate Diploma in Psychological Medicine prior to a course of instruction at the Institute of Psychoanalysis. This course consists of theoretical work combined with a personal analysis and the analysis of patients under supervision, the purpose of the personal analysis being to provide insight into his own mental processes and blind spots. Patients in private practice are selected according to such criteria as relative youth, high intelligence, good previous personality, and the general responsiveness of their type of neurosis to psychoanalytic treatment. Obviously it is necessary that they should be able to spare the time for this very time-consuming procedure — and, of course, the money. When these criteria are fulfilled the patient will be expected to attend for treatment about five or six times a week, each session lasting fifty minutes. At the actual session the patient carries on his free association while lying on a couch at the head of which the analyst sits out of direct vision, interrupting or interpreting as little as possible, although this too will depend both on the analyst and the particular patient being analysed. An orthodox analyst will adopt a strictly neutral attitude and on the whole avoid expressions of pleasure or displeasure or any sort of comments about progress which might influence the patient's attitudes; his aim is to be as unobtrusive as possible and to provide as it were a screen upon which attitudes are projected without his own personality distorting them. There is no doubt that, if psychoanalysis is the longest method of psychotherapy, it is also the most radical and the most objective one, and this distinguishes it from shorter methods in which the intervention of the analyst must necessarily be more frequent and therefore more suspect of suggestion. In fact, most orthodox analysts would claim that any other method of psychotherapy can exercise its effect only by suggestion or by the conscious or unconscious creation of a positive transference by the analyst. Freud himself was confronted by the problem of transference during his early researches, but instead of making direct therapeutic use of the patient's attachment as a means of exercising control over the neurosis, he proceeded to study transference as a scientific phenomenon and came to the conclusion that the emotions of love or hate shown him by patients were not a response to his own personality but that, on the contrary, he was being taken as a substitute for the original object of their feeling. Analysis had revived the emotions felt in early life towards significant persons, and these, projected on to the analyst, might make him at one stage the object of an exaggerated love and enthusiasm and at the next the object of distrust and hatred. One of the objects of psychoanalysis is to break down and interpret these attitudes and to deal with the resistances which prevent the patient from discovering the nature of the repressed drives which produce his symptoms, because, possibly to his surprise or even indignation, the analyst is not particularly interested in symptoms as such; to the former they *are* his illness, to the latter they are only the smell of burning which indicates something amiss in the smouldering and explosive mass beneath. Furthermore those forms of malfunctioning—palpitations, groundless anxiety, phobias, depression, paralysis, or sensory disturbances—which at least have the respectable appearance of medical disabilities, are not even the sum of the patient's symptoms, and he may be quite unaware of those defects in the field of personal relationships, attitudes to work, love, and so on which are practically speaking much more disabling. Soon he may find that his early enthusiasm to be rid of what he originally regarded as an illness causing him discomfort or distress has become somewhat weakened with the discovery that he is expected to change his whole attitude to life, and by his resistances the analyst may find himself confronted with a patient conducting a private campaign of passive obstruction which manifests itself in the many subjects which 'cannot be recalled', are 'too trivial to discuss', or which he would 'rather not mention'. Naturally resistances slow down the process of treatment, but Freud found a partial solution to the problem in the analysis of dreams, which he regarded as 'the royal road to the unconscious'. The patient finally comes to see his neurosis not as a disease in the medical sense but as an attempt to adjust at an infantile level to problems demanding a more adult approach, and since discarding past methods of handling such issues and developing new ones is by no means an easy task, the final outcome of analysis is far from being a foregone conclusion, and the selection of suitable candidates for this form of psychotherapy (especially in view of the commitments involved) is correspondingly important. Although the orthodox method has changed little since early days, it is in general true to say that the analyst's conception of what he is trying to do has shown a change in emphasis over the years. Whereas initially the main emphasis was upon bringing into consciousness that which was unconscious and thus inducing emotional release or catharsis, the later emphasis was upon the early uncovering of resistances prior to further analysis, and finally upon the transference and the analysis of the current relationship with the analyst, which of course reveals the patient's techniques of handling interpersonal situations and their early origins.

CHAPTER 3

The Early Schismatics

THE first International Psychoanalytic Congress was held at Salzburg in 1908, and the first International Journal of Psychoanalysis was published in the following year. Freud and Jung had made a lecture tour of America in 1909, but for the most part the serious study of psychoanalysis was limited to the German-speaking countries until about 1916, when for reasons to be discussed later it began to influence British psychiatry and subsequently psychiatry in America. Progress became more marked after the War, when in 1920 the Berlin Institute of Psychoanalysis was opened, primarily as a result of the work of Karl Abraham, Max Eitingon, and Ernst Simmel, and this was followed shortly afterwards by the opening of similar Institutes in London, Vienna, and Budapest. In these centres free treatment was given to those who could not afford private analyses, and courses of instruction were provided for students. The New York Institute was opened in 1931, and that in Chicago by Franz Alexander, formerly of Berlin, in 1932. However, this considerable extension of the movement was accompanied by a breaking away from orthodoxy of numbers of former disciples and by a 'closing of the ranks' on the part of those who were determined to cling to Freud's leadership, a tendency which had been apparent ever since the defections of Adler and Jung. From that time onwards orthodox Freudians began to show the peculiar intolerance to criticism which even now is one of their less amiable characteristics and, as in certain religious and political bodies but in sharp contrast to what is usually regarded as scientific procedure, those within the group were expected not to criticize its fundamental beliefs and those without were informed that they had no authority to do so. Admittedly the psychoanalytic movement had been submitted to the most bitter and often slanderous attacks both by psychiatrists and psychologists and by the lay public, which felt that traditional moral standards were being threatened, but the intolerance of the orthodox went on long after these attacks had abated. To Freud himself during the earlier part of this period, says Theodor Reik, every critic appeared as a moral hypocrite, every honest and serious judgement was considered a 'resistance'. In this atmosphere it was inevitable that those who disagreed with him left the movement not at all with the tacit agreement to differ but rather in an aura of heavy disapproval and the sort of invective that was once heaped upon the heads of heretics in the Ages of Belief. During the early 1920s, four other disciples of Freud either broke away or at any rate disagreed in various respects with the main movement, namely Otto Rank, Wilhelm Stekel, Sandor Ferenczi (who, however, never completely broke with Freud), and Wilhelm Reich. Much of the dust aroused by these early conflicts has begun to subside, since almost all those who took an active part in them are dead and the younger psychoanalysts have taken up their chosen profession with little need to feel that they are challenging the world—they may not be highly regarded by all psychiatrists, but neither on the whole are psychiatrists always well thought of by general physicians, although one seems to sense an increasing tolerance on the part of the latter since psychiatry began to make use of such authentic therapeutic methods as pills, surgical operations, and complicated electrical appliances long familiar to ordinary medicine. However, in the eyes of the rest of the world the psychoanalyst reigns supreme and psychology and psychiatry are seen either as synonyms for psychoanalysis or as rather insignificant ramifications of Freudian theory. In such a blaze of glory it might be expected that the old bitterness would be forgotten, but tradition takes a long time to die and Freudians are still touchy. From time to time their encyclicals appear to blast right- and left-wing deviationists of today or yesterday, charging them not with scientific error alone but also with possessing malignant unconscious or even conscious motives. One is led to believe that Freud, like D. H. Lawrence, was surrounded by a group of egocentric primadonnas whose highly ambivalent devotion to the Master was only equalled by their dislike of each other and the abnormal volubility which manifested itself in their writings. For the moment however we are concerned with the men mentioned above, with the exception of Reich who is discussed elsewhere.

Alfred Adler, like Freud, was a Jew and spent much of his early life in Vienna. Born in 1870, he joined Freud's seminar, where from the beginning he regarded himself as a junior colleague rather than a disciple. The strictly biological foundations of Freud's theories appealed from the outset to Adler, who had for some time been interested in the capacity of the body to compensate for organic damage. As physicians have long known, damage to certain organs in the body is sometimes followed by a compensatory reaction which from a teleological point of view may be regarded as the organism's attempt to overcome its defect. The heart with a diseased valve responds by hypertrophy of the cardiac muscle and thus to a certain extent makes good its loss of efficiency, and damage to a kidney or lung may be followed by increased compensatory functioning of the undamaged organ. While in these cases compensation occurs in the physiological sphere, Adler believed that it was possible to observe similar reactions to organic defects in the psychological one. The Greek orator Demosthenes, for example, was said to have stammered badly as a boy, and painters have suffered from defective vision or musicians from deafness. Such observations made it reasonable to suppose that it was the very inferiority of these functions which stimulated the individual to overcome his defect, to such good effect that the once inferior function became the superior one. Up to this point Adler's thesis, presented in his book *A Study of Organic Inferiority and Its Psychical Compensation* (published in 1907), was readily accepted by Freud and his colleagues as an interesting contribution to ego-psychology, but in the next four years it became clear that Adler was developing his concept, not merely as an interesting sideline, but as a key to the understanding of the whole of mental life. His basic thesis, as expressed in his own words, was that 'To be a human being means the possession of a feeling of inferiority that is constantly pressing on towards its own conquest' (*Social Interest: a Challenge to Mankind*).

But other factors than the organic ones of inferior physique, physical deformities, or defective bodily functions were to be considered as leading to lowered self-esteem and hence to an intense struggle for self-assertion. The neglected, spoilt, or hated child is likely to develop strong feelings of inferiority, and even in the happiest circumstances the normal child must feel small, helpless, and at the mercy of the world of adults which surrounds it. Thus it happens that, in order to compensate for inferiority feelings, each child develops in the early years of life his own particular strategy for dealing with the family situation as he sees it. In the light of everyday experience he develops the attitudes which collectively form what Adler described as the 'life-style', and it is upon this life-style that the adult character is based. 'The goal of the personal purposive pattern is always the goal of social significance, the goal of the elevation of personal self-esteem, the goal of superiority. This goal is indicated by a variety of manifestations. It may be crystallized as the ideal either of useful achievement, of personal prestige, of the domination of others, of the defence against danger, or of sexual victories' (Erwin Wexberg: *Individual Psychology*). Character, therefore, is regarded by Adler as an interlocking set of attitudes which has been adopted by the individual in order to deal with the types of situation to which he was exposed (e.g. his bodily constitution, his social and economic position, his sex, the family constellation and his position in the family, his education, and so on). The traits which he produces are adopted because of their functional value to him in the earliest years of life; they were the traits which seemed to give the best results, in terms of power, in the particular setting in which he was placed.

There are three possible results of the individual's strivings for superiority and his attempt to overcome inferiority feelings:

(1) *Successful compensation*, when the striving finally leads to a good adjustment to the three challenges of life—society, work, and sex.

(2) *Overcompensation*, when the striving becomes too apparent and leads to varying degrees of maladjustment—for example, the bumptious small man, the weakling who becomes a gangster either in fact or fancy, or, to quote an example with which Freud dealt scathingly, the grandiose Kaiser Wilhelm II with his withered arm.

(3) *The retreat into illness as a means of obtaining power;* for, as Adler wrote: 'Every neurosis can be understood as an attempt to free oneself from a feeling of inferiority in order to gain a feeling of superiority.'

According to this theory, then, neurosis is a state of affairs in which one who finds himself unable to attain his goal of superiority by legitimate means develops his symptoms either as an excuse to avoid situations in which he might be shown up as a failure or as a means of gaining control over others by a sort of emotional black-mail. Whereas the normal individual's aims are more or less realistic, the neurotic sets himself 'fictive goals'—i.e. goals based upon impossibly perfectionistic standards which his illness is made the excuse for failing to attain. Adler used to ask his patients: 'What would you do if you were cured?', believing that in his answer to this question the neurotic would give away the nature of the situation which he was seeking to avoid. In Adlerian theory all the phenomena which Freud considered to be sexual in nature are ascribed to the striving for superiority or the avoidance of the threat of inferiority. The Oedipus complex is stated to be used by those who fear the responsibility involved in normal sex relation-ships: '... the incest complex is not suppressed but is quite con-sciously used to this end', we are told. Homosexuality is similarly motivated, and frigidity is seen as an attempt on the part of the woman to humiliate her lover and thus gain a sense of superiority over him.

Adler died suddenly during a lecture-tour in Scotland in 1937. He had always been an active propagandist and gave many lectures to social workers, physicians, and the general public throughout Europe and the United States. In the latter country he was particu-larly highly regarded, and, during the 1920s and 1930s, his theories were widely accepted. He wrote many books, the early ones being serious scientific works, but the later have not unjustly been des-cribed by J. F. Brown as 'potboilers'. What appealed to many people about the psychology of Adler was its apparently simple and commonsense approach, the fact that it 'put sex in its proper place', and the optimistic and 'democratic' implication that treat-ment was a relatively simple matter which could be conducted on the basis of friendly chats with one's analyst who would point out the style of life with its fictive goals and give some practical advice for a more sensible future strategy. Adler, both in his personal ap-pearance and his methods, reminded one irresistibly of Frank Buchman, the founder of the 'Oxford Groups', yet in many ways he was a man of deep insights: his awareness of the personality as a unity, of the significance of non-sexual factors, of the part played by the ego, and, above all, of the importance of cultural factors, have already been mentioned. But in other respects he was a great deal too simple. It is quite impossible to believe that all the non-organic nervous disorders are produced by a 'feeling of inferiority that is constantly pressing on towards its own conquest', or that the psychoses are the result of a complete failure to conquer the feeling of inferiority in which the individual backs out of the game of life and 'refuses to play'. Adler never satisfactorily explained why one symptom rather than any other had been chosen or why one type of neurosis rather than another had developed. In his later books, he paid less attention to the power motive and correspondingly more to what he called 'social interest', the normal man's striving for significance rather than power. Although he was a convinced Socialist, it is in Adler's theory more than any other that we can see reflected the competitive capitalist society which he appears to have regarded as the normal state of affairs. Adler did not, however, accept the belief implicit in the writings of Freud that innate factors cause women to be both physically and psychologically inferior to men. Observing that women frequently feel themselves to be at a disadvantage in our present society and that they often manifest what he describes as a 'masculine protest' or reaction of jealousy in relation to men, he nevertheless denies that the supposedly feminine character traits are innate or are due to anything more than 'the reaction of the underdog in any sphere of life'.

Although Adler's school of Individual Psychology has almost ceased to exist as an organized body, there can be no doubt that many of his concepts have become integrated into the systems of other schools. With the exception of Freud it is doubtful whether any single writer has had a greater influence upon the thought of others, although doubtless the influence has often been unconscious. Following Adler, Freudian theory began to pay more attention to the ego and to non-sexual factors in the causation of neurosis, and both Karen Horney and Ian Suttie, whose systems will be described later, show the influence of Adler's thought. Wilhelm Stekel might be quoted as one who utilized predominantly

Freudian theory combined with predominantly Adlerian methods. Stekel (1868—1940) was a brilliant psychotherapist and a prolific writer who believed with Adler that the importance of the unconscious had been exaggerated. 'After thirty years' experience of analysis,' he wrote, 'I no longer believe in the overwhelming significance of the unconscious.' Freud's concept of repression was rejected in favour of a theory of 'scotomization' (a scotoma, in ophthalmology, is a blind area in the field of vision) which implied that many if not all of the patient's conflicts are not repressed in the Freudian sense of being beyond conscious recall but are rather matters to which he chooses, in the Adlerian manner, to turn a blind eye. Another Adlerian concept utilized by Stekel was that of the life-line or life-style, which was named, rather less charitably, the 'life-lie'—i.e. the patient's system of fictive goals. Stekel's method of treatment, contrasted with the passive and relatively objective Freudian method, was active: 'Day after day I attack the patient's system by storm, showing that he can get well betwixt night and morning if only he will discard his fictive aims', is a characteristic statement. The analyst using this method does not wait passively for information regarding the patient's conflicts to appear; these are deduced from the analysis of dreams and the general clinical picture, and the analyst's interpretations are thrust upon the resisting patient whose 'transference', again in the Adlerian manner, is regarded as a technique for getting the better of his physician. Resistance is seen not as an unconscious opposition to the emergence of forbidden wishes, but as a defence against the treatment itself, since the patient dreads being cured, or rather he dreads the adult responsibilities which being cured would imply. Obviously, Stekel's methods demand a great deal of intuition on the part of the analyst and this is a serious drawback, since not all analysts are as clever or 'intuitive' as Stekel. If, as he said, his system requires the 'skill of a physician, a detective, and a diplomat rolled into one', it really needs someone of Stekel's brilliance to carry it out.

Carl Gustav Jung (1875-1961) was a Swiss who left the Freudian group in 1913, being opposed as was Adler to what he felt to be Freud's undue emphasis upon sex. In his earlier years Jung devised a word-association test for tracing complexes and produced a valuable study of schizophrenia which, together with his account of temperament (*Psychological Types*, published in 1923), were highly regarded by psychiatrists of all schools. The commonly-used words 'extravert', 'introvert', and 'complex' also owe their origin to Jung. Having a wide knowledge of the religion, philosophy, myths, and symbolism of many cultures, Jung made full use of this knowledge in his psychology—so much so, that many critics have commented that the Jungian theory is more like a metaphysical system than a school of scientific psychology. It seems unfortunately to be the case that Jungians and Freudians, like Liberals and Conservatives, are born and not made, and those who sympathize with the general viewpoint of one school are likely to find that of the other incomprehensible. The present writer may as well admit that he comes into the Freudian category, and gets much the same impression from reading Jung as might be obtained from reading the scriptures of the Hindus, Taoists, or Confucians; although well aware that many wise and true things are being said, he feels that they could have been said just as well without involving us in the psychological theories upon which they are supposedly based.

On many occasions Jung denied that his approach was unscientific: 'As a scientist,' he writes, 'I proceed from empirical facts which everyone is at liberty to verify.' But, as we shall see, there is almost universal agreement outside the Jungian school that his attitude to scientific standards is somewhat unusual. This is particularly evident in his doctrine of 'psychological truth' and his theory of 'archetypes', both of which, in the present connexion, it will be useful to consider. The doctrine of 'psychological truth' or 'psychological reality' causes Jung to infer that because a belief is invested with great emotional significance it must therefore in some sense be true. For example, in *Psychology and Religion* he writes: 'In itself any scientific theory no matter how subtle, has, I think, less value from the standpoint of psychological truth than the religious dogma, for the simple reason that a theory is necessarily highly abstract and exclusively rational, whereas the dogma expresses an irrational entity through the image.' One sees what Jung means; for a religious dogma (like a myth, a dream, or a symbol) does express some sort of truth, and as Freud was the first to show, all productions of the mind must have some meaning or significance. But whether this meaning lies in the sphere of objective reality or subjective phantasy is important to the scientist and cannot be shelved by talking of 'psychological truth'. There is a sense in which everything that anyone has ever thought of is 'true', that is, significant and truly 'existing' in the mind of the person who thought it—the delusions of a paranoiac are 'true' in this sense—but we must also know whether they are objectively true and whether or not a reductive analysis might cause them to appear in an entirely different light.

Jung's theory of archetypes is a further example of his peculiar attitude to scientific method, and in this instance we find him describing the partially known in terms of the totally unknown. Freud, as we shall see later, saw all symbols, whether in dreams, myths, or art, as primarily sexual in nature, and also as being a generalized expression of a particular object. Caves, pits, bottles, chests, and similar objects were said to represent the female sex organs (e.g. the chest of Deucalion in the Greek myth), water to represent the process of birth (e.g. Moses found amongst the bulrushes of the Nile), pencils, umbrellas, swords, and other pointed objects represent the male organ, while queens, kings, and other figures of authority represent the mother and father figures. In Jung's theory, however, the symbol no longer points from the general to the particular, but on the contrary from the particularized symbol to the generalized idea in the Platonic sense of the word. This novel approach is best described by the Jungian Father Victor White in his *God and the Unconscious*: 'Behind the particularized mother's womb lies the archetypal womb of the Great Mother of all living; behind the physical father the archetypal Father, behind the child the "*puer aeternus*"; behind the particular manifestation of the procreative sexual libido lies the universal creative and re-creative Spirit. The second of all these pairs appears now, not as a phantasy-substitute for the first, but rather does the first appear as a particular manifestation and symbol of the second.' To this we feel inclined to comment that, although Freud may be wrong and Jung right, at least we have the advantage of knowing the earthly father, mother, and child, in a way that we do not know in any direct sense of the word the archetypal Father, the 'Great Mother of All Living', or the '*puer aeternus*', and it is certainly unorthodox in science to describe the partly-known in terms of the wholly unknown. Dr Gardner Murphy, one of the most knowledgeable and understanding of all psychologists, in referring to Jung has this comment to make: 'Jung's method—it is no more than a friendly exaggeration to say this—is to argue that because A is somewhat like B and B can, under certain circumstances, share something with C, and C has been known on occasion to have been suspected of being related to D, the conclusion in full-fledged logical form is that A = D. As the language of *science* this is meaningless' (*Personality: a Biosocial Approach*).

Jung's picture of the unconscious mind differs from that of Freud in the following respects:

(1) The unconscious mind of the individual is said to contain not only those primitive processes which are held repressed and forbidden entry into consciousness, but also aspects of mental life which have been neglected in the course of development.

(2) It also contains unapprehended personal experiences and ideas which have quite simply been forgotten because they have lost 'a certain energic value'.

(3) In the psychology of Jung, the personal unconscious (in the Freudian sense) is only a relatively insignificant fraction of the total mass of unconscious material. That which lies below the personal unconscious is known as the collective or racial unconscious, since it contains the collective beliefs and myths of the race to which the individual belongs. The deepest levels of the collective unconscious are the universal unconscious common to all humanity, and even, it would appear, to man's primate and animal ancestry.

With the first two points many psychoanalysts would probably find themselves in agreement; for it certainly seems to be a matter of personal experience that what is rejected need not necessarily be forbidden or censored material. Darwin for example noted in his *Autobiography* that, after many years devoted almost exclusively to scientific work, he lost the capacity to appreciate poetry and literature which he had formerly enjoyed. It seems that the ego is concerned to maintain not only some degree of ethical and intellectual consistency, but also some degree of temperamental consistency; one tends to become predominantly thinking, intuitive, emotional, or sensorial (relying on the senses), to use Jung's terminology. As Bergson has said: 'The cerebral mechanism is so arranged as to push back into the unconscious almost the whole of our past, and to allow beyond the threshold only that which will further the action in hand.' Nor need we hold too rigidly to the Freudian supposition that 'nothing is ever forgotten', for it seems entirely probable that some experiences pass completely beyond recall simply because they have 'lost a certain energic value'. But what has given rise to controversy is the Jungian concept of the collective unconscious, challenging as it appears to do the generally accepted belief that innate ideas or concepts do not exist. It is true that Freud was latterly prepared to believe that men are born with an archaic heritage which 'includes not only dispositions, but also ideational contents, memory traces of the experiences of former generations' (*Moses and Monotheism*). But he does not seem to have believed that this archaic heritage played any considerable part in the dynamics of the mind, and certainly he did not, as Jung did, make any use of this concept in his practice of psychotherapy.

When we ask what reasons Jung has to give for believing in a collective unconscious, there are, apparently, three:

(1) The 'extraordinary' unanimity of theme in the mythologies of different cultures.

(2) Jung's observation that '. . . in protracted analyses, any particular symbol might recur with disconcerting persistency, but would gradually become divested of all associative relation with any of the patient's personal experiences, and would approximate more and more to those primitive and universal symbols such as are found in myths and legends'.

(3) The content of the phantasies of psychotic (particularly schizophrenic) patients which abound in ideas (e.g. that of death and rebirth) similar to those found in mythology.

The fundamental issue in this concept of a collective unconscious is the problem of how we are to picture it. Are the archetypes, as

46

Jung named the frequently-recurring themes which appeared to originate from the collective unconscious, to be thought of as innate or acquired, and is the collective unconscious to be thought of as a sort of extension of the group mind in McDougall's meaning of the term? Concerning the first problem, Jung is not at all clear, although he tells us that '... archetypes are systems of preparedness that are at the same time images and emotions. They are inherited with the structure of the brain of which they represent the psychic aspects' (*Contributions to Analytical Psychology*). On the other hand, a modern anthropologist would probably explain the phenomenon of archetypal thought by pointing out that, in spite of the great variety of cultures, it is obviously the case that members of all cultures share certain common experiences: all individuals possess parents, are born and die, are dependent upon the sun and earth, are influenced by sexual desire, and so on. It is therefore not really surprising that they dream or create myths of the Great Father of All, the Great Mother, the child, sun-gods, birth and rebirth, and such images as are inevitably part of all human experience. Geza Róheim, the anthropologist and psychoanalyst, who has specifically rejected the theory of the collective unconscious, finds no great difficulty in explaining the phenomena described by Jung, for, as he points out, deep interpretations will always tend to be universal, while ego-interpretations stand a better chance of revealing the specific features of different cultures. Obviously the nearer the analyst is to the level of the conscious ego, the more will the data obtained relate to factors which are specific to the individual or peculiar to the patient's own society, and on the other hand the deeper he probes the closer he will come to the largely biological level of shared experiences universal to all mankind. The hypothesis of the collective unconscious is, from this point of view, a quite unnecessary elaboration to explain certain observations which can be more simply explained in another way. Concerning the nature of the collective unconscious, it appears that for Jung this is not simply a metaphorical construct to be explained away by the fact of universally-shared experience, or by the fact that, as a modern social psychologist might say, mind is a social phenomenon, for clearly Jung believes that the collective unconscious is really *there*. But the concept of a 'group mind' as something over and above the minds of individuals belonging to the group, has long been given up by psychologists who, while not disputing the facts which the hypothesis was devised to explain, find that they can be more readily and economically interpreted in other terms.

In Jung's psychology, the psyche is said to have three levels: consciousness, the personal unconscious, and the collective unconscious. His picture of the mind has often been likened to a chain of islands in the sea where the part above water is the personal conscious mind, and the part just below the personal unconscious. Deeper down, groups of individuals (or islands) are joined together in the racial unconscious (e.g. Mongolian, 'Aryan', and Semitic racial groups) and at the sea-bed upon which all islands ultimately rest is the collective unconscious, which contains the psychological heritage of humanity as a whole, of animal life, and of man's primate ancestors. The outermost crust of personality in this scheme is described as the persona (the 'persona' of Roman actors was the mask that concealed the face of the actor from the public). The persona is, therefore, that part of the personality which is exposed to the gaze of the outer world, both revealing and concealing the real self. In some ways it corresponds to the sociologist's concept of 'role'. People apprehend reality in different ways, being predominantly extravert or introvert, and within those two categories may utilize thinking, intuition, feeling, or sensousness as a means of getting in touch with the external world. In every individual either extraversion or introversion will predominate, and he will be also predominantly thinking, feeling, sensuous, or intuitive. But this applies only to the conscious mind because the unconscious mind is believed by Jung to be, like the reflection of a mountain in a lake, the mirror-image, the reverse, of the conscious. Thus the individual with a predominantly extravert and thinking temperament is unconsciously introvert and emotional, and the individual with an introvert and intuitive temperament unconsciously extravert and sensual. Corresponding to the persona of conscious life is the anima or animus, which in a man is feminine and in a woman masculine. So it comes about that what is consciously strong is weak in the unconscious and vice versa: the very masculine individual is unconsciously strongly feminine, the timid man unconsciously brave, and so on. In other words, the personal unconscious is conceived to be compensatory in function.

The motive force in Jung's psychology is known as the 'libido'. It is non-sexual, and described as a sort of life-force. There are said to be three stages of sexual development: the pre-sexual, from three to five years, is characterized by concern with nutrition (a non-sexual concept, of course) and growth; the pre-pubertal, corresponding to Freud's latency period, is for Jung the real beginning of sexuality; and finally the time of maturity extends from puberty onwards. The Oedipus complex is said to be founded upon a primitive love for the food-providing mother, and only becomes tinged with sexuality during the pre-pubertal phase. The castration complex is seen as a symbolic sacrifice or renunciation of infantile wishes which has nothing to do with literal castration. Repression plays little part in Jungian psychology and therefore is not assumed to be important in the causation of neurosis. The conflict in neurosis is not between primitive emotional drives and the demands of society, but rather between aspects of the personality which have developed unequally. It is asserted that some adaptations in life necessitate the use of thought, others the use of feelings intuition, or sensuality, and when the individual comes up against a situation with which he is unable to cope the reason is that the function by which adaptation is ordinarily made is inadequate to deal with that situation, and the opposite function has by neglect become unconscious. Facing such an issue the individual may regress, but for Jung this is not necessarily a pathological step but rather a matter of '*reculer pour mieux sauter*', since by regressing into the more archaic levels of mind a creative adaptation may be arrived at. In effect the regression is seen as a strategic retreat to call up reserves from the collective unconscious which has possibilities of wisdom denied to consciousness. If, however, no creative solution is found during this period of regression and the individual continues to follow earlier or infantile patterns of behaviour, the neurotic state has been reached. 'The archaic replaces the recent function which has failed.' Like Adler, Jung is more concerned with future goals than past history and he sees the present situation as the key to neurosis. He writes: 'I no longer find the cause of

49

neurosis in the past, but in the present. I ask what is the necessary task which the patient will not accomplish.'

Jung's system of psychotherapy is based on the concept of bringing the patient into contact with the healing collective unconscious largely through the interpretation of dreams and thereby causing him to see his own problems more clearly. In carrying out the process of free-association the analyst as well as the patient produces associations, since analysis is believed to be a cooperative procedure in which the patient cannot progress beyond the point the analyst has himself reached. As the analyst has already begun with a preconceived theory of a collective unconscious it is hardly to be wondered at that 'Jungian' material is produced. Although other systems wittingly or unwittingly indoctrinate the patient, none do so to quite such an extent as Jung's. Jung also believes that a religious outlook is necessary to the individual and encourages its development. An interesting account of a Jungian analysis will be found in John Layard's *The Lady and the Hare*.

It is difficult to give any fair estimate of the present position of Jungian psychology in the general framework of psychological thought. Certainly Jung has rarely attracted the academic psychologist, and his more recent writings, which have been almost exclusively philosophical, are even less likely to interest the scientific mind. On the other hand, some followers worship him almost to the verge of idolatry and make the most exaggerated claims on his behalf. This is particularly true of the Catholic writers, such as Father Victor White and Father Witcutt, and the latter states in his *Catholic Thought and Modern Psychology* that the system of Freud 'will soon be superseded by that of Jung'. It is, of course, wildly untrue to say that Jung has been accepted to anything like the same extent as Freud, and in fact there is every reason to suppose that, as was the case with Adler, Jung's thought has come to a dead end. His English disciples John Layard, the late H. G. Baynes, Michael Fordham, and Leopold Stein have written a number of interesting books, but on the whole Jung has not appealed to either the psychologist or the psychiatrist. Rightly or wrongly it seems that there is something in Jung's writings which '. . . must ever repulse those whose training and bias has taught them to rely upon logical reason as the only legitimate method of learning and adaptation' (J. E. Nicole: *Psychopathology*).

The system of Sandor Ferenczi need only be very briefly mentioned here, since it was more concerned with psychotherapeutic method than psychological theory. Basically, it was an altered technique of analysis, and although Freud strongly disapproved of Ferenczi's innovations, Ferenczi himself up till the time of his death in 1933 had never broken openly with the master. However, the changes in psychoanalytic technique which he introduced were significant in that they reflected an increasing concern within the psychoanalytic movement to shorten the period of analysis. As we have already seen, an analysis by an orthodox Freudian may last for two, three, or more years, during which time the patient has to visit his analyst at least five or six times a week. Clearly this limits considerably the value of the procedure, since it is not everyone who can afford either the time or the money required. Many attempts have been made to solve this problem, from the use of hypnosis or hypnotic drugs to reduce resistance to the 'active psychotherapy' of Stekel. Ferenczi initially acted on a suggestion of Freud's recommending that analysis should be carried out in a state of privation. As adapted by Ferenczi, this meant that the patient was urged to avoid sexual relations, to take as little time as possible over urination and defaecation, and not to eat or drink for pleasure. It was believed that if the libido could be denied natural expression in this way, more would be available for abreaction during analysis. (The belief that cure results from abreaction and that the more emotion displayed by the patient the better was to turn up once more during the last war in the abreaction therapy of battle-neuroses.) It need hardly be doubted that Ferenczi's methods at this time aroused strong emotions in the patient, but it became more than doubtful whether these artificially stimulated emotions were an aid to therapy, and so about 1927 he moved to the opposite extreme. Since, as was generally agreed, neurotic patients have felt themselves deprived of love and affection in childhood, the analyst was urged to act the part of the good parent: to be tolerant, to like the patient in spite of his defects, and to freely admit his (the analyst's) own defects. This of course was entirely in opposition to the Freudian rule that analysts should be as impassive and objective as possible and reveal nothing of themselves to their patients. It was Ferenczi's belief that the patient reacted to the real personality of the analyst and re-lived his infantile experiences, with the significant difference that the revived experience was carried out in a more permissive and tolerant atmosphere. Latterly he moved even further in the direction of permissiveness and encouraged the patient to dramatize his experiences as they were recollected; the patient might behave as a child, talk baby-talk, and even play with dolls, while the analyst entered into the spirit of the game. But in the light of modern thought what is significant about these innovations of Ferenczi is his recognition that the patient-analyst relationship is a two-way one. The transference is not only from patient to analyst but from analyst to patient—there is such a thing as a counter-transference, and Ferenczi was the first to emphasize the importance of what the Americans now describe as 'interpersonal relations' in the analytic procedure.

Otto Rank (1884-1939) was for many years closely associated with Ferenczi when both were concerned with finding a briefer and more effective method of analysis. But whereas Ferenczi never entirely broke with Freud in spite of the latter's disapproval of his methods and never founded a separate system, Rank was destined to move far from the parent movement. Like most of Freud's early followers, Rank was an Austrian, and as in the case of other heretical innovators began his break with orthodoxy with an observation which Freud was quite ready to accept and had, in fact, made himself: that severe attacks of anxiety tend to be accompanied by physiological features very similar to those accompanying the process of birth. Rank however went much further than this, denied that the Oedipus complex occupies the central position in the causation of neurosis, and put forward his theory that all neurosis originates in the trauma of birth. The birth trauma, the essence of which is separation from the mother, produced as it were a reservoir of anxiety in the individual which was reactivated by all the later experiences of separation. Weaning (separation from the breast) and symbolic castration (separation from the penis), together with all other situations involving separation from a loved person or object, were the basic and universal cause of anxiety. But this primal anxiety according to Rank takes two forms throughout the individual's existence, the *life fear* and the *death fear*. The life fear is the anxiety which occurs when the individual becomes aware of creative capacities within himself the assertion of which would bring about the threat of separation from existing relationships; it is 'the fear of having to live as an isolated individual'. The death fear, on the other hand, is the fear of losing one's individuality, of being swallowed up in the whole. All his life each human being is pushed forward by the need to be an individual and express himself more fully and drawn back by the fear that by so doing he will cut himself off from the rest of society. There are two possible solutions to this dilemma, that of the 'normal' person who whole-heartedly accepts the standards of his society as his own and that of the creative individual who is prepared to stand alone and create his own standards. The neurotic can accept neither of these solutions because '... his anxiety in the face of individual autonomy keeps him from affirming his own capacities, and his anxiety in the face of dependency on others renders him incapable of giving himself in friendship and love' (Rollo May: *The Meaning of Anxiety*). In short, the neurotic is a person who can neither assert his own spontaneity as an individual nor permit himself to become submerged in the mass. As Freud pointed out, he is a rebel who fears his rebellious tendencies and therefore keeps them repressed.

In this view the basic problem of psychotherapy is the resolving of the patient's separation-anxiety, and therefore Rank made it his practice to set a time limit to analysis very early in the course of treatment. When this was done and the patient informed accordingly it was found that he began to have dreams of birth supposedly brought about by the threat of separation from the analyst. The useful idea behind this theory was one which is now generally accepted by orthodox analysts, namely the idea that the effective agent in psychoanalysis is not the emergence of the contents of the unconscious but rather the emotional events of the actual treatment. What Rank in practice did was virtually to ignore the events of the past and to treat only the resistances to present emotional relationships as presented in the patient-analyst relationship. By doing so he hoped to reduce the period of treatment to a mere two or three months. In point of fact the experiment was largely unsuccessful, and, according to Ives Hendrick, '... it demonstrated conclusively that, although the conflicts which occur during the treatment are the dynamic agents of every analytic cure, the decisive ones are not fully reactivated unless the resistance to recollection of repressed infantile experience is thoroughly analysed' (*Facts and Theories of Psychoanalysis*). After making his home in America Rank utilized his theory of the birth trauma to develop a new and entirely non-analytic approach known as 'Will Therapy' which was based on 'active adjustment'. The physician's aim according to this new formulation must be to teach the patient to assert his will to health, to be 'reborn' as an individual, and to free himself from the sense of guilt which arose when he asserted himself. The self-assertive tendencies were encouraged and Freudian methods were criticized as strengthening the tendency to submit to authority. The obvious criticism of this theory is that if neurotic patients could cure themselves by will-power there would never have been any need for psychoanalysis in the first place.

Rank died in the United States in 1939, and outside America his theories are no longer the subject of discussion, although many of his suggestions have influenced others. Apart from the matters we have just been discussing and his interest for social workers, Rank made some contributions to anthropology dealt with in Chapter 5. His anthropological theories were matriarchal, in contrast with Freud's strongly patriarchal bias (in his analytical practice, he believed the analyst to represent the mother), and in this respect he resembles the British analyst Suttie, whose work we shall shortly discuss. Dr Nandor Fodor, a New York analyst, makes use of the Rankian theory of the birth trauma, which he claims to have based upon clinical rather than philosophical foundations, in his extraordinary books *The Search for the Beloved* and *New Approaches to Dream Interpretation*. Since nearly every aspect of human behaviour—not excluding constipation—is traced back in these books to the trauma of birth, it is a little difficult to see why they needed to be written at all. But if Dr Fodor is somewhat lacking in imagination as to origins, nobody can accuse him of lacking ingenuity in his interpretations. He informs us for example that children may start life with a handicap owing to prenatal influence, one of which is the violence of parental intercourse, the memory of which is said to be clearly apparent in the dreams of adult life. The fact that there exist no nerve connexions between mother and unborn child in the womb does not trouble Dr Fodor, who postulates that communication takes place by telepathy. According to this theory, then, prenatal influences and the trauma of birth play a major part in the formation of character and determine mental health in adult life. A more scientific exposition of this view has been put forward by Phyllis Greenacre, who believes that constitution, prenatal experience, birth, and the situation immediately after birth together play some part in predisposing the individual to anxiety. She notes that loud noises, maternal nervousness, and similar stimuli increase the rate of the foetal heart and the frequency of foetal movements, and supposes that these may fairly be taken as signs of anxiety. Such 'anxiety' is, of course, without mental content, but Dr Greenacre believes that it supplies an organic potential which may influence later anxiety reactions.

With the rise of Nazism, the psychoanalytic movement which had been predominantly centred in Vienna, Budapest, and Berlin broke up and left its original homes. From this time onwards it was to be divided between the United States and Britain, and we must now discuss the widely divergent developments which arose under the differing conditions in these two countries, which are in many ways so similar and in others so dissimilar.

CHAPTER 4

The British Schools

The most dramatic extension of psychoanalytic theory occurred during and after the First World War, when the unsatisfactory results of treating war neuroses as cases of 'shell shock' or 'concussion' became evident. Of course, psychiatrists in general did not accept Freudian theory as a whole at this, or indeed at any other time, but those who had to deal with such neuroses increasingly came to accept the fact that they were psychological in origin and began to make use of some Freudian concepts in order to understand them. Both in Great Britain and the United States the period from 1918 onwards saw a further spread of psychoanalytic information amongst the general public, and the first trickle of the flood of popular literature on the subject began during the early twenties. In America, G. Stanley Hall, a leading child psychologist, played a prominent part in introducing the works of Freud, and his translation of Freud's *General Introduction to Psychoanalysis*, published in 1920, was widely read. Freud's other works were translated as they appeared by A. A. Brill, the eminent psychoanalyst. In Britain about the same time many people first learned about psychoanalysis from Bernard Hart's little book *The Psychology of Insanity* which still remains a classic. Neither Stanley Hall nor Hart were psychoanalysts, however, and Dr Ernest Jones, the only native of Britain amongst Freud's early disciples, became the pioneer in this country so far as the orthodox psychoanalytic movement was concerned. Thus it came about that during the 1920s and 1930s there were, excluding the adherents of Jung and Adler, two main groups of psychotherapists in this country—the orthodox Freudians and a large number of individualists who while utilizing many Freudian concepts refused to accept the theory in all its aspects. This latter group, which might be named the Eclectics, was seen at its best at the Tavistock Clinic, founded by Dr Crichton Miller in London and associated with such names as Dr J. A. Hadfield and the late Dr Ian Suttie. In the years before the

56

Second World War, with the breaking-up of the German and Austrian psychoanalytic movements, a number of brilliant *émigrés* came to settle both in this country and in America. Amongst those who came to Britain were Wilhelm Stekel, Freud himself, his daughter Anna Freud, and Melanie Klein.

Some of the ways in which the American approach to the social sciences differs from that of Western Europe were mentioned in Chapter 1, and it was pointed out that typically it tends to under- rather than over-estimate the significance of biological factors, attaches correspondingly greater importance to environmental ones and to society generally, and shows itself prone to theory-making and the setting-up of schools. Theories in fact are no sooner created than their originators are busy looking round for some field where they may be applied.

In all these respects Britain differs widely from America, as in general does the rest of Western Europe. To begin with, the British attitude to science is different because the scientist in Europe is the descendant of the leisured gentleman of private means whose prime object was to *know* rather than to *do*, and even when the Industrial Revolution brought about the need for applied science, the man who did the applying was not the same as the one who created the theoretical knowledge. There is a sharp distinction drawn between a university and a technical college, and until quite recently applied science had a much lower status than pure science, so that even now the toast of a pure mathematician: 'Here's to pure mathematics—and may it never be of any use to anyone!' arouses a response in many hearts. Today this may be a dangerous form of snobbery, but perhaps the snobbery of the European scientist who has tended to emphasize his separateness is no greater than that of the American one who sometimes leans over backwards in order to prove that he is no intellectual but just an ordinary man. Practically speaking this attitude results in a very strict interpretation of scientific method and an impatience with any theory that is not narrowly defined by, and agreed point by point with, experimental and observational facts. British scientists in particular are wedded to facts, and so far as philosophy is concerned our main aim throughout history has been to show that there can be no such thing as metaphysics. American philosophers too are opposed to metaphysics but on entirely different grounds, and nothing could be more antithetical to the British view than James's Pragmatism when it asserts that the truth of a theory or belief should be tested by its practical consequences. In our view any scientist or philosopher who is in the slightest degree interested in practical consequences is to that degree highly suspect. The effects of this outlook are particularly evident in British psychology and anthropology. British psychology is typically experimental psychology or physiological psychology; it has no theories except of the strictly limited type necessary to any science (cf. Newton's '*hypotheses non tango*'), and since its early philosophical days little interest in schools of thought. One could read quite an appreciable portion of its literature without being acutely aware that it had anything to do with living beings at all, and the average textbook of psychology, after dealing with every conceivable aspect of perception, association and conditioning, remembering, and the rest, will close with a single chapter on Freud somewhat apologetically and as if to say: 'We don't really know what this chap is doing here, but people do carry on about him so.' Yet if anything Freud said was true, his work cannot be regarded as an isolated theory about one aspect of mental functioning because it is acutely relevant to almost all.* At its worst this sort of attitude leads to an appalling academic sterility, at its best it is a valuable check on psychologists like the ebullient Watson, who apparently set out with the express purpose of proving that what they would like to be true is true. Social psychology until quite recently was almost non-existent in Britain, and as was pointed out earlier nearly all the important work in this subject is American. In fact, at the present moment there are perhaps less than half a dozen modern British books of any significance dealing with it. This may be partially due to the realization that the more complex aspects of behaviour are less susceptible to a strictly scientific approach ('personality' too is regarded as rather a regrettable word), but the differences between British and American psychology lie deeper than this and are rooted in their widely divergent concepts of the nature of democracy. British democracy is individualist, American democracy

---

* A noteworthy exception to this generalization is Peter McKellar's *A Textbook of Human Psychology*. London: Cohen & West.

is collectivist; we like to find how different people are, not how much they are alike; we like to think that, however similar our biological processes may be, our personalities obey no rules and except in trivial ways are outside the scope of science; we are the most law-abiding nation in respect of the details that matter little except to add to the general regularity of social life, but in anything touching our private lives we are the most rebellious and anarchistic of peoples. Hence such common American concepts as 'making friends and influencing people' or the homespun 'life is with people' or even the more scientific or pseudo-scientific 'personality is the subjective aspect of culture' arouse incomprehension and even a certain feeling of repulsion. Such practical conclusions as may relate to making friends 'scientifically', to social adjustment as some perverted sort of ideal, to 'getting right with God' in the hope that He will arrange about a rise in salary or help to put through an important business deal are distasteful to people brought up to believe as are most Europeans that the only adjustment that matters is not to society but to one's own conscience and that friendship or religion have nothing whatever to do with personal advantage. From these convictions arise certain attitudes to the problems dealt with in this book—attitudes that are not always to our advantage. We regard psychology as a primarily biological science using the classical scientific and experimental method, and accordingly have little truck with its sociological ramifications and none at all with its philosophical ones or even with large-scale hypotheses. The function of science is regarded as fact-finding and the creation of strictly limited theories; what people do with the knowledge has been traditionally regarded as no business of the scientist as such. Britain has produced many great psychologists and, together with Germany, can lay claim to being the birthplace of modern experimental psychology, but many of them have taken refuge in the United States, there to permit themselves (and be permitted) wider if more speculative horizons. The British anthropologist, too, has specialized in fieldwork amongst small and primitive tribal groups rather than large-scale theorizing (with the possible exceptions of Radcliffe-Brown and Malinowski) and almost incredibly in an imperial power little practical use was made of their work until comparatively recent times. Neither have British scientists in general been prone to write 'popular' works for the layman; for although we have had our great popularizers, from Ray Lankester to Arthur Thomson and H. G. Wells, it has generally been conceded that a man's scientific ability is in inverse proportion to his ability to popularize. Our psychologists do not in general write for the layman (which, in view of the strict limitations they set upon their subject, is probably just as well) and our anthropologists and psychoanalysts rarely give their books imaginative titles, perhaps because this would belie the nature of the highly technical and extremely pedestrian material within. The intelligent layman reads Margaret Mead, Erich Fromm, or Karen Horney, but unless he has special knowledge of the subject-matter he does not read Melanie Klein or Malinowski. Amongst other terms dear to American hearts but poorly regarded here are 'culture', 'integration', 'adjustment', 'human nature', in so far as they seem to imply vague large-scale concepts or value-judgements. 'Culture' is accepted as an anthropologist's word which indeed explains why individuals in a given group possess certain attitudes and tend to behave in broadly similar ways just as they tend within wide limits to wear broadly similar clothes, but it would not be accepted as it is by some schools of thought in America as explaining anything of any great significance about an individual's personality. The study of personality and temperamental *traits* may be said to have originated in Britain with the work of Galton, but the study of personality *in itself* has aroused little interest until very recently, and few psychologists have ever taken the view that 'integration' or 'adjustment' are inherently desirable or that 'social satisfactions' are of such supreme importance as Americans would have us believe. To the British psychologist these words mean just what the dictionary says they mean, without any moral connotation whatever. Clearly one can be integrated around a very silly belief, adjusted towards a very wicked society, and if social satisfactions are important, so, he feels, is the satisfaction of being left alone, or, as Professor Berlin describes it, 'the freedom from being impinged upon'. Typically, Professor D. W. Harding points out in his extremely interesting book *Social Psychology and Individual Values* that man's social needs must be seen in relation to his other needs, to which at times they may have to be sacrificed. These comments on two differing approaches are not put forward with any intention of evaluating one or the other as superior, but what can be said with certainty is that differing historical and scientific traditions have a profound effect in influencing *what* the psychologist regards as his proper field of study and *how* he believes its problems should be attacked. The American approach is increasingly influencing European psychology in an active way as compared with the earlier and more passive interest in American ideas, but that this influence is far from complete is shown by the extreme selectivity of those who take an interest in it. For example, Britain has been interested in behaviourist theory but accepted it from Pavlov rather than from Watson; the Neo-Freudians Horney and Fromm have proved to be almost scientific best-sellers here—but were read by the intelligent layman rather than the analyst or psychiatrist; American work in social psychology has aroused interest too—but is perhaps better known to industrial management trainees and social workers than to academic psychologists. Obviously the social sciences become culture-ridden as soon as they leave their biological foundations, while the physical sciences such as atomic physics and astronomy remain relatively culture-free.

British psychotherapeutic technique of the home-grown variety has almost died out since the Second World War. It had arisen, as we have seen, almost entirely as a result of the successful application of some Freudian concepts in cases of battle-neurosis from about 1916 onwards and is departing under the same influence with the spread of orthodox psychoanalysis and the tendency to regard anything but the simplest and most direct psychotherapy as a specialized procedure requiring considerable training both in theory and practice. A further reason is the changing pattern in neurosis during the last decades, during which the older type of reaction in which a relatively integrated personality was suddenly disturbed by one or more symptoms has increasingly given way to the character disorder in which the whole personality is disturbed, so that there is no clear-cut border between 'personality' and 'symptom' with results which may well be more troublesome for those surrounding him than for the patient himself. Disorders of this type naturally require an extremely prolonged, radical, and detailed analysis and are unlikely to be influenced by any other psychotherapeutic methods. The two English Eclectics discussed here are W. H. R. Rivers and I. D. Suttie, both of whom, although differing in most other respects, share in common a disapproval of the harsher aspects of Freudian theory and an assertion of the need for a psychotherapy which should be active rather than passive, brief rather than prolonged, and above all respectful towards the patient's moral and religious beliefs. Both would probably have agreed with the view of Jacques Maritain that 'the phenomena that psychotherapy attempts to modify are pathological phenomena and not moral faults'.

W. H. R. Rivers, both a psychologist and one of the most eminent of British anthropologists, was asserting, long before Ruth Benedict and Margaret Mead, the great variability of 'human nature' from one culture to another. In 1905, together with the neurologist Head who acted as subject in the experiment, they found that when a sensory nerve to the skin of the arm was cut the restoration of various sensations as the two severed ends healed followed a definite order. Vague, crude, gross pain-sensations appeared before the clearly-localized and specific tactile ones by which we use our limbs and skin discerningly. Generalizing this distinction, Rivers came to the conclusion that there is a *proto-pathic* life that may set the limits of awareness in simple organisms which can only react crudely to pleasant or unpleasant stimuli and precedes in the course of evolutionary development the *epicritic* life of higher and more discriminating sensibility. This appeared to confirm his conviction that the distinction between primitive and discriminating, conscious and unconscious functions, existed throughout the nervous system, and that the protopathic are normally under the control of the epicritic which deals with them by fusion or at times by actual suppression. In the psyche the typical relationship between unconscious and conscious is one of 'utilization by the process of fusion', the energies of the former being made use of under higher control, while 'suppression by which experience becomes unconscious is only a special variety of the process of inhibition' (as defined by Pavlov). The violent 'all or none' reactions to which young children are prone and in which they reveal their natural tendency to completely let go or completely hold back give way in the course of development to the more discriminating and controlled behaviour of the adult. Thinking along these lines, it was natural that Rivers, who during the First World War was engaged in treating cases of battle-neurosis at Craiglockart Hospital in Edinburgh and was the psychiatrist described in Siegfried Sassoon's *Memoirs of an Infantry Officer*, should see in the reactions of soldiers in the presence of danger confirmation of his thesis. Five possible types of reaction were noted, ranging from the more discriminating towards the totally uncontrolled: aggression, flight, 'manipulative activity', immobility, and collapse. The term 'manipulative activity' denotes a phase during which there is an inability to make decisions and the individual alternates between aggression and flight, carrying out useless actions in a state of confusion; the other terms are self-explanatory. In these cases the primitive reactions were being progressively released, whereas in the typical neuroses they were still in the main suppressed but capable of manifesting themselves as symptoms. Here Rivers's position approximated to that of the early Freudian one of a symptom covering the spot where a traumatic memory lies buried and becoming superfluous when the memory is recovered. His classic example of this was in the case of a doctor who during his army career found himself unable to enter dugouts or any enclosed or underground space—a fear which proved to be traceable to an incident in childhood when he had been afraid of being attacked by a dog in a dark passage of a house he used to visit. The incident had been completely forgotten, but after it had been restored to consciousness, so Rivers informed his colleagues, the phobia disappeared. Hysterical paralyses, anaesthesias, and the like during active service all had 'the common feature that they unfit their subject for further participation in warfare, and thus form a solution of the conflict between the instinctive tendencies connected with danger and the various controlling factors which may be subsumed under the general heading of duty' (*Instinct and the Unconscious*). Curiously enough this type of symptom nearly always occurred in the rank and file, while officers and N.C.O.s tended to develop anxiety or obsessional neuroses.

The late Dr Ian Suttie was another eclectic whose theories, described in his book *The Origins of Love and Hate* (published in 1935), demonstrate a typically English response, although a more sophisticated one than that of Rivers, to Freudian orthodoxy. Where Freud's views of social and individual development were authoritarian and patriarchal, Suttie's were democratic and matriarchal, and where Freud emphasized the importance of sex, Suttie emphasized the significance of love. Thus the mother-child relationship is seen, not as a situation in which the sensual gratification of the child may, at a later stage, give rise to love for the mother as a sort of secondary elaboration, but rather as one in which 'the need for a mother is primarily presented to the child mind as a need for company and as a discomfort in isolation'. 'I can see no way of settling this question conclusively,' continues Suttie, 'but the fact is indisputable that a need for company, moral encouragement, attention, protectiveness, leadership, etc., remains after all the sensory gratifications connected with the mother's body have become superfluous and have been surrendered. In my view this is a direct development of the primal attachment-to-mother, and, further, I think that play, cooperation, competition, and culture-interests generally are substitutes for the mutually caressing relationship of child and mother. *By these substitutes we put the whole social environment in the place once occupied by mother*—maintaining with it a mental or cultural rapport in lieu of caresses, etc., formerly enjoyed with the mother.' According to Suttie, then, the child's basic need is for mother-love, his basic fear is loss of such love, and all his later social and cultural attitudes depend upon the nature of this relationship. Of course, few analysts of any school have denied this and orthodox Freudians have attached an increasing importance to separation anxiety, but Freud certainly regarded civilization as primarily suppressive in its influence upon the individual, and believed that culture arose through the thwarting of the sex-impulse and its deflection to symbolic ends. Suttie asserted, on the contrary, that culture is derived from the activity of play which 'gives the individual that reassuring contact with his fellows which he has lost when the mother's nurtural services are no longer required or offered'. This mother-love and dread of loneliness is the conscious expression of the instinct of self-preservation and arises from the biological fact of the helplessness of the human infant in the years immediately following birth.

But if love is the individual's primary need, hate, so far from being an innate tendency to destruction, is a reaction to situations in which loss of love is feared. 'Anger is aimed, not at the direct removal of frustration or attainment of the goal of the moment, still less at [the mother's] destruction, but *at inducing the mother to accomplish these wishes for the child.*' It is an insistent demand for the help of others, a standing reproach to the hated person which owes all its meaning to a demand for love; basically it is always ambivalent, a mingling of love and aggression.

The infant's need for love and security may, however, be thwarted by many factors such as the mother's neurotic inability to give affection, the advent of a second baby, cultural factors (e.g. bowel-training), or class-factors (e.g. the working mother's need to return to the factory). The child's attempts are then directed towards removing the cause of his anxiety and thereby changing the feelings of anxiety and hate into feelings of love and security. The technique (in Adlerian terms, the life-style) which he adopts in order to do so influences his later personality development and his attitude towards others. Four possible attitudes may arise at this time:

(1) The child may argue: 'Mother is always good—if she does not love me it is because I am bad.' This may lead to later depressive states or to what Adler described as an 'inferiority complex'.

(2) Conversely, it may argue: 'Mother is bad for not loving me—I will not trust her.' This is the attitude of the individual who develops persecutory attitudes towards society.

(3) The solution of regression results from an attitude which says, in effect, 'If I become a baby again, mother will be as good to me as she was before.' Hence arises the tendency to hysterical invalidism and in severe cases to schizophrenia.

(4) Delinquency and criminality arise from an attitude which says: 'You must love me or I will bite you—I *will* get attention somehow.'

Suttie was the first, and almost the only, English psychologist to realize the significance of cultural factors. He accepted Freud's general observations concerning the sexual development of the child, but saw that they might be strongly influenced by the culture in which the child grows up. Thus the anal stage is, to some extent at least, an artefact produced by the significance attached in our culture to physical cleanliness. The Oedipus complex as described by Freud is not universal but contingent upon certain circumstances affecting the mother's character and emotional relationships to son and husband: e.g. the neglected wife will tend to lavish excessive affection on her son. Many of Suttie's views were closely in line with those of Adler (for example, his theory of the development of neurosis shows traces of the Adlerian concept of 'lifestyle' in which the desire for power is replaced by the desire to regain lost love), but he pointed out that Adler's power drive, so far from being a universal tendency, is 'an anxiety-reaction to a particular mode of upbringing and hence contingent upon certain cultural influences'. He was particularly interested in what he described as the modern 'taboo on tenderness'. Why is it, he asked, that the modern individual is so afraid of being thought tender or sentimental? Epithets such as 'mummy's boy', 'milksop', 'soppy', or 'crybaby' reveal antifeminist tendencies when contrasted with the idealization of toughness, aggressiveness, and hardness, which are regarded as praiseworthy. Suttie suggests that this type of character-formation is in part the result of a reaction against the early weaning habits of modern times—it is a revenge upon and a repudiation of the weaning mother. (This question is also discussed by J. L. Halliday in his *Psychosocial Medicine* and dealt with similarly.) Suttie was opposed to the patriarchal and antifeminist bias of Freud which caused him to infer that women are basically jealous of the male's sexual organs. He did not dispute the existence of 'penis envy' in some cultures but demonstrated the existence of its equally important complements: (a) the father's jealousy of the infant's possession of the mother, and (b) the male jealousy of the female's ability to produce children, described as 'Zeus jealousy'. The Aranda, a tribe of Australian aborigines, perform rites based upon the phantasy that men really can bear children and this may be explained as the expression of an unconscious wish. Finally, in opposition to the Freudian view of religion as the 'universal obsessional neurosis', Suttie saw religion as performing the function of a psychosocial therapy, since both religion and psychotherapy exercise their influence in maintaining or regaining mental health by love. This observation is of interest in connexion with the French sociologist Durkheim's findings in his famous study *Le Suicide*, which seem to show that satisfactory integration in a religious or other group is an important factor in preventing suicide. Jung too has commented that few of his patients were practising Catholics, an appreciable number were Protestants, and the majority were agnostics; here again it may be supposed that participation in the affairs of a well-integrated group conduces to psychic health, whereas individualist attitudes in religious or other matters seem to be correlated with neurosis. On the other hand, of course, one might explain these facts the other way round, for it might reasonably be assumed that those who are neurotic have difficulty in becoming integrated into social groups.

The history of child-analysis dates back as far as 1906 when Freud published the famous case-history of 'Little Hans' in his article 'Phobia of a Five-year-old Boy'. In dealing with Hans, Freud suggested the interpretations to the father (who had himself been analysed), and the latter passed them on to his son. The child was seen on only one occasion by Freud, who subsequently wrote: 'No one else (but the father) could possibly have prevailed upon the child to make any such avowals. The special knowledge by which he was able to interpret the remarks made by his five-year-old son was indispensable, and without it the technical difficulties in the way of conducting a psychoanalysis upon so young a child would have been insuperable.' Evidently at this time Freud assumed that analysis was only possible in such young children if analyst and parent were the same person. In 1913, the earliest work on child-analysis in its modern form was carried out by Hermine Hug-Hellmuth, who combined the analytical approach with advice and encouragement through the parents. Mention might also be made of August Aichhorn's work with older delinquent children. But it is only since the 1930s that it has been possible to apply a fully analytic approach to children, and here we shall discuss the theories and views based on experience with children and adolescents held by the Continental School of Anna Freud and the English School of Melanie Klein. While Anna Freud's work relates mainly to the older age groups, that of Melanie Klein has been with the very young and her experience in this field has led to the development of an increasingly biological outlook in what has virtually become the mainstream of orthodox psychoanalysis in Britain.

The publication of Anna Freud's *Das Ich und die Abwehrmechanismen* in 1936 (English translation, *The Ego and the Mechanisms of Defence*, published a year later) emphasized a new tendency in psychoanalysis to attach greater importance to the ego or conscious mind than had previously been the case. Miss Freud pointed out that the term 'psychoanalysis' could not properly be applied to any technique which concentrated attention upon the id to the exclusion of all else. Of the analysis of dream-symbolism she writes: '... by translating symbols we may reveal the contents of the Id without really gaining any deeper understanding of the individual with whom we are dealing'. It is therefore only by the analysis of the ego's unconscious defensive mechanisms that we can understand the transformations which the instincts have undergone. 'Without a knowledge of these we may, indeed, discover much about the contents of the repressed instinctual wishes and phantasies, but we shall learn little or nothing about the vicissitudes through which they have passed and the various ways in which they enter into the structure of the personality.'

The analyst inevitably comes on the scene as a disturber of the ego's peace, since in the course of his work he must inevitably remove repressions and destroy compromise-formations which, although rightly considered pathological, represent from the point of view of the ego laboriously built-up defence systems in an attempt to master the instinctual life. The dangers against which the ego tries to defend itself are three in number: the protests of the superego, the dread of the strength of the instincts, and objective anxiety from the environment which predominates in the young child before the superego comes to be formed. 'The infantile ego fears the instincts because it fears the outside world. Its defence against them is motivated by dread of the outside world, i.e. by objective anxiety.' What the child fears at this stage is punishment or the withdrawal of affection brought about by instinctual manifestations. In addition to these three powerful motives for erecting defence mechanisms, Anna Freud mentions a fourth which recalls Jung's category of incompatible opposite tendencies: 'The adult ego requires some sort of harmony between its impulses', she writes '... and so there arises a series of conflicts... between opposite tendencies, such as homosexuality and heterosexuality, passivity and activity, etc.'

Five mechanisms of defence are described in this book: denial in phantasy, denial in word and act, restriction of the ego, identification with the aggressor, and 'a form of altruism'.

Denial in phantasy: A seven-year-old boy used to please himself with the phantasy that he owned a tame lion which terrorized others but loved him. It came at his call, made its bed in his room, and followed him like a dog wherever he went. This phantasy is interpreted as follows: the lion was a substitute for the father, who was hated and feared as a rival in relation to the mother. In his imagination the boy simply denied a painful fact and turned it into its pleasurable opposite. The anxiety-animal became his friend, and its strength, instead of being a source of terror, was at his service. Such stories for children as *Little Lord Fauntleroy* in which a small boy or girl is pictured as taming a bad-tempered old man are regarded as coming into this category. Denial in word and act is illustrated by the behaviour of the child when he tries to reassure himself in face of dread of the external world. 'I am as big as daddy' or 'I am as clever as mummy' or 'I *don't* dislike this medicine —I like it very much' are all examples of denials of reality which protect the child from a knowledge of his helplessness and dependence.

Restriction of the ego is illustrated by the case of a small girl of ten who went to her first dance full of pleasurable expectation. She admired her new dress and shoes and fell in love at first sight with the best-looking boy at the party. But although the boy had the same surname as herself, and she had already imagined in phantasy that there was some sort of secret bond between them, she was chided by him during their first dance together for her clumsiness. From that time onwards she avoided parties and took no trouble to learn to dance, although she liked watching others do so. Finally she compensated herself for this restriction of her ego by giving up feminine interests and setting up to excel intellectually, and by this roundabout means she later won the grudging respect of a number of boys of her own age.

Identification with the aggressor is a method of mastering anxiety by assuming the opponent's qualities through a process of intro-jection. Thus the little boy who has undergone dental treatment will play at being a dentist with his sister as patient.

A form of altruism describes the contrary mechanism of satisfy-ing one's own desires through the lives of others, as in the case of a young governess who as a child was possessed by two desires: to have beautiful clothes and to have many children. In later life she was plain and unassuming, indifferent to her clothes and childless. But her childhood desires had not disappeared and manifested themselves in her interest in the lives of others. She took work look-ing after other people's children and was intensely concerned that her friends should have pretty clothes. As Anna Freud points out, the most detailed study of this altruistic surrender in literature is to be found in Edmond Rostand's play *Cyrano de Bergerac*—the French nobleman who, handicapped by an ugly nose, but the possessor of all the cultural graces, helps a suitor win the hand of a girl he himself loves by sending her poems allegedly by the suitor and defending his rival with his sword to keep all other rivals at a distance.

These observations of Anna Freud were made, of course, upon children, but the mechanisms not unnaturally apply with equal force to adults, whose day-dreams and sometimes their actions may also reveal denial in phantasy, word, and fact, of unpleasant or frightening realities. Restriction of the ego has been noted by Lazarsfeld amongst unemployed workers, when, after a long pe-riod of unemployment, the worker's interests tend to shrink and he begins to adopt a way of life much narrower than his former one. Identification with the aggressor is mentioned by Alexander as occurring in Nazi concentration camps when prisoners sometimes acted towards their fellow-prisoners with the same brutality they themselves had suffered at the hands of guards, and presumably match-making old maids may be regarded as coming into the cate-gory of compulsive altruism. Other and more familiar types of defence mechanism were described earlier both by Freud himself and by other members of the psychoanalytic school. Of these *re-pression, anxiety* (a warning of a threatened breach in the defences

70

created by repression), *reaction formation*, and *sublimation* have already been described, and *rationalization* ('the giving of bad reasons for what we do upon impulse' as Bradley described it) is too familiar to require further explanation. *Displacement* is said to occur when an emotion is detached from its original object and attached to another unrelated one. For example, a man who is frustrated at work and gets rid of his fury by quarrelling with his wife at home is said to be displacing his aggression, and the phenomenon of love on the rebound is similarly a displacement of affection in the absence of its former object. *Projection* is another important mechanism, in which basically sexual or aggressive impulses intolerable to the individual possessing them are attributed to an outside person or agency. This at any rate is its ordinary significance in psychopathology, although more generally Freud pointed out that 'the projection of inner perceptions to the outside is a primitive mechanism which, for instance, also influences our sense perceptions, so that it normally has the greatest share in shaping our outer world'. In this wider sense whenever the internal and subjective becomes confused with the external and objective we may speak of projection. But sometimes the reverse process occurs and the external comes to be incorporated as part of the self, as in the case of the parental prohibitions and demands which by *introjection* become the superego. Introjection and projection form the foundations of the 'English School' of Melanie Klein, who was one of the leading figures in modern European psychoanalysis although her work had made comparatively little impact on America. The main points at issue between the English school of Klein and the Continental school of Anna Freud will be briefly summarized at the end of this chapter, but it is necessary at the moment to glance briefly at the theories of the former, which are now held by a large number of orthodox analysts. The methods of Anna Freud conform in general to those used in adult psychotherapy and therefore apply to children old enough to cooperate and with an adequate command of speech to express themselves. Melanie Klein, however, originated a technique of analysing the free-association play of children which makes it possible for psychoanalytic methods to be applied to those of only two to six years old. The controversy between the two schools of thought partly concerns the problem of whether this method is a valid one, for if, as the analysts of the Continental school believe, it is not then obviously any information obtained by the use of the method is suspect. But if we accept Melanie Klein's methods there can be no doubt that the new insights they give into the earliest years of child life are of the greatest possible importance. Ot these methods Susan Isaacs, who studied young children at the experimental Malting House School for many years, wrote: 'Scepticism is sometimes expressed as to the possibility of understanding the psychic life at all in the earliest years—as distinct from observing the sequence and development of behaviour. In fact, we are far from having to rely upon mere imagination or blind guess-work, even as regards the first year of life. When all the observable facts of behaviour are considered in the light of analytic knowledge gained from adults and children over two years, and are brought into relation with analytic principles, we arrive at many hypotheses carrying a high degree of probability and some certainties regarding early mental processes.' In addition to Susan Isaacs, other prominent analysts such as Joan Riviere, D. W. Winnicott, Geza Róheim, and R. E. Money-Kyrle have given support to the views of Melanie Klein, as did the late Dr Ernest Jones, Freud's biographer, one of his original pupils, and formerly the doyen of British psychoanalysts.

Many years ago Freud had noted the rather surprising fact that the superegos of children are often more harsh than the attitudes of fairly tolerant parents would lead one to expect if, as was believed to be the case, the superego was derived from the introjection of parental standards. This fact was interpreted by supposing that what was really introjected was the parental superego rather than the conscious attitudes of the parents. Freud wrote: '. . . the superego of the child is not really built up on the model of the parents, but on that of the parents' superego, it takes over the same content, it becomes the vehicle of tradition and of all the age-long values which have been handed down in this way from generation to generation' (*New Introductory Lectures*). In this view, the concept of the superego may be compared with the biological concept of the germplasm which, in Weismann's theory, is handed down from one generation to another unaffected by the changing fortunes in the lives of the individuals who bear it. The theories of Melanie Klein may throw a new light upon the origins of the superego, which was believed in orthodox Freudian theory to originate following the dissolution of the Oedipus complex at about the age of four. In Kleinian theory they must be traced even further back into the earliest months of life.

During these early stages the child, it must be supposed, makes no distinction between his own ego and the surrounding world. It follows, therefore, that unlike the adult, who regards the emotional responses called out by external objects as purely personal feelings within his own mind, the child attributes them to the object itself. What gives him pleasure is regarded as a 'good object', what gives him pain as a 'bad object', and in this way his world comes to be peopled with good and bad objects which he expects to behave towards him in terms of the qualities he has attributed to them. Now the child's first object is the mother's breast, which may sometimes supply milk easily to satisfy the child's needs and at other times may give little or none. To the baby hunger is a frightening situation—not only because feeding is important to him, but also because '. . . the very young child, with no more than a minimal appreciation of time, is unable to bear tension; he does not possess the knowledge, so consoling to older human beings, that loss, frustration, pain, and discomfort are usually but temporary and will be followed by relief. Consequently a very small change in the situation (e.g. a less comfortable posture or pressure of his clothes, a less easy grasp of the nipple or a less ready flow of milk) will convert a pleasant satisfying stimulus into an unpleasant dissatisfying one. Thus the child can both love and hate the same objects in rapid succession or alternation, and his love and hate alike tend to work on the all-or-nothing principle—there are not the qualifications and quantitative variations that are found in later life' (Professor J. C. Flugel: *Man, Morals and Society*). This all-or-nothing type of emotional response in the young child and the fact that its emotions are projected into the outside world means that, in effect, it lives in a world peopled by gods and devils—a world which appears sometimes a heaven and at other times a very hell. (In fact Money-Kyrle has suggested that these concepts are derived from the forgotten memories of early childhood.)

Hate and aggression, the emotions which form the child's hell, must be particularly terrifying, for, according to Joan Riviere, while in this state '... the child is overwhelmed by choking and suffocating; its eyes are blinded by tears, its ears deafened, its throat sore; its bowels gripe, its evacuations burn it' (Paper: 'On the Genesis of Psychical Conflict in Earliest Infancy' quoted by Flugel, *op. cit.*).

In the earliest months two physical processes are of dominant importance—taking in and giving out. Milk from the mother's breast is taken in by the mouth and following the process of digestion faeces are given out. It seems likely that the child's earliest mental states are based on these biological facts, so that what he takes in or gets rid of in his imagination plays an important part in forming his concepts of himself and the surrounding world. Psychologically speaking, the process of taking in is what is described as 'introjection' and that of giving out is 'projection'. The child wishes to take in only good objects, for example, the satisfying breast, and in so far as he does so he is able to think of himself as good and 'whole' and not merely a mass of conflicting sensations. Money-Kyrle suggests that the concept of an enduring self is based on this type of introjection. But, whether because his greed in taking the breast in partly aggressive in nature, or because introjection is also used as a means of controlling or destroying bad objects, it sometimes happens that bad objects seem to have got inside, and these manifestations of his own aggression have to be got rid of either by the process of projection or by destruction. What is described by Melanie Klein as the 'persecutory position' arises when the projected bad objects, the representatives of the child's own aggression projected into the outer world, return to plague him. The temper tantrums and negativistic states of the teething period when the child may refuse food and scream with rage are believed to be due to this sense of persecution which is the counterpart of the delusions of persecution of the paranoid adult. For the most part, however, such states are largely outgrown in the normal child, although a residual persecutory element always remains to become incorporated in the later sense of guilt which is a feature of all civilized beings.

At a later stage the child makes a new and very painful discovery when he finds that the good and bad objects of his early months are different aspects of the same person—his mother. Occurring at a time when reality and imagination are not as yet differentiated and aggressive wishes are believed to be magically destructive, the child comes to believe that he is in danger of destroying, or has already destroyed, the person he most needs and loves. This stage leads to feelings of depression and is accordingly described as the 'depressive position'. Just because this state of affairs is so painful, a tendency develops at this time to regress to the persecutory position of separate good and bad objects, and it is supposed that numerous alternating states of persecution and depression may occur before the depressive position is fully reached and ultimately left behind. The child outgrows its depressive period when the continued existence of the mother gradually brings the realization that aggressive wishes are less potent than had been feared. Yet, as in the case of the persecutory position, relics of the depressive position will always persist. The depressive element in guilt-feelings and the adult's tendency to exaggerate the 'goodness' or 'badness' of all he meets are such relics. Since elements of both the persecutory and depressive positions become incorporated in the individual's sense of guilt, it is suggested by Money-Kyrle that two extreme types of conscience or superego may be defined, although clearly a whole range will extend between the two extremes: there is at one extreme the type based almost exclusively upon fear of punishment (the persecutory type) and at the other the type based predominantly upon fear of injuring or disappointing something that is loved (the depressive type). The former will tend to respond to guilt-feelings by propitiation, the latter by reparation. The first personality will tend to be authoritarian, the latter humanistic.

At the age of two or three months, when the persecutory position begins to develop, the baby's notions of aggression are conditioned by the fact that it is at the oral level of development. Aggression therefore takes the form of phantasies of biting, tearing, and sucking out, which, when projected upon the mother, lead to the picture of a terrifying figure who will tear, rend, eviscerate, and destroy. (The witch of many fairy-tales may be derived from this phantasy.) From what has been said concerning these theories it is apparent that if we accept them many of our beliefs concerning the upbringing of children and the influence of social conditions must be changed. For if it is the case that the real aggressiveness of parents is comparatively unimportant compared with the aggressiveness which the child projects upon its parents, then there can be little hope that more enlightened methods of child-rearing will in themselves radically affect the development of character. Social betterment cannot be achieved from the social or even from the family level but must rather begin with the analysis of the individual in order to remove the early infantile anxiety which even the most enlightened upbringing could not have avoided. It is just this remedy which Melanie Klein suggests in an essay 'The Early Development of Conscience', contained in the symposium *Psychoanalysis Today* edited by Dr Sandor Lorand. She writes: 'The repeated attempts that have been made to improve humanity—in particular to make it more peaceable—have failed, because nobody has understood the full depth and vigour of the instincts of aggression innate in each individual. Such efforts do not seek to do more than encourage the positive, well-wishing impulses of the person while denying or suppressing his aggressive ones. And so they have been doomed to failure from the beginning. But psychoanalysis has different means at its disposal for a task of this kind. It cannot, it is true, altogether do away with man's aggressive instinct as such; but it can, by diminishing the anxiety which accentuates these instincts, break up the mutual reinforcement that is going on all the time between his hatred and his fear. When, in our analytic work, we are always seeing how the resolution of early infantile anxiety not only lessens and modifies the child's aggressive impulses, but leads to a more valuable employment and gratification of them from a social point of view; how the child shows an ever-growing, deeply-rooted desire to be loved and to love, and to be at peace with the world about it; and how much pleasure and benefit, and what a lessening of anxiety it derives from the fulfilment of this desire—when we see all this, we are ready to believe that what now would seem a Utopian state of things may well come true in those distant days when, as I hope, child-analysis will become as much a part of every person's upbringing as school education is now.'

In order to bring out the differences between these two important schools of thought within the bounds of a necessarily limited amount of space, we may summarize them as follows:

In respect of theory:
A.

(1) Anna Freud accepts the orthodox Freudian theory while attaching more significance to the ego and its defences than was formerly the case.

(2) Accepting the orthodox theory, she therefore believes:

(a) that although unconscious and instinctual factors are of great importance, such environmental factors as the parent's attitude towards the child are equally important. To a considerable extent the child's problems change with a changing environment.

(b) that the superego arises during the fourth year or thereabouts in the manner already described in Chapter 1.

(c) that the important drives are the sexual ones.

B.

(1) Melanie Klein also accepts orthodox theory, but, as noted above, claims to have opened up a hitherto unexplored region in the pre-Oedipal stages.

(2) Differing from the orthodox school in this respect, she therefore believes:

(a) that environmental factors are much less important than had previously been believed.

(b) that forerunners of the superego are demonstrable during the first two years of life.

(c) that for this reason any analysis which fails to reach back to the stage of infantile anxiety and aggressiveness in order to resolve them is necessarily incomplete.

(d) that the important drives are the aggressive ones.

In respect of practice:
A.

(1) With the methods of Anna Freud, children from three years onwards may be analysed.

(2) The details of the method used depend upon the age of the child. In younger children (i.e. before the latency phase) relaxation

upon a couch for free association cannot be expected, nor can it always be used in older children. The child, therefore, may walk about, talk, tell stories and dreams, or play games, and all these activities are used in interpretation which as in the adult is gradual.

(3) There are two essential differences between the young child and the adult, so far as analysis is concerned:

(a) the young child's ego is undeveloped and his main problem is that of achieving control over his primitive instincts. This is the reason why, in the child as in the psychotic, caution is needed in analysis when interpretations are being made.

(b) the young child does not develop a typical transference neurosis; he is constantly reacting to the actual situation and does not reproduce the experiences of the past in his reaction to the analyst.

(4) The cooperation of the parents is sought, both in sustaining the regularity of the child's visits to the analyst, and in giving information and reports on progress. The analyst makes no attempt, as was done in the earlier history of child-analysis and ordinarily today amongst non-analytic child-psychologists, to give advice or change the home situation. On the contrary, it is in the analyst's interest to maintain the home situation unchanged during treatment, since he wishes to discover how the child's symptoms and character have developed.

B.

(1) Children as young as two years old are treated by Melanie Klein.

(2) The method is centred around the phantasy life of the child as revealed in play. Interpretations are given directly and even the deepest interpretations may be given during the first meeting.

(3) The cooperation of parents is not sought, firstly because their reports are likely to be distorted by their own unconscious conflicts and secondly because little significance is attached to the reality situation.

(4) The material recovered (at any rate as interpreted) includes a wide range of sexual and aggressive phantasies from the first year of life, including Oedipal wishes, the wish to destroy the mother's body, and the desire to incorporate the father's penis.

There is stated to exist even at this age an awareness of parental intercourse which is conceived as taking place orally by analogy with the nipple. A main source of conflict between classical Freudians and Kleinians in respect of adult psychoanalysis is that, if the latter are right in ascribing these important phantasies to the earliest months of life, it follows that orthodox analysis has been seriously incomplete in failing to deal with aggression in its most primitive form and the baby's first attempts to handle the problems associated with it.

In view of what was said earlier it seems not unlikely that Freud attracted sympathetic interest in Britain fundamentally because of his strictly scientific approach, because his conception of adjustment was adjustment of the individual to *himself* rather than to society, and because of the biological emphasis further stressed by the Kleinians, who are now regarded by many as the main movement in orthodox psychoanalysis. The problem of loneliness and social adjustment emphasized by the Neo-Freudians and by Riesmann and other American writers may become more important here as populations become increasingly mobile both geographically and socially; but there is no doubt at all that, so far from being regarded as a problem, loneliness in the sense of not being bothered by neighbours or being unnecessarily spoken to on the train—not being 'impinged upon'—is an English middle-class ideal, and so far as social adjustments concerned the English have always cherished their eccentrics, at least in retrospect. Rivers of course is one of the great names in anthropology, but although his analysis of the nervous mechanisms involved in conflict and regression is essentially correct, it was not original, whilst his observation of epicritic and protopathic sensation in cutaneous nerves, if broadly true experimentally, is not now explained by physiologists in the same way, nor are the findings believed to be connected with the concept of higher and lower levels in the central nervous system. His psychological observations made in the relatively restricted field of war-neuroses are still quoted by psychiatrists but much less by psychologists or psychoanalysts, partly, at least, because Rivers's concept of causality is a physiological one rather than one based on psychic determinism. Thus in discussing dreams Rivers suggests that both the ideational and the emotional content of a dream are determined by recent happenings, that wish-fulfilment dreams are a special case of the more general state of affairs in which any emotion or current problem may be worked through as in a day-dream, and that the infantile or distorted nature of the manifest content is due, not to repression or symbolism, but to physiological regression to more primitive levels of the nervous system under the influence of sleep. Psychologically this resembles the view of Adler that dreams attempt to solve contemporary issues but are not to be regarded as determined in every detail and that the most important feature of a dream is its emotional tone. But Rivers's concept of regression is conceived in neurological terms of the 'series of levels in the nervous system' first described by Cabanis during the French Revolution and elaborated by the great British neurologist Hughlings Jackson a century later. However, his account of the primitive reactions to fear is still unequalled and is important as demonstrating a type of behaviour apparently unrelated to culture and common to both men and animals, although there can be no doubt that the point at which breakdown actually occurs is influenced by social, individual, and physiological factors. Psychoanalysts on the whole tend to ignore these reactions, although clearly they reveal a great deal about how the mind works at the most primitive level of fight or flight. Nor have psychoanalysts satisfactorily explained the very definite cultural and class incidence of hysteria and other neuroses noted by Rivers and confirmed even more strikingly during the last war. It is difficult without straining credulity to the utmost to see why in the First World War hysterical reactions were largely confined to the private soldier, while in the last war its grosser manifestations were almost unknown in any army of a civilized country and were restricted to the more primitive troops from Asia, Africa, and Southern Europe, if hysteria is to be regarded as a regression to the phallic level at which fixation has previously occurred. Observation suggests that the cultural and educational level may be at least as significant as the emotional one, yet at a time when most psychiatrists are increasingly interested in and puzzled by the changing patterns of the neuroses, by the virtual disappearance of gross conversion hysteria and the corresponding increase of character disorders, all that Fenichel can say in his large volume *The Psychoanalytic Theory of Neurosis* is that, while it would be a fascinating task to investigate the cause of this change, it 'lies outside the competence of the analyst', and although the change must have important implications for psychoanalytic theory it is dismissed in a single page. Another issue inevitably raised by the work of Rivers is the question of brief therapy as contrasted with the psychoanalytic position that only complete analysis is adequate and that any other form of therapy must be based primarily on suggestion. Both these questions must be raised from time to time in the following discussion, but for the moment it is worth while noting the view of non-Freudian psychotherapists that it is difficult to see (a) why one should aim for a perfectionist goal when the patient is simply asking to be relieved of certain sources of discomfort, and all the more so in that there must be very few people who, from the Freudian standpoint, do not require to be analysed, although in reality this would be an impossible task, (b) why it is not permissible to make use of Freudian theory to actively interpret or understand a patient's observed behaviour in therapy when precisely this sort of approach is used with children by the Kleinians. Why, in short, is it necessary to wait for a patient's interpretation of a symptom when we already know on theoretical grounds what its main significance is? Of course, economy in time and money was not the only reason for brief psychotherapy such as that practised in England by T. A. Ross and based on the rather dated views of Déjerine or by William Brown based more soundly on Freud and McDougall. There was first of all the medical conviction that neurosis is a 'disease' the patient 'has', just as he may have pneumonia, and secondly the moral conviction that one is not entitled to interfere unnecessarily with a patient's personality as shown in his ethical or religious outlook. The first belief was originally held by Freud himself, but since it is now quite clear that neurosis is not a disease in the medically accepted sense and that it is not something a person *has* but rather something that he *is*, neither of these views is tenable in spite of the protestations of Maritain and Dalbiez to the contrary. It is however still possible to hold the opinion that in the steadily decreasing number of cases in which overt symptoms appear as the presenting problem, interference should be reduced to a minimum except when a complete analysis is intended.

Suttie's theories at first attracted a good deal of attention and are still quoted by social psychologists and sociologists to whom Freud's biological and individualist bias does not readily appeal, but otherwise they have been used more as a stick to beat Freud than as an approach to psychotherapy. His attack on orthodox views and in particular on Freud himself is vehement and gives the impression that the fact that Freud made a particular statement is the best of reasons for asserting precisely the opposite. But in spite of this his discussion is lucidly presented and carefully argued, and as one of the more detailed native English dynamic theories of personality, its relative neglect is rather surprising, although possibly to be explained by the fact that *The Origins of Love and Hate* was published at a time when the Freudian movement in Britain was rapidly gaining momentum even in the Tavistock Clinic itself. Suttie's opposition to Freud seems fundamentally to have been against his patriarchal authoritarianism, in place of which Suttie attempted to substitute matriarchal and democratic tendencies; but psychologists have shown most interest in his criticism of two of the least satisfactory Freudian assumptions relating to the nature of aggression and the nature of society. Finding the question of the innate nature of aggression both meaningless and irrelevant, the psychologist can see that experimentally it results from frustration of a drive, which is precisely the position taken up by Suttie on clinical grounds, and the Freudian view that the social impulse arises from the binding together of basically hostile individuals by goal-inhibited sexual impulses, which is also poorly regarded by psychologists, is attacked by Suttie as a circular argument, since it is difficult to see why sexual desire should be inhibited except as a *result* of social organization, and what arises as a result of social life can hardly be its *cause* as well. Suttie's argument is commended by D. W. Harding who nevertheless points out that to derive social desire from the affection felt by the child for its mother in infancy is an example of a fallacy common to analytic schools in general—the fallacy of supposing that the first manifestation of a tendency is its origin. Harding concludes that 'it would be at least misleading to say that the grown cat's mousing was "derived from" the kitten's aptness to chase and pounce on blown leaves and bits of paper that move; it is equally misleading to say with Susan Isaacs that the desire for property arises from the infant's wish to possess the breast securely; or to say that social desire is "derived from" the affection felt by the infant for the mother'. However, granting the logic of this argument as a cogent criticism of a too facile assumption, it becomes apparent that the alternative view, that there is no reason why we should not postulate an innate disposition to social behaviour which manifests itself in different ways at different times, is even more untenable. On this view, drawn to its logical conclusions, we should have to assume, not only an innate social disposition but also an innate acquisitive one and so on, until we end up with the original instinct theories propounded by McDougall and others from which it has been generally accepted that Freud had rescued us —and these lead to circular arguments with a vengeance and to futile explanations that are not explanations at all. 'Why does this man strive for money?' Because of his acquisitive instinct. 'But why does he strive more than other people?' Because his acquisitive instinct is innately more powerful. 'What is this instinct, and how do you identify it?' It is the instinct to possess or acquire, and one observes it in this man's striving for money. Whatever their failings, the analytic schools have spared us the absurdity of asking ourselves whether juvenile delinquents are suffering from an overdeveloped aggressive instinct or whether maternal neglect is the result of an underdeveloped maternal one.

The British schools so far discussed have, on the whole, made little impact either upon the United States or upon the rather less than 250 psychoanalysts scattered throughout the rest of Western Europe, and it is therefore worth while concluding this chapter with a brief account of the work of a British psychoanalyst of whom the reverse is the case. The views of Dr W. R. D. Fairbairn of Edinburgh have received scant appreciation in British psychoanalytic circles where a more or less strict orthodoxy discouraging any fundamental departure from Freud's original position still reigns, but are highly regarded by leading authorities in the United States. The reason for this is not far to seek; for Fairbairn in his book *Psychoanalytic Studies of the Personality*, first published in 1952, largely discards Freud's biological emphasis with its picture of a basically pleasure-seeking libido striving for satisfaction through the medium of various eroto-genous zones (oral, anal, phallic, etc.) which develop from one stage to the next by a process of inevitable evolution also biologically determined. In its place we are given a genuinely psychological psychology based upon the concept of a central ego seeking to relate itself with objects where it may find support, and we have seen that such an outlook is in line with current American trends. Thus Dr T. S. Szasz of New York comments in his important study *The Myth of Mental Illness* (Secker & Warburg, 1962) which has as its main thesis the belief that mental 'illness' is not a disease entity but a form of communication employing the language of illness: 'Fairbairn has been one of the most successful exponents of a consistently psychological formulation of so-called psychiatric problems. Em-phasizing that psychoanalysis deals, above all else, with observations of, and statements about, object relationships, he has reformulated much of psychoanalytic theory from the vantage point of this ego-psychological (and by implication, communicational) approach... it was Sullivan and Fairbairn who gave impetus to the fuller ap-preciation of the communicative aspects of all types of occurrences encountered in psychiatric and psychotherapeutic work.'

Whilst attaching fundamental significance to the events of the two oral phases, Fairbairn regards the anal and phallic phases de-scribed by Freud and Abraham as artefacts and rejects completely the Freudian thesis that each type of neurosis represents a regression to a specific earlier level, e.g. the obsessional to the anal level, the hysteric to the phallic one. On the contrary, he writes, '...my own findings leave me in little doubt that the *paranoid, obsessional,* and *hysterical* states—to which may be added the *phobic* state—essentially represent, not the products of fixations at specific libidinal phases but simply *a variety of techniques employed to defend the ego against the effects of conflicts of an oral origin*'. Libido, in this view, is essentially object-seeking and the so-called erotogenic zones merely channels mediating these aims of the ego, whilst ego-development must be conceived in terms of relationships with objects, and in particular with those which have been internalized during early life under the pressure of deprivation and frustration. What this means we shall see shortly, but broadly speaking development is regarded as a process of growing away from the early stage of infantile dependence based upon primary identification with the object towards a state of adult and mature dependence based upon differentiation of the object from the self. In schematic terms, the course of normal development can be represented as follows:

(1) Stage of Infantile Dependence, characterized by an attitude of taking, which is subdivided into:

(a) Early Oral—incorporating—sucking or rejecting (Pre-ambivalent).

(b) Late Oral—incorporating—sucking or biting (Ambivalent).

(2) Stage of Transition between infantile dependence and mature dependence, characterised by dichotomy into good and bad incorporated objects and their gradual exteriorization into the outer world.

(3) State of Mature Dependence, characterised by an attitude of giving when both accepted and rejected objects have been exteriorized.

During the early oral phase the natural object is the breast of the mother and insofar as this appears to be good its contents are incorporated. Under conditions of deprivation, however, anxiety arises lest the object together with its contents has been incorporated and thus destroyed. Since at this stage the hate-love situation of ambivalence has not yet arisen, the problem facing the frustrated infant is that he may have unintentionally destroyed his loved object and that consequently his love is destructive and dangerous. This is the basis of the schizoid state. In the late oral phase the position is entirely different; for by this time the natural object has become the mother with the breast and, insofar as it presents itself as bad, the object may be bitten and its bad aspect incorporated in order to control it. Ambivalence, with its confusion between love and hate, arouses in the infant frustrated at this period the basic problem of how to love the object without destroying it by hate. This is the foundation of the depressive reaction. It will be seen that the schizoid individual faces throughout life the devastating experience of feeling that his love is bad and destructive—hence he tends to avoid deep emotional relationships; the depressive, on the other hand, can feel that his love at least is good and consequently remains capable of relationships with outer objects. His trouble is that, although his aggression has been differentiated, he has failed to take the further step described in the outline above as dichotomy of the object, i.e. instead of being free to direct his hate towards rejected objects and consequently a love relatively uncontaminated by hate towards accepted ones, his relationships must always be ambivalent.

Since nobody passes without scars through the period of infantile dependence or the transition period which succeeds it, Fairbairn believes that there is present in everyone either an underlying schizoid or an underlying depressive tendency according as they were subjected to difficulties in infantile object-relations predominantly during the early or the late oral phases. These two states are a sort of basic neurosis or characterology comparable to Jung's extravert-introvert or Kretschmer's cyclothymic-schizothymic types, and the various neurotic reactions of later life represent attempts to deal with difficulties and conflicts relating to object-relationships in consequence of the persistence of incorporated objects, although the actual course of events will depend upon the circumstances which the individual is called upon to face. Hence all psychopathological conditions originate at a stage long before the development of the superego and are based on the relationships of various parts of the ego to internalized objects and to one another as objects. This leads to Fairbairn's concept of mental structure which is that of 'a multiplicity of egos', because, in his own words,...
I was led to set aside the traditional classification of mental structure in terms of ego, id and superego in favour of a classification couched in terms of an egostructure split into three separate egos – (1) a central ego (the 'I'), (2) a libidinal ego, and (3) an aggressive, persecutory ego which I designate as the internal saboteur.' The first corresponds roughly to Freud's ego with the important differences that it is a primary and dynamic structure which does not arise out of the id and is not dependent upon energy or impulses coming from the id. On the contrary, it is the primary structure from which the others take their origin. The libidinal ego, although corresponding to some extent with the Freudian id, is therefore a derivative of the central ego and, like it, is a dynamic structure differing mainly in its more infantile character. The internal saboteur is also wholly an ego structure comparable to Freud's superego

but operating at a lower level of mental organization. Whilst rejecting Freud's concept of the id, Fairbairn retains his concept of the superego without which he feels no satisfactory explanation of guilt is possible.

Comparisons between this theory and that of Klein are inevitable, but it must be remembered that Klein accepted all the main tenets of Freudian theory to which Fairbairn most strongly objects—her own, of course, was largely a supplement to Freud's. Moreover, she attached a fundamental significance to the 'depressive position' whilst Fairbairn's theory arose originally from a study of the schizoid one. His concept of multiple egos has spread within the orthodox analytic movement in the United States—Karl Menninger, for example, speaks of 'observing' 'regressive', 'reality' egos and so on, but how far these specifically correspond to the central and libidinal egos and the internal saboteur (later described as the 'anti-libidinal ego') it is difficult to say. Anthony Storr, an English psychiatrist with a Jungian training, has shown in his book *The Integrity of the Personality* how useful an aid to understanding Fairbairn's theory can be; for, behind an unfamiliar terminology, it emphasises the child's need to be loved 'as a person' and the inadequacy of Freud's concept of maturity as the mere attainment of genital sexuality. Throughout his writings it is clear that he is concerned with people as whole persons whose goal must be to attain that maturity of object-relations with others of which a genital attitude is but one element.

CHAPTER 5

The Psychosomatic Approach

PSYCHOSOMATIC disorders, strictly speaking, belong to the borderland territory between psychoanalysis and physical medicine. Nevertheless, it seems worth while to say something about them here, firstly, because psychoanalysis played the major part in creating the psychosomatic point of view, and secondly, because it provides an excuse to discuss certain writers who have made contributions in this field. Georg Groddeck, Wilhelm Reich, Franz Alexander, and J. L. Halliday have all applied Freudian theory, in one way or another, to the problems of organic and social diseases, and accordingly it is convenient to deal with them here.

Up to the eighteenth and early nineteenth centuries psychological factors such as loss of fortune, the death of a loved one, or disappointment in love, were quite naturally accepted by physicians as playing an important part in the causation of disease. But later in the nineteenth century the growing knowledge of pathology and the introduction of new methods in microscopy led the German pathologist Virchow and others to assume that all diseases were organic, that unless demonstrable cell-changes could be discovered under the microscope no disease could be said to exist. This belief had the effect in psychiatry of distracting attention away from psychological factors and concentrating it upon physical ones, and the approach seemed to be fully justified when in a number of mental disorders an organic cause was actually found (e.g. the discovery that general paralysis of the insane is a form of syphilis of the nervous system). However, by the beginning of this century the work of Freud, Janet, and Kraepelin brought the concept of psychologically-produced disorders once more to the attention of psychiatrists, although it is only in comparatively recent years that we have come to realize that organic diseases as well as mental ones may be psychological in origin. Many people, when told that psychological factors are capable of influencing the course of organic disease or even initiating it, are very vague as to what exactly is postulated to be happening. Are we to suppose, they may ask, that an intangible entity described as 'mind', an entity which cannot be demonstrated by any known scentific method, can possibly be the cause of quite tangible results? One possible answer to this question is that the existence of mind is a philosophical problem which cannot be answered by the scientist, although conceivably at some future date he might be able to show that the hypothesis of mind was an unnecessary one to explain his observations; but we are not directly concerned with this problem when we talk about psychological factors in disease. The physician or psychoanalyst leaves the problem of mind on one side, since the question as to whether materialism, idealism, or one or other of the dualistic philosophies is true is of little practical importance in curing a disease. What we do mean is indicated by William White in his book *The Meaning of Disease:* 'The answer to the question: What is the function of the stomach? is digestion, which is but a small part of the activity of the total organism and only indirectly, though of course importantly, related to many of its other functions. But if we undertake to answer the question, What is the man doing? we reply in terms of the total organism by saying, for example, that he is walking down the street or running a foot race or going to the theatre or studying medicine or what not. ...If mind is the expression of a total reaction in distinction from a partial reaction, then every living organism must be credited with mental, that is, total types of response.' Thus, a mental or psychological factor may, for practical purposes, be regarded as one relating to the total reactions of the individual, and a 'psychosomatic' or 'psychological' disease is one which cannot be fully understood without taking into account the relationships of the patient as a unique person to his environment, to himself, and to other people.

Although Freud himself made few direct contributions to the study of psychosomatic diseases, his theories made it possible for psychologically-produced illness to be taken seriously, initially, as we have seen, in the field of neurosis. The first analyst to interest himself in the psychological aspects of organic disease was Georg Groddeck (1866–1934) of Baden-Baden, who in *The Book of the It*, *The World of Man*, and *The Unknown Self*, propounded a somewhat bizarre and largely intuitive theory based upon his experiences in analysing cases of heart disease, nephritis, cancer, and other serious organic illnesses. The individual according to this theory does not live his own life and has little to do with his fate. He is, in fact, lived by the 'It' which seems to be conceived as a compound of the Freudian 'Id' with the wisdom of the Jungian collective unconscious. It was the 'It' which decided when the individual would be born, and it also decides when he will die, whether or not he will succeed, and when and how he becomes ill. Every disease, from a wart to a cancer, is an expression of the omnipresent and omnipotent 'It'. For example, a woman with a small wart on the inner aspect of her thigh was told by Groddeck that she wished to become a man and had therefore produced (or, rather, her 'It' had produced) a miniature penis. A woman with a tumour of the uterus had obviously developed the tumour because, lacking a child, the 'It' had caused this deadly substitute 'child' to grow within her. A fracture case would be asked: 'Why did you break your arm?' and a case of laryngitis: 'Why do you wish to be unable to speak?' (Alfred Adler, at any rate in the case of minor ailments, seems to have held similar views concerning what he described as organ jargon.) The following quotation, taken from *The Unknown Self*, is an example of Groddeck's approach: '[Psychoanalysis] turns to the patient himself, to his psyche, to his conscious mind, and still more to his unconscious, with the question, "Why have you infected yourself? What was it that drove you to cause some of the germs around you and within you to multiply so that you were able to use them to make yourself ill?" And to these questions, if one uses the method given to us by Freud, one will receive an answer, and apparently a true answer, or at least a useful one, since often, indeed very often, the "It" gives up being ill as soon as it is questioned in a way it can answer. It would seem that illness is often only a means of flight from something not understood, and a defence against what is unbearable. Here we have the explanation why children are particularly liable to infection, since to children life brings the hardest things to bear. In other words, without Freud and psychoanalysis we should not know what we do now, that every illness has a definite meaning to the sufferer, that it is intentional, consciously or unconsciously intentioned, and that it can be treated by discovering this intention, this meaning.'

It is easy to dismiss Groddeck's account of the manifestations of the 'It' as totally absurd, and obviously it would be wrong to suppose that all disease can be so simply explained. But in holding the views he did Groddeck was much nearer the truth than, at the other extreme, were the wholly mechanistic physicians of his time. Bones are sometimes broken to satisfy unconscious drives, and therefore 'Why did you permit yourself to be injured?' may be a perfectly sensible question to ask. People commonly develop voice defects because they do not wish to speak, and recent evidence suggests that there may be some relationship between sterility or frigidity and cancer of the genital organs. What was wrong with Groddeck's theory was that it included too much and that he never took the trouble to give any acceptable account of what really went on. It is not very enlightening to be told that the 'It' produces disease, if we do not know (a) what the 'It' really is, and (b) how it produces its effects.

This defect has been partly, at least, remedied by Franz Alexander of Chicago, whose book *Psychosomatic Medicine* gives an account of the subject from a combined physiological, psychological, and wholly scientific point of view. Alexander, the Director of the Chicago Institute of Psychoanalysis, is a Freudian who has disagreed with orthodox theory in various relatively minor respects which can only briefly be mentioned here:

(1) He holds an unorthodox view, first put forward by Ferenczi, as to the nature of sexuality.

(2) He is inclined to pay less attention to the stages of infantile sexuality as described by Freud and has replaced them by a theory of three elementary tendencies which he designates as: to receive or take, to retain, and to give or eliminate.

(3) He attaches considerable significance to repressed aggression.

(4) He is more inclined to grant importance to cultural factors than the orthodox Freudians, although less so than the so-called cultural schools of Fromm, Horney, and Sullivan.

(5) He makes use of an abbreviated form of analysis.

The only one of these points which need be further elaborated is the first, relating to the nature of sexuality. Alexander believes that sexuality is not qualitatively different from other behaviour, but that the distinction is rather a matter of quantity. In his own words, 'the surplus energy left over from other activities is discharged in erotic behaviour'. It follows that any strong overflow of emotion, when not purposefully integrated with other reactions, may become erotic: e.g. hostile feelings in sadism, guilt feelings in masochism, curiosity in scoptophilia (i.e. pleasure in looking), and pride in exhibitionism. All non-sexual emotions have sexual equivalents: 'It is not their quality but the degree of tension involved and the mode of discharge which makes them sexual.'

In order to understand the genesis of psychosomatic diseases (strictly speaking, all diseases are psychosomatic, but we are using the word now in its more limited sense to refer to those organic disorders in which there is reason to believe that emotional stress has played a major part in their development), it is necessary to say something about the anatomy and physiology of the nervous system. As has already been noted, there are various levels in the nervous system, ranging from the highest and most conscious to the unconscious and more or less automatic centres where postural adjustments are made, balance maintained, and movements coordinated. But, in addition to the central nervous system, comprising the brain and spinal cord with the sensory and motor nerves which pass to and from the cord, there is a more primitive one known as the autonomic nervous system, which takes the form of two thin nerve-chains with ganglia or knots of nerve-cells at intervals lying on either side of the spine at the back of the abdomen, pelvis, and chest. The solar plexus in the upper abdomen is one of these ganglia, and just as the nerves of the central nervous system going to the skin and voluntary muscles are of two main types—motor (concerned with movement), and sensory (concerned with sensation)—so the nerves of the autonomic nervous system supply the internal organs and are subdivided into parasympathetic and sympathetic groups. The controlling centre of the autonomic nervous system lies in the base of the brain in an area known as the hypothalamus. The system supplies the stomach, intestines, heart, blood-vessels, and other organs, including the important endocrine glands, and its importance lies in the fact that here is situated the physiological basis of emotion.

Alexander compares the life of the organism with the life of a nation in which there are two extreme conditions: war and peace. War represents the state of affairs when the organism has to deal with an emergency, peace when it is in a state of rest and relaxation. 'War economy means priority for war goods and prohibition of certain peace-time productions. Tanks are produced instead of passenger cars, munitions are produced instead of luxury goods. In the organism, the emotional state of preparedness corresponds to war economy and relaxation to peace economy, as certain organ systems which are needed in the emergency become stimulated while the others are inhibited' *(Psychosomatic Medicine)*. It is the sympathetic part of the autonomic nervous system which prepares for emergency or in biological terms for fight or flight, and when the sympathetic nerves are stimulated certain bodily changes occur: the heart beats faster, the pupils dilate, gastric activity (a peace-time process) is inhibited, sugar is released from the liver, and so on. These activities are accompanied by the secretion of the hormone adrenalin from the suprarenal glands above the kidneys, which intensifies their effect. The dilated pupils, the pallor of the skin (due to constriction of the smaller blood-vessels), and the rapid pulse are the observable external signs of such emergency responses in fear or anger which serve the function of making activity (fight or flight) more effective. When, on the other hand, the organism is at rest—for example, after a large meal or after sexual intercourse or sleep—the reverse changes occur as a result of parasympathetic stimulation: the heart beats slowly, the stomach proceeds to digest its contents, the skin is flushed, the pupils contracted, and sugar is stored in the liver. Sympathetic activity therefore is a breaking down (katabolic) process, while parasympathetic activity is a building-up (anabolic) process, and these two fundamental reactions are useful to animals in that they prepare the organism for activity or relaxation. But human beings differ from animals in two very important respects. Firstly, in animals and to a certain extent in the normal human being these physiological changes last only so long as the need persists; with the animal particularly, 'out of sight is out of mind'. Animals live in a perpetual present, whereas the human individual, by reason of his capacity to visualize the past and the future, may be fearful or resentful about both. Sympathetic stimulation is necessary when the individual is confronted by actual danger or the need for increased activity, but when he is angry or afraid about events of yesterday or the possible events of tomorrow what was intended as an emergency reaction becomes a prolonged and chronic one. For example, the useful temporarily raised blood-pressure of emergency may become the pathological and permanently raised blood-pressure of prolonged resentment and frustration. Another difference between animals and human beings is the capacity of the latter to see emergencies in situations where the danger is not to life and health but only to pride or self-respect. For instance, the student before an examination shows the rapid pulse, the pallor, and other changes which were biologically intended for life or death situations, and even more so the neurotic with, for example, claustrophobia becomes anxious and his sympathetic system is stimulated in a situation where there is no objective danger at all but only a symbolic one. The animal, and in normal circumstances the man, whose sympathetic system has been stimulated works the emergency state off in action, whether in fighting, running away, verbally expressing his hostility, or in more constructive behaviour; but of course it is characteristic of the neurotic that he tends to inhibit or repress these emotions, and instead of the emergency reaction being worked off in action, the appropriate behaviour — fight, flight, or constructive action — is never consummated. He comes to be in a constant state of preparedness in face of a threat which may be purely subjective and never results in his doing anything. The result is that the physiological changes described above may become permanent and fixed instead of temporary emergency reactions. This is the physiological foundation of the psychosomatic disorders.

But, as Alexander points out, there are two extreme types of individual: those who in the face of emergency tend to respond by activity (i.e. by sympathetic stimulation), and those who in a similar situation respond by what is described as 'vegetative retreat' (i.e. by parasympathetic stimulation). In the former condition the neurotic inhibits his aggressive impulses, and hence is likely to develop such psychosomatic illnesses as high blood pressure, diabetes, rheumatoid arthritis, and exophthalmic goitre. 'In essential hypertension the increased blood-pressure is chronically sustained under the influence of pent-up and never fully relieved emotions, just as would happen temporarily under the influence of freely-expressed rage in normal persons. Emotional influences upon the regulatory mechanisms of carbohydrate metabolism probably play a significant role in diabetes mellitus. Chronically increased muscle tension brought about by sustained aggressive impulses appears to be a pathogenic factor in rheumatoid arthritis. The influence of this type of emotion upon endocrine functions can be observed in thyrotoxicosis (i.e. toxic goitre). Vascular responses to emotional tensions play an important role in certain forms of headaches. In all these examples, certain phases of the vegetative preparation for concentrated action are chronically sustained because the underlying motivating forces are neurotically inhibited and are not released in appropriate action.' In the second state, that of parasympathetic stimulation, the individual withdraws from action in the face of emergency into a dependent condition, and his organs return to a peace-time basis when they should be mobilizing. Such people, instead of facing the emergency, tend to turn for aid like helpless children. Prolonged parasympathetic overstimulation leads to such disorders as dyspepsia, duodenal ulcer, chronic diarrhoea, colitis, and constipation, for example the stomach goes on digesting when no food is present until it digests its own lining, forming an ulcer. Thus many diseases are not as is usually thought misfortunes that merely 'happen' to the unoffending individual because in a quite real sense he creates them himself—he is an active agent in bringing them about and they express personality traits just as neurotic symptoms do. Hence we cannot discuss disease usefully without considering the type of person who has become ill. Dr Flanders Dunbar, of the Presbyterian Hospital in New York, believed that certain diseases occur predominantly to individuals of a particular personality-type. The stomach ulcer type may, on the surface, be ambitious, hard-driving, and tough, but underneath he shows dependent and feminine characteristics. The individual with high blood pressure may, on the surface, be friendly and calm, but it can be demonstrated that this superficial attitude is a reaction-formation against strongly repressed aggressive trends. Coronary thrombosis and angina pectoris are an increasingly frequent cause of death in those obsessional and over-conscientious individuals who shoulder great responsibilities, such as physicians, lawyers, and executives in industry—they are, as Alexander says, almost occupational diseases. There are also specific personality-types in the case of those who are prone to accidents and fractures and indeed a specific psychopathology discussed by Karl Menninger of the Menninger Clinic, who has made use of Freud's theory of the Life and Death instincts in order to explain many of these manifestations of inwardly directed aggression. He includes in this category such partial or total forms of self-destruction as suicide, asceticism and martyrdom, neurotic invalidism, alcoholism, antisocial behaviour, self-mutilation, purposive accidents, and polysurgery (i.e. frequent resort to surgical operations). Here, however, we shall only consider the problem of what is described as 'accident-proneness'.

More than twenty years ago, K. Marbe, a German psychologist, observed that the person who has already had one accident is more likely to have another than the person who has never had one at all, and Theodor Reik, in *The Unknown Murderer*, has pointed out the frequency with which the criminal betrays himself and even brings about his own self-punishment by a purposive accident. Freud too describes the case of a man who, rejected by a woman whose lover he had been, stepped 'accidentally' in front of a car when he met her in the street and was killed before her eyes *(Collected Papers,* Vol. 3). In 1919, M. Greenwood and H. M. Woods investigated the distribution of accidents in a shell factory and made the now commonplace observation that a majority of accidents happen to a small minority of individuals—in this instance it was found that 4 per cent of the women had 28 per cent of the accidents. The basis of such 'accidental happenings', says Menninger, is the belief prevalent in our culture that suffering expiates guilt, and the individual, applying this same principle within his own personality, acts as an internalized judge who demands suffering for his wrongdoings. Suffering relieves the pangs of a guilty conscience and brings back some degree of inner peace. The accident-prone person is commonly one who originally held rebellious attitudes towards his parents and retains these attitudes in later life towards those in authority combined with a sense of guilt at his rebelliousness. In the case of road accidents the National Safety Council of the United States found that amongst automobile drivers 'the people with four accidents were about fourteen times as numerous as they should have been on the basis of the theory that bad luck might be only pure chance, while people with seven accidents each during the time of study were nine thousand times commoner than the laws of chance would require'. Furthermore, those persons who had numerous accidents showed a pronounced tendency to repeat the same type of accident, and Menninger states that, in his experience, analysis of those who, as the saying is, 'drive as if they wished to kill themselves' often convincingly reveals that this is precisely what they wish to do.

Dr J. L. Halliday of Glasgow, combining Freudian theory with his experience in Public Health, published his *Psychosocial Medicine* in 1948. This is a highly significant piece of research which, whether we agree in detail with his thesis or not, indicates a relatively new direction in the field of psychological medicine. Basically Halliday is concerned with the problem of psychological and psychosomatic disease as a community phenomenon and in order to illustrate this point he produces medical statistics which are believed to demonstrate certain interesting trends in the health of Britain during the years 1900–39. There can, of course, be no question that the nation's health has greatly improved throughout these years, but if the indices of ill-health are divided into two groups, the one relating to physical ill-health and the other to psychological ill-health, it will be found that, whereas the former conditions show a dramatic decrease, the latter have tended to increase in an equally striking manner. Thus the general death rate, the infant mortality rate, the proportion of stunted and rickety children, and the incidence of typhoid fever, rheumatic fever, diphtheria, and tuberculosis, have gone sharply down. But on the other hand indices of mental ill-health—the infertility rate, the suicide rate, the gastric and peptic ulcer rate, the exophthalmic goitre, diabetes, and cardiovascular diseases rates—disorders which come into the 'psychosomatic' category—have all gone up. For example, between 1911 and 1936, the death rate from exophthalmic goitre rose in England alone by 400 per cent in males and 230 per cent in females. In the initial fifteen months of the First World War, medical discharges of soldiers from gastritis and peptic ulcer together numbered only 709, whereas in the first twenty-seven months of the Second World War the discharges from peptic ulcer *alone* numbered 23,574.

Halliday then goes on to elaborate his concept of the 'sick society' in which, in addition to the indices of mental ill-health mentioned above, he notes the following symptoms:

In the economic and industrial spheres:
(1) Increasing sickness rates.
(2) Increasing absenteeism.
(3) Increasing fall of output per worker.
(4) Unemployment.
(5) Increasing strikes.
Criminal indices:
Increasing juvenile delinquency (said by Halliday to have increased by 60 per cent between 1913 and 1938).
Cultural indices:
(1) The increasing intrusion of manifestations of the primitive and visceral, including sex.
(2) Increase in 'escapism' —gambling, etc.
(3) Decline of religious faith (i.e. the loss of a sense of origins, purpose in life, and cosmic destiny). This recalls Fromm's frame of orientation and devotion' —see p. 154.
(4) Increasing intellectualism and obsessional planning.
Political indices:
(1) Social fragmentation (e.g. in class war, and the revival of regional nationalism).
(2) Mass emigration (group dispersal), and increasing 'restlessness'.
(3) The emergence of 'leadership for destruction'.

At the cultural level, Halliday seems to explain this social disintegration in terms of a changing technology which has brought about the decay of old institutions before they have had time to be replaced by new ones. He writes: 'The increasing development and application of science to the physical environment led in time to

the industrial revolution of the eighteenth century and to the introduction of many new ideas and inventions, and these in turn inevitably brought about changes in the pre-existing family patterns,
religious patterns, cultural patterns, occupational patterns, and
economic patterns, so that the total social system became changed
at an ever-accelerating rate, until a point was reached (perhaps
about 1870) when the national equilibrium was so seriously upset that disintegration set in.' At the family and individual level he
is particularly interested in the changes in patterns of child-rearing
which occurred between the eighteen-seventies and the nineteen-
thirties in response to these developments. During the late nineteenth century, breast-feeding was universal (or nearly so), feeding
times were not arranged 'by the clock', and, since the 'pram' was
unknown outside the wealthier classes, the infant had the comfort
of physical and emotional support in his mother's arms. Little
attempt was made at bowel-training until the second or third year,
and the child was often wrapped in swaddling-clothes; for bad
smells, in those days of poor sanitation, and in particular faecal
and urinary smells, were simply ignored. Furnishings were plain
and simple, and there were no dangerous pieces of apparatus in
the home, so the child was given considerable freedom of movement and was able to explore and manipulate objects. The family
was large, which meant that children were less likely to be fussed
over or spoiled, and early social impulses were given free play.
In short, there was a large measure of toleration during the three
early years—until, in fact, the patriarchal father began to play a
part in the child's education. It was not until the genital phase was
reached that there was any great frustration of emotional growth,
and Halliday suggests that this may have some connexion with the
relatively high incidence of hysteria in Victorian days (it will be
recalled that hysteria, in Freudian theory, is a regression to, or a
fixation at, the genital stage). Halliday concludes: 'Viewed physi-
ologically, the child's environment was appallingly bad. Dirt,
absence of pure water supply and adequate sanitation, overcrowd-
ing, bad housing, poverty, malnutrition, and long working hours—
all contributed to tragically high rates of bodily impairment and
death. Viewed psychologically, however, the child's environment
was not so bad, in that during the early years emotional growth was

largely permitted to develop and unfold in its own way and in its "own good time".'

When we turn to the nineteen-thirties, the picture is completely altered. Overt conditions are of course much better, but psychological conditions are less favourable. Breast-feeding has almost disappeared, and feeding by the clock is the rule; toilet training often begins in the first months of life, since faecal smells are distasteful to a more educated public. Elaborate and often dangerous furnishings are common, and electric points and delicate equipment such as radios make the child's explorations limited in scope. Families are small, and, at the age of four or five, or even younger, the child is pushed out to a nursery school where it will be 'out of the way' and the mother can go to work if she so wishes. The babe in arms has become the infant in the carriage. Partly because of the smallness of her family, partly no doubt from a sense guilt, the mother tends to fuss over her child when it is in the house. Outside in the street fast cars and heavy traffic make the world a perilous place. This relatively high degree of frustration in the first two years of life may, Halliday believes, be responsible for the increasing incidence of psychosomatic disorders, predisposition to which seems to be developed during these years: 'The life, instead of being allowed to unfold naturally with the concomitant maturing of bodily order, was subjected to an imposed system of conditioning which prematurely provoked, or predisposed to, bodily disorders by inducing tensional states or dysfunctions in the gastrointestinal tract, the respiratory system, the cardiovascular system, the voluntary muscular system, and so on. The third phase of infancy, however, was probably less frustrated than in the previous century in so far as more notice and attention was given to children; the phallic father was no longer in fashion, having been replaced at first by daddy (who was kind) and later by pop (who was ineffective, even contemptible); and there was less positive indoctrination of the sense of sin and guilt before an all-seeing and almighty God.'

Wilhelm Reich is included here because, although originally an orthodox Freudian, he was interested in the influence of social factors – particularly in the political field – on character formation. His later biological formulations are regarded by most authorities as bizarre in the extreme, but his earlier work on body tensions expressed in the book *Character Analysis* exerted considerable influence on analytic practice at the time. Reich put forward the interesting theory that body tensions were a frequent mode of expressing habitual emotional states. Certain postures and expressions (e.g. a drooping mouth, a rigid abdomen, grimaces, typical stance, and so on) were stated to be the outward signs of characteristic ways of reacting. He believed that these and other character resistances should be attacked prior to the actual analytic procedure and broken down by repeatedly calling attention to them and to the emotional tensions producing them in all possible situations. This was described as 'education for analysis'. Reich denied the existence of a Death instinct and believed that sadism and masochism, seen by Freud as combinations of Eros and Thanatos, were the result of 'disastrous social conditions'. Thus his position was primarily a socio-political one which bears some resemblance to the later work of Fromm, Kardiner, and others. It is expressed in *Character Analysis* as follows: '…every social order creates those character forms which it needs for its preservation. In class society the ruling class secures its position with the aid of education and the institution of the family, by making its ideologies the ruling ideologies of all members of the society. But it is not merely a matter of imposing ideologies, attitudes, and concepts on the members of society. Rather it is a matter of a deep-reaching process in each new generation, of the formation of a psychic structure which corresponds to the existing social order, in all strata of the population.' Reich was concerned in another book, *The Mass Psychology of Fascism*, to understand the psychological factors which lead to totalitarianism and cause the members of a society to abdicate initiative and self-direction in favour of dictatorship. Since in the individual the first clash with authority occurs in the field of sexuality, it is here, according to Reich, that we must seek to comprehend the pattern of later submissiveness. The child's sexual play is dealt with by punishment, by deprivation of love, and by threats, until it is virtually forced to suppress any overt manifestations of sexuality. But this suppression, once achieved, spreads far beyond its original goal; for the restrictive pattern radiates throughout the personality, curbing many other impulses and riddling the mind with conflicts. The crippling of spontaneous sexual expression leads to the crippling of the whole personality, the child's spirit has been broken, and from this time on he will tend to behave submissively towards all figures in authority. Should such an individual attempt to break the bonds of his servitude he will inevitably fail, since any revolt he may make against authority will reveal its origins in frustration. If he attempts sexual freedom, he becomes pathologically preoccupied with sex; if he attempts rebellion or defiance, it becomes delinquency, gangsterism, and tyranny over others. The dictator who has overthrown the old order is merely a successful delinquent, and world politics is delinquency upon a world scale. Reich's hypothesis, then, is that slavery is thrust upon the individual through interference with healthy sexual development and it follows that the solution to the problem is to be found in sexual freedom. A. S. Neill, the educationist, who accepts Reich's thesis, says in his *Problem Family* that 'a child left to touch its genitals has every chance of growing up with a sincere happy attitude to sex'. Of course, in order to validate this theory one would have to show that societies with restrictive sexual morals are more prone to develop authoritarian forms of government, and while it seems possible, even probable, that societies in which upbringing is permissive do not often put dictators into power, it is quite certain that many societies with strict sexual morals do not become dictatorships either. Neill's statement, which seems to suggest that happiness is localized in the genitals, is, as it stands, absurd; it is not the parental attitude towards this one matter which is important to the child's later development but the total attitude in all spheres. The parent who is not shocked by his child's sexual play is usually a parent who is permissive and tolerant in all respects, and in this case Neill's view would be justified. But it is certainly not justified if taken literally as meaning that the mere fact of permitting free sexual play is the keynote to a happy life, because obviously there are many parents who are 'permissive' in this respect out of indifference and a happy and well-balanced adult is hardly likely to develop in a soil of parental neglect. Sexual freedom cannot be isolated from freedom in general.

Reich's later writings went far beyond Freudian therory when he took the extreme position that sexuality as expressed in the orgasm is of fundamental importance in understanding the problems of the individual and society. His last books deal with entities described as 'bions' and 'orgones' which are apparently to be regarded as physiological in nature (although unknown to physiologists) and in *The Cancer Biopathy* he put forward a psychosomatic theory as to the origin of cancer. None of these beliefs were accepted by any-one outside Reich's own school, and he left the orthodox move-ment in 1933. However, it is as a pioneer in the field of character analysis that Reich is most likely to be remembered, for it was he who noted that reactive character traits were an armour used by the ego to protect it against both instincts and a thwarting environ-ment. Such character traits as ambitious behaviour, which covers inadequacy, or arrogance, which hides deep feelings of inadequacy, do indeed protect the ego, but they have the serious defect that they are maintained indiscriminately regardless of their appropriate-ness in a given situation and, because they insulate the individual from external stimuli, he becomes less susceptible to re-education. Being essentially ambivalent such characteristics derive basically from pregenital sources. Reich made the two important points (1) that character disorders are a specific form of neurosis even al-though they may be unaccompanied by 'symptoms' in the formal sense and are often more troublesome to the individual's associates than to himself, (2) that all neuroses have their root in character, that is, in the adjustments which the ego has made to the instincts as well as to the external world. His method of pointing out to a patient his characteristic attitudes towards others has proved ef-fective with difficult character problems and was made use of and further developed by Horney and Sullivan.

There are two main categories of psychosomatic disorders: those in which unconscious instinctual attitudes influence organic functions in a physiological way without the changes having any specific psychic meaning, and the conversions of hysteria which express a phantasy in 'body language' without any structural change being present. It is in the main with the former that the present chapter has been concerned, and it is only in cases of this type that conflict arises between the psychoanalyst and the physi-cian, who is likely to demand answers to such questions as: Granted that a certain mental state and a certain physical one coexist how can you prove that the former brought about the latter? Supposing, for the moment, that one does not grant their coexistence in *all* cases of the disease, how on the basis of the small numbers you deal with can you prove this supposition wrong, and how would you explain the other cases? What is the therapeutic significance of your claims when Freud himself said that 'organ neuroses' could not be treated by psychoanalysis? Now, strictly speaking, the psychoanalyst does not regard the disease and the mental state as separately coexisting, for to him they are both aspects of the same thing, the biologically-conceived individual, but to the ultra-conservative physician whose conception of 'psychological factors' is a state of affairs found in the odd case which obviously retards progress by causing worry in a significant degree (for example becoming bankrupt, having one's house burnt down or one's son charged with murder, being on the verge of suicide), it is difficult to understand how an immaterial mind floating about somewhere in the region of the cranium can really affect the human machine with serious chronic diseases which in many cases have been shown to be due to previously unrecognized physical maladjustments. Lack of exercise and over-consumption of cholesterol-containing foods, he will point out, are correlated with a high incidence of coronary thrombosis, so it seems much more satisfactory to assume that the frequency with which it appears in top business executives is due to their sybaritic way of life and physical laziness rather than to their prolonged mental stress. But even a fairly broad-minded physician might draw the line on being told that an asthma attack is 'an anxiety equivalent, a cry for help, directed towards the mother, whom the patient tries to introject by respiration in order to be permanently protected' as Fenichel defines it. Statistics in such cases are on the whole not very satisfying and in the above example, for instance, we should like to know how the asthmatics came to see a psychoanalyst in the first place if it were not that they were more concerned about their mental condition than their asthmatic one or that they were referred by physicians who considered their condition not typical of the general run of sufferers. We should like to know how many people with a similar personality problem did not have asthma, as well as how many asthmatics had no personality problem worth mentioning or a wholly different one. It does not take very much critical thought to see, as Flanders Dunbar showed by comparing the past history of accident cases in a casualty ward with the accident history of patients in a ward of chronic or serious heart cases which acted as a control series and demonstrated the much greater incidence of accidents in the former group, that people with long and serious illnesses of any type are hardly likely to be in a position to have many accidents. Even on the thesis that accidents are produced by inwardly-directed aggression, the account given will not do; for chronic disease in itself is sufficient punishment for even the most guilt-ridden, and indeed the placidity and comparative cheerfulness of such patients has been attributed to the fact that guilt has been assuaged by suffering. Accidents are not only physically less likely but psychologically unnecessary. Similarly it is possible to agree with Dr Halliday's psychosocial thesis as being a very feasible attempt to explain social trends everyone has noticed without at the same time failing to see that his figures need to be taken with a grain of salt. To begin with, they are presumably based on statistics gathered from that most fallible of sources, the doctor's certificate. This is not a reflection on the ability of the G.P. to diagnose, but rather on his attitude towards certificates and what he regards as his duty to his patients. When we are told that certain infectious diseases are on the increase we have every reason to accept the doctor's statement as evidence, since he conceives it to be both in the public interest and that of his patient that the condition should be known—but would he in all cases regard it as his duty to tell officialdom that his patient has syphilis or gonorrhoea? Certainly he would not, since to do so would be felt by his patient as a breach of professional secrecy which if it became known might lead to concealment of the disease in others. Nor for obvious reasons would he write 'cancer' on a certificate he had to give to the patient himself, and although it seems likely that the incidence of peptic ulcer is actually increasing, the figures of army discharges from this cause during the two world wars tell us very little and prove nothing whatever except that popular attitudes towards the condition have changed and army policy as to what type of case should be discharged has changed with it. At a time when X-ray diagnosis was infrequent and dyspepsia was accepted as something ordinarily treated at home and not necessarily made worse by environmental changes, something one just 'had' that drugs could only ameliorate, many patients never saw a doctor at all and others never saw a specialist or had an X-ray unless in an emergency. Again, a considerable part of the period under consideration (1900 to 1939) was a time when unemployment was high, and during such times doctors will tend towards leniency in granting certificates for such nondescript categories as 'fibrositis' or 'bronchial catarrh', since it is better to be 'off sick' than 'out of work'. What unfitted a man for army service in the last war might to all appearances be much more trivial than in the first because past experience had given a clearer insight into the sort of soldier who was likely to prove a liability; similarly the concept of 'juvenile delinquency' has been widened to include behaviour that previously was not so regarded. Statistical results in medicine are influenced quite as much by changing viewpoints on the part of doctors and the changing age-structure of the population as by actual changes in the incidence of a disease, and of course in respect of any one group of investigators they are influenced by the type of patient seen, who may not be typical of sufferers in the population as a whole.

The fact is that the concept of psychosomatic disease or organ neurosis did not arise initially because psychoanalysts began to take an interest in organic disease but because, as Freud realized, it was inherent in his monistic and biological outlook. Equally, the concept was not accepted from this source by physicians in general because it was not inherent in their dualistic and basically mechanistic one. But a further reason for their non-acceptance (for it was this rather than total rejection) was the psychoanalyst's adherence to a jargon which was all but incomprehensible even to those with some smattering of knowledge of Freudian theory. Tell the average physician that his asthmatic patients are highly-strung and that their attacks are frequently brought on by emotional stimuli or even by a conditioned reflex, as when the patient allergic to roses has an attack in the presence of a bunch of artificial ones, and he will agree with you. Tell him that the asthmatic is often of a particular character-type, tends to be over-sensitive, and shows a need for dependence, and he will agree with this too, just as he is likely to agree that his migraine patients are often intelligent, overconscientious, and driving types. Whether the character is causal to the disease or vice versa he would not presume to know, nor would he regard it as particularly relevant to a condition which in any case requires a physical approach. Nor is he opposed to the view that stress in some unspecified way may aggravate physical disease, or perhaps even cause it in those who are predisposed, since he has for long used sedatives in cases of stomach or duodenal ulcer and in hypertension—but tell him that an asthma attack is brought about by separation-anxiety and means that the patient is trying to inhale his mother so that he can keep her safely inside his chest in order to be permanently protected, that sometimes he has phantasies that she is already within and this brings about a struggle between his ego, and the respiratory apparatus 'containing' her, and he will think you are either joking or mad. Hence the major influences in the creation of modern psychosomatic medicine—at any rate in Europe—have not been Freudian and stem rather from the doctor's own observations in a social climate where the infective disorders were becoming a less serious problem than the disorders previously classified as hereditary or degenerative, and war experience was making increasingly clear the relationships between stress, personality, and disease. Finally this point of view, which had been based on what were regarded as merely interesting observations without any clear-cut scientific foundation, was supplied with one, not by a psychiatrist, but by a physician and physiologist. The work of Hans Selye of Montreal showed the physiological pathways, both neurological and biochemical, by which stress could produce organic disease and furthermore demonstrated in the laboratory that prolonged exposure to fear-producing stimuli led to such results or even to death in experimental animals. Selye's 'stress syndrome' rather than Freud's psychoanalysis is likely to form the rationale of modern psychosomatic medicine, but it is finally to psychoanalysis that the physician must turn in order to discover the nature and significance of stress for the individual with all its psychological variations which physiology unaided is powerless to explain.

Psychoanalysis and Society

Totem and Taboo, Freud's first book to apply psychoanalytic knowledge to social and anthropological problems, was published in 1913, to be followed by a series of others: *Group Psychology and the Analysis of the Ego* (1922), *The Future of an Illusion* (1930), *Civilization and Its Discontents* (1930), and finally *Moses and Monotheism* in 1939. Here we shall discuss briefly Freud's views on the origins of society, on the nature of groups and leadership, and on culture generally, together with those of other analytic schools and the anthropologists who have been influenced by him, before dealing in subsequent chapters with the American culturally-orientated schools of Fromm, Horney, Sullivan, and others

Freud shared with Jung the belief in a collective unconscious, an archaic heritage appearing without learning in every individual which includes '...not only dispositions, but also ideational contents, memory traces of the experiences of former generations'. He supposed that there exists a sort of mass psyche or group mind which is the source of these traces, so that the sense of guilt from events occurring many thousands of years ago may still survive and influence individuals living today. The essential differences between the two are that Freud made no direct use of the group mind or archaic heritage in psychotherapy, whereas it is basic to Jung's system and psychotherapeutic method; that, although both conceive of collective symbols as in some way inherited with the physical structure of the brain, Freud insists on this to an extent that Jung perhaps does not; and that the Freudian concept is quite limited, consisting mainly of certain forms of symbolism and, possibly, the experiences of the primal horde, in contrast to the vast Jungian collective unconscious upon the surface of which the tiny ego is a mere excrescence. Modern Freudians make little use of the concept and some actively reject it, but it is worth recalling that the English school of Melanie Klein emphasizes primitive symbolism occurring at a very early age and seems to infer that the infant has an innate awareness of parental intercourse and other happenings or objects relating to the processes of birth and sex. On either side these theories raise very formidable scientific difficulties, although of course this has never had the slightest effect upon those who support them. Both views, for example, necessitate an acceptance of the inheritance of acquired characters which is almost universally rejected by biologists in any form and totally rejected in the original one—even Ernest Jones pointed out that Freud's 'biological contributions were marred by adherence to a peculiarly simplistic form of the long-abandoned Lamarckian views on heredity'. But the greater absurdity lies in supposing that any theory of evolution, no matter what its mechanism, could be used to explain the inheritance of memory traces of the experiences of former generations. Here, from *The Integration of the Personality*, are some of Jung's views on the collective unconscious: 'This psychic life is the mind of our ancient ancestors, the way in which they thought and felt, the way in which they conceived of life and the world, of gods and human beings... as the body is a sort of museum of its phylogenetic history, so is the mind. There is no reason for believing that the psyche, with its peculiar structure, is the only thing in the world that has no history beyond its individual manifestation. Even the conscious mind cannot be denied a history extending over at least five thousand years. But the unconscious psyche is not only immensely old, it is also able to grow increasingly into an equally remote future.' The psyche, we are told, is 'increasing infinitesimally with each century'. Of course Jung is barking up the wrong tree by separating body and mind and then arguing that, because the body has evolved and shows traces of its evolutionary past in its present structure, the mind must have done the same and should show traces of its psychic evolution, when in fact there is no reason at all to suppose that there has been the slightest change in man's bodily structure since *homo sapiens* appeared. The notion that the psyche is 'increasing infinitesimally with each century' confuses psychological with sociological observations instead of with physiological ones, as in the first instance; because, although it is true that human experience and knowledge increases very rapidly century by century, this has nothing whatever to do with mental changes but rather with the social fact that each individual born today has more available information from past generations to put into his head. Anyone who suggests that an intelligent and healthy infant taken from a Chinese or Eskimo village and reared as an English child will not in all respects be psychologically like other English children, racial unconscious or no, *may* be right—but he will find it hard to find a single psychologist or biologist who would be prepared to believe him. Evolution takes place slowly over millions, not thousands, of years; it takes place by natural selection based on chance variations and mutations, and the effect of civilization, if any, is to reduce the influence of selection by reducing competition; so far as we have been able to discover the brain contains no innate ideas of any sort, much less archetypes of the elaborate kind described by Jung; the 'mind', however one defines the term, 'evolved' in the period we have knowledge of by accumulating past experience. In the matter of a racial unconscious Jung is supported by no scientist anywhere, since there is no evidence that the biological equipment of any race is basically different from that of any other. But the strangest thing about this problem is that one cannot see how it ever came to be regarded as worthy of discussion when the obvious explanation of all the facts is ready to hand, and it does not take deep thought to see that the child or primitive is likely to explain the unknown universe in terms of the known family situation or that he is heir to the modes of thought and experiences of the past. Of course certain ways of reacting are innate since they are basically protective mechanisms: the child does not need to be taught to be aggressive or show anger when his desires are frustrated or to start on hearing a loud noise, but this is no more mysterious than that he should feel the need to do something when he is hungry or thirsty. Some forms of symbolic thought other than those based on direct experience are obviously not only not mysterious but even inevitable, and one is inclined to feel that psychoanalysts or analytical psychologists go a long distance out of their way to complicate what is perfectly simple. Why, for example, should Rank and others insist that bowls and containers represent the enveloping womb when there is no other conceivable means of containing, and why should child analysts suppose that a child pushing a train through a tunnel is simulating parental intercourse when, apart from the important question of why trains and tunnels are supplied in the first place unless they represent an archetype or fixed idea in the mind of the analyst, it seems obvious that, short of ignoring the whole thing, there are only two things a child could do with a train and tunnel — obligingly push the train in or smash both of them. The supposition that children must possess innate concepts of this sort leaves us to draw the logical conclusion that monkeys poking straws into holes in their cage or even birds and rodents carrying out the same or similar actions must have the same or similar problems and desires as the child. This demonstrates a peculiar trait of the analytic schools which has not endeared them to scientists in general: the habit of carrying on their investigations and making their statements in a scientific vacuum beyond which they do not come into conflict with other views but simply continue as if they did not exist. For examples we need seek no further than their use of the group mind or the observations made by psychoanalysts from time to time on such subjects as intelligence, memory, child development, or anthropology, to find that they rarely refer to other views supporting their claims or in disagreement with them coming from those who have been studying the subjects for years within long-established scientific disciplines; they ignore them completely. Whereas most scientists nowadays who felt the need to make use of such concepts as the group mind or the inheritance of acquired characteristics would do so with an elaborate defence of their position, and rather defiantly, because of their awareness of its general unacceptability, one may doubt whether analysts are always aware that there is a contrary view or that anyone had ever thought on the subject before. Freud, of course, was widely read and at the times when his major theories were being worked out obviously had a considerable acquaintance with late nineteenth-century psychology and anthropology, but if Jung has read any modern science this is certainly not apparent in his works, which seem to take a leap from patients who may be chronic schizophrenics or deteriorated elderly gentlemen and pass by way of the murky forests of Teutonic affairs straight into the arms of Indian and Chinese mysticism. It is therefore less strange than might at first appear that Jung has made almost no impression at all in precisely those fields of social psychology and anthropology where one might have expected his interests to lead him, although even Freud, who made a very considerable impression, does not appear to have kept abreast of modern knowledge in the social sciences outside his own field. He does indeed mention with approval Trotter's *Instincts of the Herd in Peace and War*—but Trotter was Ernest Jones's brother-in-law.

Psychoanalysts who are also anthropologists, such as Abraham Kardiner and Geza Róheim, have made considerable use of Freud's theories, but significantly those aspects which they find most useful are not the specifically anthropological ones but rather those dealing with individual development. Kardiner, who is essentially an arm-chair theoretician, has found inspiration in the Freudian emphasis on the importance of infantile experience and the irrational nature of the unconscious, while making little use of the stages of libido development, and Róheim, more orthodox and with considerable experience of field-work, lays even more emphasis on infantile experience by taking up the Kleinian position. But neither has derived much help from Freud's cultural and social theories as a whole, and both reject the theory of a group mind or collective unconscious, which, as we have seen, plays little or no part in Freud's general theory. Perhaps the only exception to this is his theory of dreams, which makes use of the collective unconscious with its archaic heritage in order to explain the occurrence of fixed symbols. *The Interpretation of Dreams* was considered by Freud to be his most important work and the significance of dreams as the 'royal road to the unconscious' is accepted as a major aspect of psychoanalysis; the symbol is one of the means whereby forbidden wishes from the unconscious id are allowed to manifest themselves in disguised form in consciousness when they would otherwise clash with the moral demands of the superego. It is the function of the dream to preserve sleep by permitting expression to the wishes in such a form as not to shock the ego and so awaken the dreamer, and it thus happens that the manifest content of the dream (i.e. the dream as recalled upon waking) differs considerably from its latent content (i.e. its unconscious significance). However, by the process of free-association the latent content can be revealed, in spite of the fact that it has been carefully disguised by the processes of condensation, displacement, plastic representation, and fixed symbolism. Condensation means that some parts of the latent content are left out and elements possessing a common trait are fused together, so that a figure appearing in a dream may be a composite image of several people in real life. In displacement, elements which are invested with great emotional significance may be made to appear insignificant and vice versa in order to conceal their importance from the dreamer. Plastic representation is described by Freud as 'a plastic, concrete piece of imagery, originating in the sound of a word'. For example, the dreamer's impression of climbing a high mountain from which he has a wide *view* of the surrounding land is connected by free association with the recollection of a friend who is publishing a *Review* on the subject of foreign relations. The dreamer is identifying himself with the 'reviewer', since he is making a survey of his own life in his analysis. In fixed symbolism, Freud drew attention to his belief that certain modes of symbolic expression in dreams have a fixed meaning which cannot be further analysed, since they are not individual but common to all humanity. Examples of such fixed symbols have been given in Chapter 3, and in the Freudian sense the meanings are usually sexual ones. As if these disguises were not enough, there is a final process which complicates dream analysis: that of secondary elaboration. On awaking, the dreamer recalls the dream's manifest content, but his mind soon sets to work to give to what he only vaguely remembers some semblance of order and coherence, a coherence which it did not originally possess, so that the dream as told is a much more orderly and rational entity than it was when originally presented during sleep. Thus the latent content is disguised to form the manifest content and this is further distorted by secondary elaboration.

The problem of symbolism brings us into contact with Freud's concept of man's archaic heritage. For the fixed symbols, according to this theory, have never been individually acquired by any man. Nor are they limited to dreams, but are to be found in mythology, fairy tales, art, religion, and in many other fields. The dream-censorship, in other words, makes use of an archaic language which was lying ready to hand in order to make the forbidden wishes of the unconscious as incomprehensible as possible to the conscious mind of the individual. Freud supposes that during the course of development of civilization it became necessary to repress primitive drives and wishes which nevertheless continued to press upwards towards satisfaction and fulfilment. These wishes—aggressive, sexual, and incestuous—had to be disguised according to the degree of civilization attained at any particular period, and in their disguised form are to be found in mythology. Hence the early myths are full of such themes as parricide, castration, devouring monsters, and incestuous relationships, whereas the later ones conceal their primitive content more carefully. Of course many attempts have been made in the past to explain the origins of myths and folk-tales, although in most cases these were descriptive rather than causal, explaining what was believed to have brought myths into being without explaining why they should exist at all, much less why their content should be so extraordinary and yet so stereotyped. The *historical* theory asserts that the events described are based upon actual history which has been grossly distorted in the process of transmission, so when Danae in her prison is said to have been impregnated by Zeus with a shower of gold we are asked to believe that this represents the money with which her guards were bribed. Others have supposed that myths and folk-tales are *parables* with a moral purpose as in the case of Aesop's fables, or that they are *allegories* representing significant natural events. In this case divine incest may represent the daily fusion of the Sun with his mother Dawn, tales of death and rebirth the burial of the seed and its resurrection in spring, and so on. A modification of this theory is due to the philologist Max Müller, who suggested that what had been everyday words became transformed into proper names—the name for the sun was once 'apollo' and for dawn 'daphne', so that the statement that the sun follows the dawn could give rise to the myth that Apollo pursues Daphne. Andrew Lang interpreted them on the other hand as 'just-so' stories by which man in his state of primitive animism attempted to explain the world; they were in effect *early scientific theories*. Lastly, according to Lord Raglan, myths which others have supposed to have given rise to ritual are actually the offspring of ritual—they are, as it were, the stage directions for the ritual drama. For example, Raglan derives the Oedipus myth from a ritual parricide and incest originally carried out to magically rejuvenate nature. It need not be supposed that all these theories are simply untrue, since obviously myths, once they had been created, might be modified into tales, utilized as primitive science, or mingled with historical moral elements and descriptions of real persons. Myths basically relating to sexual phenomena may have become associated with agricultural rituals and magical attempts to increase the fertility of crops. But Freud denied that these explanations were in any sense fundamental and postulated that myths are 'thinly-disguised representations of certain fundamental unconscious fantasies common to all mankind'.

Classical mythology, the plays based upon it by the Greek playwrights, and the more primitive myths and folk-tales of less sophisticated peoples, all show a remarkable similarity of content: accounts of parricide and incest with the mother, castration, punishment and reparation, matricide, cannibalism, and dismemberment, form part of the mythology of all peoples. So the real issue from the psychoanalysts' standpoint is to explain how these similarities arise. But in order to do this we need not seek far; for, as noted elsewhere, such phantasies are universal during the earlier years of life. The small child during the phase of the Oedipus complex wishes to kill his father and commit incest with his mother, he fears castration by the father, and at a later stage, since he not only hates but also loves his father, thoughts of reparation and self-punishment begin to arise. Oedipus blinding himself is expressing a deep-seated urge to make reparation. The theories of Melanie Klein help to explain the tales of cannibalism and dismemberment, of matricide and primary aggression in greater detail, since in Kleinian theory aggressive feelings towards the mother arise long before the hate felt towards the father during the Oedipus stage, and this aggression projected upon the mother is reflected back upon the child in the form of images of a wicked devouring witch with long teeth who eats little children. But it was originally the child who, during the oral stage, wished to devour his mother.

Freud believed that, at a remote period in the history of man, human beings lived in a state of 'heedless sexual and primitive egoistic motives', and throughout this time, of course, they had neither the ability nor the need to create myths since repression was unnecessary. In *Totem and Taboo*, making use of such anthropological material as was available in the first decade of this century *(The Golden Bough,* and other works of Sir George Frazer; the totem theory of Robertson Smith; and some of the views of Darwin), he proceeded to examine the origin of social institutions, of totemism and exogamy, and the prohibition of incest in the light of the following theory: he assumes that the earliest type of human society must have been the 'primal horde' described by Charles Darwin, over which a powerful male, the father of the horde, was absolute ruler. The father subjected the younger males to his absolute power and kept all the women for his own use. Thus subjected, the sons were forced to live in complete abstinence and obedience, until one day they revolted and banding together killed the father and ate his body. As is well-known, many primitive peoples live in groups which are represented by a 'totem', a sacred animal or plant which it is forbidden to eat or kill; yet, on ceremonial occasions, a feast is held during which the ordinarily forbidden animal is killed and the meat eaten ritually. This ritual, according to Freud, is a symbolic representation and commemoration of the original parricide. Behind the hatred for the old man of the primal horde lay an ambivalent feeling of affection, and the sons soon after their criminal act felt the need of atonement and reparation. This need led to their forbidding the killing of the totem animal which represents the father, its deification as the leader of the tribe, and the institution of a ceremonial feast at which the original crime was re-enacted in ritual form. But since the women of the tribe had been the original cause of the murder a danger existed that competition between the sons might lead to a repetition of the crime. They therefore forbade marriage with the liberated women and created a taboo against killing within the tribe. Henceforth it was compulsory to marry outside the group (exogamy, prohibition of incest) and new laws forbade the killing of one's bloodbrother. In this way the competition for women between brothers no longer existed as a serious threat to the social organization of the tribe, the large patriarchal family group. Freud's theory therefore assumes that society has arisen out of the need to curb man's unruly sexual and aggressive drives and that its function is primarily suppressive. In a single hypothesis, he explains the origin of society, of religion and law, of totemism, of the incest taboo and exogamy, and of ritual and myths. Law curbs the sexual and aggressive drives, religion, myth, and ritual commemorate the crime and assuage guilt, and society is the overall mechanism of control. In the course of time the myths relating to the ritual (the ceremonial representation of the original act) led to the drama of Sophocles and Aeschylus which still makes use of the material supplied by myths, and at a further remove the modern theatre. Surely no theory has ever explained, or attempted to explain, so much.

Religion represents the externalization of man's unconscious conflicts and their raising to the cosmic level. In one of its aspects it provides substitute gratifications for primitive drives, in another it acts as a suppressive force against primitive drives. Religion is 'the universal obsessional neurosis of humanity' in which is perpetuated the illusion of a loving heavenly Father who promises happiness in the hereafter in return for the renunciation of instinctual desires on earth. This is the thesis of *The Future of an Illusion*, and in *Civilization and Its Discontents* Freud asserts that civilization, suppression, and neurosis are inevitably associated in such a way that the more civilization, the more neurosis and conversely the less suppression, the less neurosis and the less civilization. Society, by an ever-increasing tendency to suppression, makes man more and more unhappy, and he seeks relief in substitute gratifications: drinking and smoking or drug-taking, religion, and love—sublimation is only a possible answer for the superior few. When the inhibiting forces of civilization are removed, however, we see men in their true light, as 'savage beasts to whom the thought of sparing their own kind is alien'.

Otto Rank followed Freud into speculations upon social and religious origins but based them upon the hypothesis of the 'birth trauma'. According to Rank the function of the father in the primal horde was to thwart the sons' desires to return to the mother, since there exists a 'perpetual insatiable tendency to force one's way completely into the mother' and thus undo the trauma of birth. Because they were thwarted in this way, the sons killed the father and thereafter renounced the coveted mother. Only the youngest son, we are told, is permitted to return to the mother because he was the last to occupy the womb. He is the 'Hero' of mythology, and his superiority consists in the fact that '... he comes last and, so to speak, drives the others away. In this he is like the father, with whom he alone, and from the same motives, is able to identify himself'. It is the youngest son who, after the murder of the primal father, and following a period of rule by the mother or the women of the family (matriarchy), becomes the leader. In a matriarchy right and justice spring from the protecting aspects of the mother (her womb), and on the other hand fear of her terrifying aspects relating to the birth trauma. In a patriarchy the ruler is the one who prevents return to the mother, and the primal anxiety of the mother is transformed into respect for the king or ruler. Increasing masculine domination results from the desire to exclude women in order to keep repressed the memory of the birth trauma, but periodically the wish to return to the mother asserts itself and revolutions against masculine dominance occur. Religion in this view 'tends ultimately to the creation of a succouring and protecting primal Being to whose bosom one can flee away from all troubles and dangers and to whom one finally returns in a future life which is a faithful, although sublimated, image of the once lost Paradise' (the mother and her protecting womb). In Christianity, the Son becomes God and the primal mother Mary, while the primal father is the Lord of Hell. The crucifixion is a punishment for rebellion against the Father and is followed by resurrection—that is, birth. It is a symbolical representation of the process of birth and the dogma of the Immaculate Conception asserts that Christ was not born in the ordinary way, that in fact Christ the 'Hero' has conquered the birth trauma. Art takes its roots from the 'imitation of one's own growing and origin from the maternal vessel'. Receptacles were first created in imitation of the maternal womb, and at a later stage, of the child and its head: the vase gets 'a belly, ears, and beak, etc.' Every discovery is a rediscovery of something latent, so that dwellings imitate the protective womb, and swords, guns and so on the male sexual organ. In general, Rank sees in cultural development a gradual withdrawal from the primal birth trauma into sublimated forms as a substitution for the primal state.

During the 1920s and 1930s anthropologists increasingly began to concern themselves with actual field-work in primitive cultures: Malinowski in the Trobriand Islands, Firth with the Tikopians,

Deacon and Layard in Malekula, Margaret Mead, Bateson, Rivers, Radcliffe-Brown, and Boas, all brought back new data concerning primitive cultures, which although influenced by them did not always fit in with Freudian anthropological theories. Bronislaw Malinowski found in the Trobriand Islands a state of affairs in which not the father but the maternal brother was the child's guardian, and he therefore suggested that the Oedipus complex was not universal. For this he was criticized by Jones and Róheim, who had himself done fieldwork in primitive cultures; if, says Róheim, Malinowski did not know Freudian methods and had not been analysed, how could he test the Oedipus theory? Rivers accepted Freud's findings guardedly but with interest, as did the Seligmans and many others about this time. Róheim himself accepted the Freudian theory of the Primal Horde, but rejected the hypothesis of a racial unconscious, basing his propositions on the thesis of 'man's delayed infancy'. His theory is summarized in the following paragraph taken from an essay 'Psychoanalysis and Anthropology' included in Lorand's symposium *Psychoanalysis Today*: 'The specific goals of primitive societies are by no means conditioned by their environment or by practical considerations. They are a series of solutions offered by various human groups for the pre-Oedipal and Oedipal conflicts inherent in the infancy situation. Growing-up from the point of view of the unconscious is an attempt to regain the "paradise lost" of infancy. Our specific ways of adapting to reality are based on inventions and these inventions are sublimations of infantile conflict situations. Culture itself is the creation of a substitute object; the substitute object partakes both of narcissistic and object erotic qualities, represents both the mother and the child. In this respect it is identical with the mechanism of play: a defence against separation anxiety based on a transition from the passive to the active position. Mankind is the only animal that *produces food* (restitution mechanisms with food as symbol of the child) and that lives mainly by cooperation (= symbiosis = mother-child situation).' Here, as the reader will note, we see traces of the ideas of Klein and Rank, and a confirmation of Suttie's thesis that culture is related to play and that cooperation arises from the mother-child situation. But it should be made clear that the theories of Róheim, Freud, and Rank are almost completely rejected by the non-psychoanalytic anthropologist who has little use for the theory of a primal horde or any other Freudian constructs relating directly to anthropology. On the other hand, many anthropologists have made use of the Freudian concept of the importance of the early years in personality development or have utilized his theories concerning mythology. Amongst this latter group are the Americans Edward Sapir and Abraham Kardiner. Roughly speaking, then, anthropologists may be divided into three groups: those who go the whole way with Freud, such as Róheim and a very few others; those who make considerable use of Freudian concepts but reject, for the most part, his anthropological formulations (e. g. Kardiner, Kluckhohn, and Sapir); and those who make almost no use of Freudian theory at all. The latter group is, perhaps, still in the majority, at any rate in Britain and the rest of Europe.

It is now believed that the culture or way of life of each society tends to produce different personality types, and in his book *The Individual and His Society* Kardiner elaborates his concept of the 'basic personality structure', in which he combines a psychoanalytic approach with a realization that cultural and environmental factors may also play a large part in determining psychological phenomena. Kardiner and his colleague Linton define the basic personality structure as 'the constellation of personality characteristics which would appear to be congenial with the total range of institutions comprised within a given culture'. It includes modes of thinking and constellations of ideas, superego formation, and attitudes to supernatural beings, and therefore represents those aspects of personality which distinguish the members of different cultural communities. Character, on the other hand, is 'the special variation in each individual to this cultural norm'. In other words, the special conditions obtaining in each culture tend to produce a particular type of individual with psychological traits suited to that culture. This 'normal personality' for a given culture is the basic personality structure, and the variations upon this common theme which differentiate one individual from another in the same culture and constitute his individuality are described as character. Clyde Kluckhohn, Ralph Linton, and others attempt to reconcile the Freudian doctrine of a permanently fixed personality determined during the first five years of life with the fact that in certain respects, personality appears to change. They speak of 'nuclear' and 'peripheral' regions of personality. 'Changes in the nuclear region, though sometimes trivial in themselves, always modify the personality policy and are necessarily of the either-or variety. Changes in the peripheral region may be purely quantitative and may occur without altering other personality traits. The major stages (oral, anal, genital) require nuclear changes, but together with these are those more superficial adaptations to status and role which every culture expects of persons of a given age, sex, and office. In most cases the periphery is where there is relative freedom to make adjustments' (Kluckhohn: *Mirror For Man*). Cultures have the same properties as the individual personality in that they possess nuclear and peripheral areas of organization, and we might picture each culture (culture is to society what personality is to the individual) as a huge jig-saw puzzle with its centre composed of closely-fitting interlocked pieces, while nearer the periphery lie more loosely-organized pieces and even pieces which are not interlocked at all. Like the basic personality of the individual, the nuclear or central area of a culture is resistant to change—to continue the metaphor we might say that if a particular piece of the puzzle is removed we can only replace it with a similarly-shaped piece. Thus if an attempt is made to stop the practice of head-hunting in a primitive society by sheer suppression, the whole society may begin to disintegrate; for we must consider first of all what function head-hunting plays in the society as a whole. (In New Guinea the killing of a wild boar was substituted for the practice of head-hunting with satisfactory results.) In short, the central or nuclear parts of a culture or a personality cannot be changed piecemeal or by force without risking its total destruction as a functioning entity.

The Freudian assumption of the fixity of human nature began to fare badly in the 1930s when Ruth Benedict and Margaret Mead produced a series of studies which demonstrated how very flexible human nature is when observed against different cultural backgrounds. Margaret Mead, an American anthropologist, found for instance that the storm and stress which is taken for granted as typical of adolescence in Western civilization does not occur amongst girls in Samoa, where custom permits early sexual experience. Similarly, sexual differences between male and female cannot be said to be due to innate biological factors, as Freud supposed, if, as Mead found in New Guinea, neighbouring tribes with differing cultures show variations in masculine and feminine traits which in some cases amount almost to a reversal of the roles as we know them. 'The Arapesh ideal is the mild, responsive man married to the mild, responsive woman; the Mundugumor ideal is the violent aggressive man married to the violent aggressive woman. In the third tribe, the Tchambuli, we found a genuine reversal of the sex-attitudes of our own culture, with the woman the dominant, impersonal, managing partner, the man the less responsible and the emotionally dependent partner.' These cultural differences extend into all fields of personality; the Arapesh are cooperative, unaggressive, and gentle towards their children, the Mundugumor uncooperative, aggressive, and harsh. Aggression is so distasteful to the Arapesh that it appears to hold an equivalent position to that of sex in Victorian society, and enterprise, self-assertion, competitiveness, or anger are strongly disapproved of, so that the mere sight of anyone in a temper shocks them profoundly. Children are never punished and during its early life it is incessantly suggested to the child that everything is 'good'—good sago, good house, good uncle, and so on. Amongst the Mundugumor, on the contrary, 'social organization is based on a theory of a natural hostility that exists between all members of the same sex, and the assumption that the only possible ties between members of the same sex are through members of the opposite sex'. The late Ruth Benedict, another American anthropologist, found that the Zuñi Indians of New Mexico resemble the Arapesh of New Guinea in their lack of assertiveness and initiative—the Zuñi *try* to lose a race, and *insist* on not occupying positions of importance, so that leaders have to be forcibly put in positions of authority and are poorly regarded once they are there. While we in Europe and America strive to collect money, the Kwakiutl of Puget Sound prefer to burn it and tear it in pieces at their 'potlatch' ceremonies, and the Dobu live in such a state of persecutory suspicion that a European psychiatrist would unhesitatingly diagnose any Dobuan outside his own society as a paranoiac requiring psychiatric treatment. War is unknown amongst the Eskimos, and suicide amongst many other tribal communities. Bali, says Róheim, is '...the unthinkable; a schizophrenic culture'.

Without the appropriate experience it is difficult to assess these new formulations in anthropology, and the reader will have to draw his own conclusions from Ruth Benedict's *Patterns of Culture* and Mead's *Coming of Age in Samoa, Sex and Temperament in Three Primitive Societies*, and other books. But if the observations described are even approximately valid, then clearly they give a much more optimistic view of the possibilities for the human race than one obtains from Freud and Melanie Klein. The Neo-Freudian schools too reject Freud's biological approach and are more concerned with the influence of society and culture in building personality than with its instinctual foundations, and amongst psychologists today one finds at the one extreme the orthodox Freudians with their biological theory of a relatively fixed personality dependent upon the instinctual drives and originating in the early years of life, and at the other extreme the thoroughgoing sociological schools (with which we are not concerned here) which assert that personality traits are not to be viewed as 'inside' the individual, being merely consistent modes of behaviour organized around the roles the individual plays in society. (See, for example, *Social Psychology* by Lindesmith and Strauss.) Margaret Mead attaches primary significance to the child-rearing pattern in creating the basic personality structure of a culture, whereas Ruth Benedict seems to attach more importance to the total cultural situation—for example in *The Chrysanthemum and the Sword*, a study of modern Japanese personality structure, she takes into account Japanese history as well as child-rearing patterns. Geoffrey Gorer's *The Americans* and *The Greater Russians* are studies along the lines set by Mead of American and Russian personality patterns. But to the strictly analytically-minded Róheim all talk of culture (whether in the form of technology, environment, economic factors, of child-rearing) creating personality boils down to the old problem: does the hen (culture) come from the egg (childhood situation) or the egg from the hen? 'Do people develop in a particular way because of what has happened to them in their childhood (psychoanalytic viewpoint)—or do parents

behave in a particular way to their children because "society" or
"culture" makes them do just those things (sociological viewpoint)?' In his view, the solution of Kardiner to the effect that both
answers are correct is tantamount to saying that half a hen lays an
egg and from that egg we get the other half of the hen. There are no
environmental influences, according to Róheim, which for example
make the Balinese mother behave cruelly to her children, so the
sociological thesis cannot reasonably be maintained.

But whether Róheim be right or wrong there can be no doubt
that the recent tendency in psychology has been towards an increasingly sociological emphasis, and it will be interesting to see
how far this enables us to find answers to problems which an approach based on the individual has failed to solve, for the acceptance of the sociological viewpoint has quite momentous implications, not only in psychotherapy, but also in psychology, medicine,
and many other spheres. In medicine it would withdraw attention
from the sick patient to the 'sick society' in Halliday's phrase, and
as L. K. Frank has proposed: 'Instead of thinking in terms of a
multiplicity of so-called social problems, each demanding special
attention and a different remedy, we can view all of them as different results of the same disease. If, for example, we could regard
crime, mental disorders, family disorganization, juvenile delinquency, prostitution and sex offences, and much that now passes
as the result of pathological processes (for example, gastric ulcer)
as evidence not of human wickedness, incompetence, perversity, or
pathology, but as human reactions to cultural disintegration, a
forward step would be taken.' Of course, in making generaliza-
tions about modern psychological thought one is apt to ignore the
fact that a very large number of psychologists—perhaps even the
majority—have no particular interest in either society or personality, and it would be more accurate to say that personality theory
today gives less attention to the isolated individual and proportionately more to social determinants, and that social psychology
begins with the group rather than the individual as its unit. The
modern social psychologist finds much of Freud's work not so
much factually in error as practically irrelevant to his own purpose; he does not particularly concern himself with the individual's
fundamental drives, with the problem of whether aggression is

innate or not or the nature of the emotional ties binding individual members of a group to its leader and each other, because this way of looking at group behaviour is foreign to an approach which is basically behaviouristic. The group is studied *as a group*, some sort of social impulse is taken for granted simply because it can be observed in action, and its strength or weakness, positive or negative quality, in any individual member is deduced from his behaviour. That conflicts may arise between individuals and thereby disrupt group unity is obvious, but the social psychologist would probably interpret the fact that they had been allowed to do so as arising either from perplexity over the task confronting the group or, more fundamentally, from defects in its social organization. This attitude arises, not because he dissents from any particular theory of personality, but because he sees the group as a cross-section of average people the behaviour of which cannot be explained by reference to the psychopathology of individual members; for example, a paranoid individual will ordinarily find himself isolated in a group which is functioning under normal circumstances, and will only attain a position of power if the group as a whole is confronted by a 'paranoid' situation in which it feels itself unjustly treated in terms of reality. This is the sort of phenomenon which gave rise to the theory of a group mind, because the group in this case behaves in a way which is quite different from what one might expect on interviewing its predominantly non-paranoid members in other situations, but today we can see that it is best explained in terms of the real situation or the way the group is organized. If the leader proved to be strongly paranoid in the psychiatric sense, the social psychologist would not suppose that he had been able to exert his personality on the group by virtue of his ability to dominate, but would ask himself why the group felt sufficiently resentful and suspicious to put him in charge. The fallacy of the group mind or of the individual mind in a dualistic philosophy arises from the error of ignoring the fact that natural phenomena have to be dealt with in terms of their own level of organization. If we begin by assuming that the body is a machine, then sooner or later we shall have to drag in the concept of a separate mind—the ghost within the machine—in order to explain why in some respects an organism does not behave as a mechanism; if we assume that a group is a collection of individuals which can only be understood in terms of individual psychology, we shall have to introduce the concept of a group mind to explain why, no matter how we add up our results, we cannot account for its collective reactions. In fact it is simpler to realize from the beginning that an organism does not show the same reactions as a machine, nor a group the same reactions as a number of unrelated people regarded as isolated personalities. Freud, of course, saw the group in an entirely different light, and his own theory of group behaviour stems from his picture of the family and the primal horde which is centred around emotional relationships towards a patriarchal leader. The need for a leader and the quality of the relationship to the leader derive from infantile relationships with the parent which influence the individual's attitude to subsequent parent figures, as sibling jealousy influences his attitude to group members who become competitors for the father-leader's approval. The primary group is described by Freud as 'a number of individuals who have substituted one and the same object for their ego-ideal and have consequently identified themselves with one another in their ego'; the members are siblings who, instead of killing each other, direct their love and hate on the leader as the focus of group emotions, leaving them free to unite in brotherly love. This is an interesting thesis, but one's natural response is to feel that it bears a rather distant relationship to the groups one actually knows in Britain or America, where formal and informal leadership are not necessarily synonymous, where the father may be in a legalistic sense the 'head of the family' without being necessarily or even frequently its emotional focus, where working groups have a formal leader whose main *raison d'être* is his real or assumed technical knowledge while he plays a comparatively insignificant part in the emotional dynamics of the group, and, above all, where the informal group with a wholly social function often has strong feelings of disapproval towards any form of authoritarianism or even implied supremacy on the part of a single person. In closely-knit groups in these cultures each member may show supremacy in relation to a specific situation (as e.g. the best cook, the best fighter, the best entertainer, the best swindler outside but not within the group), yet few would care to claim general supremacy, and the formal leader who wishes to be socially approved will frequently play down his authority, attributing it not to innate ability so much as to imposition from without. On the other hand Freud's theory may relate more closely to what one observes in German social groupings, where a spontaneous differentiation into leaders and led is more frequent and clear-cut. Nevertheless there is a clear distinction between Freud's view based on the pattern of the family, which has a certain biological unity, and the social psychologist's view frequently based on the study of work-groups or at any rate groups which are doing something, which sees leadership as a function of the group and the task it has to handle; the former sees leadership as static, the latter as dynamic and liable to alter as the task alters. In the one the leader is the recipient of the group's ambivalent emotions and takes the place of a superego, making brotherliness possible between members, in the other the leader is the tool used by the group to accomplish a particular task and the neighbourliness of members can be seen as, at least in part, brought about by the channelling of aggressive energies into work or striving towards a goal.

The form taken by a scientific statement depends upon what one wants to do with it. There is no contradiction involved in saying that epidemic diseases spread by insanitary conditions are cured by antibiotics and sulphonamides, while noting that historically they ceased to be epidemic in England largely owing to Chadwick's Water Board or Lord Leverhulme's popularization of cheap soap. One is the private doctor's, the other the public health point of view, and it is possible to agree with both statements. Nor is it incorrect to describe milk as 'homogenized' if one is a milkman and non-homogenous if one is a chemist. But it would be absurd if the individual physician criticized the public health authorities on the grounds that clean water and soap could not cure a case of typhoid or dysentery, or the latter announced that aureomycin was useless; if the milkman and chemist disagreed because one rightly asserted that his milk was homogenous *as milk* while the other equally rightly asserted that it was not *as an emulsion* homogenous chemically. Yet this is the sort of argument that goes on all the time between the psychologist (in this case the social psychologist) and the psychoanalyst, although the fact is that when either steps outside his own field to apply his findings he is liable to talk nonsense. The Freudians have adopted on the whole an almost hostile attitude towards any form of social therapy in neurosis, and we know in advance that if, for example, Alchoholics Anonymous claim good results in stopping people drinking themselves to death, we shall be told that this is not a 'real' cure because the infantile oral roots of the trouble have not been dealt with and the fixation remains to express itself in other ways. Obviously, the reply must be that the symptom for which treatment was required was removed and to imply that the patient should be made perfect as well is asking too much because social cure and analytic criteria of cure are not the same thing. If leaders are to be equated with the father and every stick with a penis, good and well; but if this symbolism is practically important it is difficult to explain why we treat different leaders or sticks differently and why there is usually a considerable consensus of agreement about the qualities of any specific one. Freud's analysis of myths and of group life is brilliant, but we are left wondering why a racial or group unconscious and the doctrine of innate ideas should be postulated when it was Freud himself who made them unnecessary; for if a myth is a collective dream rooted in the family experiences of each individual in relation to inevitable emotional tensions, it is unnecessary to bring inheritance into the picture at all. His account of the group is applicable to the family group and to others in so far as they have qualities in common with the patriarchal family—but by no means all groups do so nor indeed do all families, and the clear-cut polarization into leaders and followers is, in fact, very far from typical. However, the main reason why social psychology has moved in other directions than those pioneered by Freud and McDougall is that already given: social psychologists deal with groups as such, Freud deals with individuals inside a group. With certain exceptions, social psychology and psychoanalysis do not contradict each other—they no longer speak the same language.

CHAPTER 7

The Theories of Karen Horney

THE two main movements in the history of psychoanalysis have been a response to Freud's biological assumptions which stimulated on the right wing an ever deeper penetration into infantile experience (as in the Kleinian school) and on the left wing an opening-out into the individual's social and cultural background (as with Horney, Fromm, and Sullivan). The right-wing approach was of course implicit in Freud's own work, since it was in large measure a filling-in of gaps along lines he himself in part foresaw, and it is not surprising that Jones, the Huxley to Freud's Darwin, who lived nearly twenty years longer than his master, regarded the work of the Kleinians favourably. But the left-wing socially orientated movements aroused considerably more hostility amongst the orthodox because in their desire to emphasize the modifiability of human nature which is usually implicit in a socially-orientated theory it was found necessary in the long run to attack the very foundations of orthodoxy. The inevitability of anatomy in determining the psychological differences between the sexes, the inevitability of the stages of libido development and the Oedipus complex, were rejected and the importance of interpersonal relations and the cultural background emphasized, and in psychotherapy an attempt was often made to substitute short and active methods for prolonged and passive ones. When this left-wing tendency first became apparent is difficult to say, because those who later came to be regarded as its supporters do not seem initially to have been at all clear where their thought was leading, and it is obvious that Adler, who has the greatest claim to originating the trend, was quite as individualistic and biologistic as Freud in his early works. However, three personal characteristics of Adler may have played a part in the later development of his school; his own inferiority complex, his lack of understanding of the scientific method, and his Socialism. The first led to his self-assertive insistence on appearing as Freud's colleague rather than his disciple and to his never-ending lectures to the lay public rather than to his professional equals; the second to his dropping scientific determinism, as is revealed in the casual disregard for detail and logical argument in most of his later works; and the third to a quite genuine feeling for the underdog and an appreciation of the need to spread the advantages of psychoanalysis beyond the sphere of a small group of well-to-do bourgeois citizens. But in the end he had collected a motley crowd of strangely-assorted disciples ranging all the way from formerly perplexed school-teachers and nursery workers who, having found the truth, went about eagerly button-holing anyone who would listen, to socialists, strong in political conviction but short in formal education, who felt that this was the ultimate answer to Freud's deliberate attempt to obfuscate psychological issues and confuse the workers. Inevitably too there were general practitioners glad to find that patients could be so simply understood and some psychiatrists who were secretly pleased to find that sex was really unnecessary, while the dynamic approach they had appreciated in Freud was retained. Adler's brilliant intuitions petered out in mediocrity because he had spread his gospel too widely and grossly simplified the issues in a theory which left no room for further development and had little appeal for scientists, or even non-scientists of a moderate degree of sophistication. Adlerians have tended to be 'hearties' with a strong sprinkling of health cranks and members of organizations of elderly women concerned with social issues; but neither here nor in America, where it was at one time widely spread, has the Adlerian movement attracted many deep thinkers or, in the conventional sense, 'great' men. It might seem reasonable to include Jung and Rank in the psychoanalytic left-wing groups, but these two very brilliant men belong to a category of their own, for although Jung is concerned with myths which are ordinarily considered to be social products, his mystical theory has repelled many; and Rank, whose account of the individual's relationship to society still applies to some American social workers, is in matters of detail equally obscure. The beginnings of interpersonal theory in analysis appears with Ferenczi, but in its modern form interpersonal theory derives from Horney, Fromm, and Reich, who were associated in Germany prior to assuming American nationality, and of course from a long line of American social psychologists.

Horney, Fromm, and Reich practised as analysts in Berlin, where for over fifteen years Horney was an orthodox Freudian teaching at the Berlin Psychoanalytic Institute. In the United States she became Associate Director of the Chicago Institute and lecturer at the New School for Social Research, but it was as a staff member of the New York Psychoanalytic Institute that she began to stress the part played by social factors in neurosis and to challenge the biological assumptions of the orthodox Freudians. Ultimately her views had departed so far in the social direction that she left the main body, and at the time of her death in 1952 she was Dean of the new American Institute for Psychoanalysis. As might be expected, this break was not unaccompanied by tensions both before and afterwards, particularly as Horney and her associates proceeded to carry out analyses without the concepts of instinct theory or libidinal development as defined by Freud and interpreted against the background of American industrial civilization as described in *The Neurotic Personality of Our Time*, one of her more important books. Her books, indeed, may have contributed even more than her therapeutic following or direct influence as a teacher in building up her considerable position in the United States. For, like Adler in his later works but unlike the earlier analysts in general, she appealed to a wide public almost over the heads of her colleagues. Intelligent readers all over the world read such books as *New Ways in Psychoanalysis, Our Inner Conflicts, Self-Analysis*, and *Neurosis and Human Growth*, but it seems fair to say that those who read rarely had influence and those who did were unlikely to be impressed unless a pre-existing dissatisfaction with orthodox theory was seeking a peg to hang its cloak. Nor did the numerous patients who turned up to analytic sessions with a copy of Horney under the arm during a negative phase in the transference relationship necessarily stimulate their psychoanalysts to a sympathetic interest in Horney's 'new ways' for treating the neuroses of 'our time'. In fact, outside the United States her influence is virtually non-existent amongst psychoanalysts, although it is not inconsiderable among psychologists in their more speculative moods.

The direct influences upon Horney herself are not far to seek. There was firstly her long-standing distaste for Freud's anti-feminist bias, as revealed in almost all her early papers: 'On the Genesis of the Castration Complex in Women', 'The Flight from Womanhood', 'The Dread of Women', 'The Denial of the Vagina' (*International Journal of Psycho-Analysis*, v, 1924; VII, 1926; XIII, 1932; XIV, 1933) are typical titles of papers attributing sexual differences to social rather than biological factors. Secondly, although unadmitted, must have been the Marxism which during the 1920s she shared with Fromm, Reich, and of course the vast majority of Socialists and progressive thinkers in Central Europe throughout that decade, even if it did not survive the end of the Popular Front. Thirdly, there was the debt to Adler, which caused Adlerians to accuse her of plagiarism (there is no nonsense about the universality of science amongst analytic schools, whose criticisms have a tendency to regress to a more homely level with anguished shrieks of: 'get out of my back garden!' and 'I know what *your* dad did before he came here!') and brought about Horney's equally sincere rejection of their claim. The truth would seem to be that, although her way of looking at problems is decidedly Adlerian, Horney's technique was largely Freudian; as Gardner Murphy says, '...the psychoanalytic tools and fundamental psychodynamic assumptions are retained in so far as one can retain them without laying any stress whatever upon fixed, inalienable biological trends or instincts' (*An Historical Introduction to Modern Psychology*). Lastly, and most emphasized by Horney herself, was the influence of America, where, as she describes in *New Ways in Psychoanalysis*, she found following her arrival in the early 1930s that '... the greater freedom from dogmatic beliefs ... alleviated the obligation of taking psychoanalytical theories for granted, and gave me the courage to proceed along the lines which I considered right. Furthermore, acquaintance with a culture which in many ways is different from the European taught me that many neurotic conflicts are ultimately determined by cultural conditions.'

Horney has criticized the theories of Freud in great detail, and it seems worth while to give her main criticisms here, since they give a very clear picture of the main points at issue between the orthodox viewpoint and that of the Neo-Freudians. Freud's great contribution to modern psychology in her view was the fundamental triad of concepts, that psychic processes are strictly determined, that actions and feelings may be unconsciously motivated, and that the motivations are emotional in nature. But it becomes clear that Horney's way of looking at these concepts is not the Freudian one; for, although she accepts psychic determinism, she feels that the concept of unconscious motivation is often too formalistic. 'Awareness of an attitude comprises not only the knowledge of its existence but also the knowledge of its forcefulness and influence and the knowledge of its consequences and the function which it serves. If this is missing it means that the attitude was unconscious, even though at times glimpes of knowledge may have reached awareness' (*New Ways in Psychoanalysis*). Regarded in this light Stekel's concept of scotomization and Adler's fictive goals are unconscious mental processes, since any mental process may be described as 'unconscious' when the individual is unaware of its full implications, power, and results. Freud's concept of unconscious motivations is not unique because he showed that unconscious mental processes exist (in fact, as we have already seen, this discovery was never claimed by Freud); what is important about it is, firstly, the discovery that to thrust strivings out of awareness, or to refuse them admittance to awareness, does not prevent them from existing and being effective, and secondly, the discovery that unconscious motivations remain unconscious because we are interested in not becoming aware of them (i.e. because of repression). Freud's third great contribution to psychology was his realization that these unconscious motivations are emotional in nature, and this led to the modern concept of personality as dynamic in contrast with the old static and mechanistic picture of the mind produced by the Associationist and Herbartian schools of the early nineteenth century. More specifically, the dynamic theory of the personality postulates that the motivations of our actions and attitudes lie in emotional forces, and that in order to understand the human personality it is necessary to take into account emotional drives which are often in conflict. In addition to these three basic postulates which Freud contributed to the science of psychology there are, says Horney, three major contributions which he made to the practice of psychotherapy. These relate to transference, to resistance, and to the method of free-association. She does not consider the Freudian theory that transference is essentially a repetition of infantile attitudes towards the analyst, who represents the original parental figure, a particularly useful one, but the underlying assumption that the observation of the patient's emotional reactions to the analytical situation constitutes the most direct way of reaching an understanding of his character-structure and, therefore, of his difficulties, is, she thinks, extremely important. 'I believe', she wrote, 'that quite apart from its value to therapy, much of the future of psychoanalysis depends on a more accurate and deeper observation and understanding of the patients' reactions. This conviction is based on the assumption that the essence of all human psychology resides in understanding the processes operating in human relationships' (op. cit). The concept of resistance is based upon the assumption that the patient has good reasons for wishing to be unaware of certain drives, and therefore it follows that the more we are able to recognize the ways in which the patient defends his positions (the ego-defences), the more effective will psychotherapy become. Free-association is '...the specific factor in psychoanalysis which renders an accurate observation possible', and is based upon the principle that a continuity of thoughts and feelings exists even if it is not apparent. 'The idea of free associations, as it is used in therapy, belongs among those analytic concepts whose potential value is far from exhausted' (op. cit.).

But, while recognizing Freud's genius, Karen Horney believed that certain of his basic assumptions were influenced by the outlook of his time, being determined by philosophical beliefs prevailing in the nineteenth century. The first of these basic assumptions is the *biological orientation* which is apparent in his instinct theories, in his emphasis upon hereditary and constitutional factors, and in his tendency to explain the psychological differences between the sexes on the basis of anatomical differences. Freud repeatedly pointed out that the instincts lie on the borderline between organic and psychic processes, and it is clear that he supposed the oral, anal, phallic, and genital phases, and presumably the Oedipus complex, to be innately determined and therefore relatively unaffected by environmental or cultural factors. His concept of the differences between the sexes is based on the supposition that woman's wish to be a man is brought about by her wish to possess a penis, whereas the man's ultimate dread is of castration.

A second influence from the nineteenth century, this time a negative one, is *Freud's ignorance of modern knowledge in anthropology* and *sociology*. The 'culture concept', which implies that human societies may differ from each other in quite radical and striking ways, is of recent origin, and the prevailing trend at an earlier period was to ascribe the peculiarities of one's own culture to human nature in general. Freud seems to have assumed that 'human nature is the same the whole world over', and in his theories cultural phenomena are regarded as having developed from essentially biological and instinctual origins.

Yet another characteristic trait in Freud's psychology is his *tendency to dualistic thinking*—that is to say, he tends to think of psychic factors as pairs of opposites: Ego and Id, Life and Death instincts, masculinity and femininity—these are not only pairs, but rigidly contrasted groups which stand in opposition to each other. His theoretical models are mechanistic and conceived on the analogy of physical systems—for example, he assumes on the analogy of physical forces that energies spent in one system automatically are lost to another one, so that giving love to others is said to impair one's self-love. This sort of dualism, which separates entities into rigid and opposed categories, is typical of nineteenth-century thought, as also is Freud's *deliberate abstention from moral judgements*. Karen Horney comments on the latter trait that it is based on the example of the physical sciences and is really only justified when recording and interpreting observations. Outside this sphere, the psychologist cannot, and should not, claim to be neutral.

Finally, Freud's thinking is what she describes as '*mechanistic-evolutionistic*' in its outlook. Darwin's theory of evolution implied that things which exist today have not always existed in the same form but have developed out of previous stages. Mechanistic-evolutionistic thinking is a special form of this point of view which implies that present manifestations are not only *conditioned* by the past (a quite reasonable assumption), but that they contain *nothing but* the past. So in the case of water turning into steam it emphasizes the fact that steam is merely water appearing in another form, whereas non-mechanistic thinking would point out that, although steam has developed out of water, in so doing it has assumed entirely new qualities, regulated by different laws and producing different effects. (This observation in the Marxist philosophy of Friedrich Engels is described as the 'transformation of quantity into quality'.) In relation to psychology Freud's mechanistic outlook appears in his assumption that the attitudes of an adult are *nothing but* a repetition of the same attitudes in childhood, that nothing much happens in our development after the age of five, and that later reactions are to be considered as a repetition of past ones; another example is his assertion that, since birth is the first manifestation of anxiety, later forms of anxiety are to be regarded as a repetition of the original anxiety of birth. Clearly, Horney says, it is one thing to say that the experience of birth is the original anxiety-producing situation and quite another to suppose that later anxiety is the *same* thing all over again.

These philosophical beliefs seem to have led Freud to be quite unnecessarily pessimistic about human nature. Karen Horney points out that Freud's libido theory seems to assert that '...not only the striving for power, but every kind of self-assertion is (to be) interpreted as an aim-inhibited espression of sadism. Any kind of affection becomes an aim-inhibited expression of libidinal desires. Any kind of submissive attitude towards others becomes suspect of being an expression of a latent passive homosexuality.' The infant's love for his mother is presumed to be founded on his need for the being who satisfies his libidinous desires, and, worse still, the theory of the Death instinct asserts that we have to destroy others in order not to destroy ourselves. That this is an unpleasant belief is apparent enough, but there are good grounds for believing that it is also an illogical one; for if the process of natural selection has the effect of eliminating traits which are harmful to survival, it seems strange that innate human aggression should be so strong that the only solution is universal analysis. And if man is naturally self-centred and aggressive, his sociability purely a manifestation of aim-inhibited sex, how did he ever come to form social groups in the first place? Or, to take the evidence of cultural anthropology, if aggressiveness is innate, how do we explain the lack of it in such social groups as the Arapesh of New Guinea, described by Maragaret Mead in her *Sex and Temperament in Three Primitive Societies*? It is difficult to see why we should accept the belief that, whereas aggressiveness at all levels is primary and innate in man, friendliness is in some sense secondary and merely an expression of aim-inhibited sexuality. Horney refuses to accept this belief of Freud's and comments upon it as follows: 'That over-kindliness may be a reaction-formation against sadistic trends does not preclude the possibility of a genuine kindliness which arises out of basically good relations with others. That generosity may be a reaction-formation against greediness does not disprove the existence of genuine generosity.'

The drawback to Freud's libido theory in Horney's view is that it is an instinct theory which, although it enables us to see the manifold ways in which a single trend manifests itself in a personality, makes the mistake of assuming that libido is the ultimate source of all trends. An analyst's interpretation may be described as deep when it reaches down to repressed strivings, feelings, and fears, but to suppose that only those interpretations are deep which can be connected with infantile drives is a dangerous illusion for three main reasons: (1) it distorts one's views on human relationships, the nature of neurotic conflicts, and the role of cultural factors; (2) it leads to a temptation to understand a whole machine out of one wheel instead of trying to show how the interrelation of all parts brings about certain effects; (3) it leads to the analyst assuming final limitations to therapy (based on biological factors), when they do not exist.

The Freudian argument concerning the Oedipus complex is based upon a typically psychoanalytic heads-I-win-tails-you-lose type of reasoning. As McDougall long ago pointed out, the little boy who shows strong affection for his mother is alleged to be manifesting all the signs of an Oedipus complex; if, however, no such signs are to be noted, it is assumed that the complex has been successfully repressed. Such an argument is hardly likely to convince those who do not share Freud's belief in the biological nature of the complex. Karen Horney's views concerning this complex closely approximate to those of Ian Suttie and Adler. She does not believe that the complex is universal or that it is caused by innate factors but rather that it arises from two possible environmental situations: firstly, the witting or unwitting sexual stimulation of the child by the frustrated father or mother, and, secondly, from an anxiety on the part of a child to compensate for hostile tendencies in a frustrating home situation. 'If a child, in addition to being dependent on his parents, is grossly or subtly intimidated by them and hence feels that any expression of hostile impulses against them endangers his security, then the existence of such hostile impulses is bound to create anxiety. One way to allay this anxiety is to cling to one of the parents, and a child will do so if there is any chance of thus receiving reassuring affection.' The resulting picture may look exactly like the Freudian complex; for there will be passionate clinging to one parent and jealousy towards the other or, indeed, towards anyone interfering with the claim of exclusive possession, but this, so far from being biological in origin, is an early manifestation of neurotic conflict.

The desire for self-aggrandizement which Freud ascribes to self-love or narcissism and Adler to a desire for superiority and power over others is also treated by Horney along much the same lines as by Suttie. The individual feels that 'if others do not love and respect [him] for what he is they should at least pay attention to him and admire him. The obtainment of admiration is substituted for love—a consequential step.' Thus the desire for self-aggrandizement, so far from being an expression of self-love, is rather an expression of the failure to obtain love. 'It is true', says Erich Fromm, in his *Man for Himself*, that selfish persons are incapable of loving others, but they are not capable of loving themselves either.' Similarly, Freud's interpretation of the fact that women often wish they were men in terms of the woman's innate biological inferiority is criticized by Horney along Adlerian lines. 'It is necessary not to take at face value a woman's tendency in one way or another to base her inferiority feelings on the fact that she is a woman; rather it must be pointed out to her that every person belonging to a minority group or to a less privileged group tends to use that status as a cover for inferiority feelings of various sources, and that the important thing is to try to find out these sources.'

This view is in strong opposition to those of such Freudian writers as Helene Deutsch, who has supposed that women are basically masochistic, wishing to be violated and raped in intercourse, and humiliated in mental life.

Freud's view of human nature has already been discussed; it implies, as he himself wrote, that 'Hatred is at the bottom of all the relations of affection and love between human beings; hatred in relation to objects is older than love' (Freud: 'Triebe und Triebschicksale', *Internationale Zeitschrift für Psychoanalyse*, 1915). But, as Horney again points out, the disputable issue is not the undoubted fact that man can be hostile, destructive, and cruel, but whether such manifestations of aggressiveness are instinctual in nature. 'The extent and frequency of destructiveness are *not* proof that it is instinctual'; for if the impulse is innate, why is it the case that during the process of psychoanalysis the release of anxiety in the patient is followed by an increased capacity for affection and genuine tolerance for himself and others? If man is inherently destructive, is it useless to strive for a better future, and from the anthropological point of view, the acceptance of such a theory must lead anthropologists to 'assume that whenever in a culture they find people friendly and peaceful, hostile reactions have been repressed'.

In her own theory Karen Horney begins with the categorical statement that there is no such thing as a universal normal psychology; for behaviour regarded as neurotic in one culture may be quite normal elsewhere, and vice versa. What constitutes normality or abnormality can only be decided when we consider the culture within which the individual is functioning. There are, however, two traits which she believes to be present in all neurotics; rigidity in reaction, and a discrepancy between potentialities and accomplishments. By 'rigidity in reaction' she means that, whereas the normal individual behaves in a manner which is flexible and suited to the requirements of the objective situation, the neurotic brings to all his human relationships a tendency to act in predetermined ways. In other words a normal person treats each situation as it arises on its own merits, while the neurotic brings to it his own fixed ideas. Thus the former becomes suspicious only when the insincerity of the person confronting him tends to make him so, but the latter brings his suspicions with him (if suspiciousness is one of his neurotic traits). Of course this rigidity can only be considered 'neurotic' if it deviates from the culture patterns of the social group to which the individual belongs (e.g. the modern industrial executive's drive to work hard and accumulate wealth would have been considered eccentric in the Middle Ages, but today, although sometimes due to a neurotic compulsion, it has to be looked at in the context of an industrial society). Similarly, a discrepancy between accomplishments and potentialities may be due to external factors, and the individual may be frustrated by harsh realities which cause him to fail in spite of himself, but the neurotic brings about his own failure. The former is frustrated by external events, the latter by conflicting tendencies within himself. A neurosis, as defined by Horney, is: 'A psychic disturbance brought about by fears and defences against these fears, and by attempts to find compromise solutions for conflicting tendencies' (*The Neurotic Personality of Our Time*). Whereas Freud saw the Oedipus complex as the foundation of all neurosis, Karen Horney explains neurosis in terms of 'basic anxiety'.

A normal person may develop what Horney describes as a 'situation neurosis' when his relatively normal mind is confronted by an external situation full of conflicts. Thus an individual compelled to face the horrors and risks of war on behalf of a group for which he feels little affection and for whose views he feels nothing but contempt or indifference is likely to develop a 'battle neurosis' which is predominantly situational in origin. The true neurosis, however, is the 'character neurosis,' and in this case, although external factors may accentuate or bring out certain personality defects, we may readily observe that the defects were there, although possibly latent, long before the situation was met. All genuine neuroses are based upon disturbances of character which have existed since childhood, and it therefore follows that mere removal of symptoms such as may be carried out by means of hypnosis or suggestion can have no permanent value whatever. But the mental conflicts of the neurotic are not, as Freud supposed, fundamental conflicts of human nature arising from biological foundations, but on the contrary are based on the motivating forces and conflicts of the individual's society. The neuroses of modern industrial man are therefore based on conflicts inherent in our own culture, although they take their energy from what Horney describes as the child's basic anxiety'.

Basic anxiety is described as a feeling of being 'small, insignificant, helpless, endangered, in a world that is out to abuse, cheat, attack, humiliate, betray, envy' (*The Neurotic Personality of Our Time*). Such feelings arise in childhood in the case of children whose parents fail to give them genuine warmth and affection (usually because of their own neuroses), and who therefore have lost, or never experienced, 'the blissful certainty of being wanted'. Unconditional love is an essential for the child's normal development, and when this is refused the environment comes to be dreaded because '...it is felt to be unreliable, mendacious, unappreciative, unfair, unjust, begrudging, and merciless. According to this concept the child not only fears punishment or desertion because of forbidden drives, but he feels the environment as a menace to his entire development and to his most legitimate wishes and strivings. He feels in danger of his individuality being obliterated, his freedom taken away, his happiness prevented. In contrast to the fear of castration this fear is not fantasy, but is well founded on reality. In an environment in which the basic anxiety develops, the child's free use of energies is thwarted, his self-esteem and self-reliance are undermined, fear is instilled by intimidation and isolation, his expansiveness is warped through brutality or overprotective "love" ' (*New Ways in Psychoanalysis*).

For such reasons as these the potentially neurotic child has to repress his hostility (his fear of desertion, his helplessness, his need to be loved, and his feelings of guilt all act to this end), and he grows up feeling that the world is a frightening and dangerous place, that he should not assert himself, that he is 'bad', and that loneliness is his natural lot. Because of this natural weakness he wishes to be protected and taken care of, to put all responsibility upon the shoulders of others, yet on the other hand his suspicions of the intentions of others makes it almost impossible to trust them. Since somehow he needs to escape from his anxiety, he tends to develop certain neurotic personality trends against it. These are described by Horney in her earlier books as: affection, submissiveness, withdrawal, and power.

(1) *The neurotic striving for affection.* Whereas in normal love the primary need is for affection, the neurotic striving for affection is based upon the need for reassurance: 'If you love me you will not hurt me.' There arises, therefore, an excessive need for affection or approval which can never be satisfied. Fearing dislike or disapproval, the neurotic individual possessing this trait will do everything possible to avoid them. He dislikes being alone, and in his sexual relationships (whatever their overt pattern) he shows himself to be compulsive and indiscriminate. Sex is to him a means of buying affection and thus reassurance. But because of the sort of childhood situation described above, he cannot really trust people and feels himself to be unworthy of being loved. This situation brings about the conflict that, while he is always seeking 'love', he can never return it since he fears emotional dependency. An intimate or prolonged relationship being impossible, he falls in and out of love and may become sexually promiscuous. The neurotic demands unconditional love and because of his need for reassurance expects to be loved regardless of his failure to love in return and regardless of his provocations.

(2) *The neurotic striving for power.* This, the trait which Adler saw as fundamental, is seen by Horney as only one of several neurotic traits. While the desire for power is not in itself necessarily neurotic and may spring from identification with a cause or from the possession of superior abilities, the neurotic drive for power arises from fear, anxiety, and feelings of inferiority. The power-driven neurotic wishes to be right all the time, to control everyone and always to have his own way, hence his three characteristics: (a) that he wishes to be superior in everything and competes even with those whose goal is different from his own—he would resent a greengrocer his possession of a knowledge of vegetables; (b) that his drive for power is based upon hostility to others, and he therefore wishes to disparage, frustrate, and defeat them; (c) that he fears retaliation from others, and since he also wishes to be loved by them finds himself in an inescapable dilemma. His motto is: 'If I am stronger than you, you cannot harm me.'

(3) *Neurotic withdrawal.* Neurotic withdrawal is based upon the neurotic's belief that, if once he becomes self-sufficient, he will be

safe. He therefore wishes to be emotionally independent of people: 'If I avoid people, they cannot harm me.'

(4) *Neurotic submissiveness.* With his ever-present feelings of helplessness the neurotic tends to accept traditional views and conventional opinions or those of the powerful and influential. He may repress all demands of his own, allow himself to be abused, avoid criticizing others, and become indiscriminately 'helpful' to anyone he meets. The feeling which lies behind this personality trend is: 'If I submit to the will of others or help them, I shall avoid being hurt.'

Later, in *The Neurotic Personality of Our Time,* Horney described several additional neurotic trends, making ten in all, but with these we need not concern ourselves here. 'At that time,' she says, 'I regarded [the neurotic character structure] as a kind of macrocosm formed by many microcosms interacting upon one another. In the nucleus of each microcosm was a neurotic trend' (*Our Inner Conflicts*). But, as she later came to see, this simple enumeration of so-called neurotic trends caused them to appear in a too isolated fashion and with further consideration it became evident that all the traits concealed only three basic attitudes: moving toward people, moving against people, and moving away from people. The theory of neurosis now presented by Horney was as follows: The initial cause, or at least the predisposing cause, is found in the 'basic anxiety' of childhood, and in dealing with such harassing conditions, the child seeks for ways to keep going, to cope with a menacing world. He develops *ad hoc* strategies, but also lasting character traits which become part of his personality. Although at first a rather chaotic picture may present itself, in time three main lines of strategy crystallize out: the individual may move *toward* people, *against* them, or *away from* them. In the first strategy, he may accept his own helplessness, and in spite of his fears try to win the affection of others and lean on them; in the second, he accepts and takes for granted their hostility and determines to fight; in the third, he wishes neither to belong nor to fight but to keep apart. In each of these three attitudes one aspect of the basic anxiety has been overemphasized—helplessness in the first, hostility in the second, and isolation in the third. If it were possible to hold consistently to any one attitude, the individual might be able to get through life reasonably safely. But the person suffering from basic anxiety cannot adopt any one move whole-heartedly, since, in the conditions under which they have developed, all three attitudes are bound to be present. Although one attitude may predominate and influence actual conduct more strongly than the rest, the other tendencies have not ceased to operate, and they inevitably clash with each other. Also, since the neurotic is not flexible, he demonstrates these traits regardless of their suitability in any particular circumstances. It is Karen Horney's contention that the conflict between these three tendencies constitutes the core of any neurosis and it is therefore described as the 'basic conflict'. But the basic conflict is only the beginning of the neurosis; for the individual, even if he reaches some kind of equilibrium for a brief period, is soon torn by the new conflicts which his attitudes have generated. The new conflicts require new remedies, and the individual is soon lost in a tangle of self-created problems, Horney describes her theory of neurosis in the form of an allegory, which, since it gives the clearest account of a rather complex, picture, is best recounted here: 'Let us assume that a man with a shady past has found his way into a community by false pretence. He will, of course, live in dread of his former state's being disclosed. In the course of time his situation advances; he makes friends, secures a job, founds a family. Cherishing his new position, he is beset with a new fear, the fear of losing these goods. His pride in his respectability alienates him from his unsavoury past. He gives large sums to charity and even to his old associates in order to wipe out his old life. Meanwhile the changes that have been taking place in his personality proceed to involve him in new conflicts, with the result that in the end his having commenced his present life on false premises becomes merely an undercurrent in his disturbance' (*Our Inner Conflicts*). The individual begins with a 'shady' past (his basic anxiety); he proceeds to cover up his dread by respectability and a complex series of solutions (the basic conflict); but, in doing so, he is involved in new conflicts and new solutions (defence mechanisms), until the original conflict is relatively insignificant in comparison with the vast superstructure which has been built over it.

Horney describes the following defence mechanisms which are used by the individual as 'second-line defences' to solve the problems created by his basic conflict: firstly, part of the conflict may be *'eclipsed'* and the opposite trend given prominence (reaction-formation), or the individual may *isolate himself* from people (moving away from people, it appears, may be a defence mechanism as well as an aspect of the basic conflict). Again, he may form an *idealized image* of himself ('I am not really the miserable creature you may take me to be—look at my high ideals of generosity, independence, honesty, and purity—*that* is the person I really am'). Lastly, the neurotic may *externalize* his conflicts, seeing them not in himself, but rather in the external world. Feeling oppressed by his own problems, he may show indignation at the oppression of small nations: anger directed towards others may really represent his own self-dislike; or he may feel despair in others, but not in himself. What Horney describes as the 'idealized image' and regards as a neurotic defence mechanism is equated with the Freudian superego and Adler's fictive goals, so the existence of the superego in this view, far from being a natural state of affairs, represents a neurotic one. Ideals, she says in effect, are all very well, but they must be dynamic and arouse some attempt to approximate to them. The 'superego' or the 'idealized image' is a hindrance to growth because it either denies shortcomings or simply condemns them. 'Genuine ideals make for humility, the idealized image for arrogance.'

There are three final points of contrast between Horney and Freud which we might mention here. Firstly, she reverses the Freudian concept of libido development so that instead of explaining certain character traits as originating from the physical manifestations of the oral or anal stages, she asserts that these physical manifestations arise from the character traits which in turn are a response to the sum total of childhood experiences. Retentiveness in relation to bowel control is therefore only one expression of a character which is resolved to give nothing away, and oral greed only one expression of a general tendency to greed. Secondly, Freud attempted, rather unsuccessfully in Horney's view, to explain why neurotic drives are compulsive and forceful in a way that normal drives are not. This he attributed to two facts

—that the neurotic is ruled by the pleasure principle and therefore cannot tolerate frustration, and that he is infantile in his outlook. Horney saw the compulsive nature of neurotic drives in a quite different light; for, as her theory makes clear, the neurotic's overt drive for 'love', 'power', or 'withdrawal' is not really a drive for these things at all, but basically a search for security and freedom from anxiety. He does not want to give affection but needs to receive the assurance that he will not be hurt, he does not want power as the normal person wants power but in order to escape from the anxiety produced by his feelings of inferiority. Therefore to obtain these assurances is a matter of life and death in his eyes; neurotic drives are compulsive because they are motivated by anxiety.

The last point is of particular interest, irrespective of whether one agrees with Horney's general theory or not; for it takes issue with the Freudian position that the individual manifests resistances only in relation to the primitive contents of the id. Many analysts of various schools take the view that the Freudians have greatly exaggerated the 'horrific' and 'disgusting' nature of unconscious drives; for, as H. G. Baynes, a Jungian, pointed out some years ago: 'Only a sophisticated mind is shocked at the facts of his own instinctual nature, and only a sophisticated attitude could continue to assume that perfectly real objections to the Freudian dogma are invariably based upon an unwillingness to accept the "horrible" 'truth' (*Analytical Psychology and the English Mind*). This is a matter of some importance, because Freudians have always insisted that the main resistance to accepting their theories is precisely the horrific nature of the id drives. This undoubtedly was the case in the early days of psychoanalysis when people were more easily shocked than they are now; but most psychiatrists have met patients who, so far from manifesting resistance *against* these 'shocking' facts, are very glad to accept them as justifying their own 'evil' thoughts and actions. It may be recalled that according to Suttie many people are more embarrassed at revealing their tender feelings than their often quite gross shortcomings, but Alexander, himself a Freudian, has made the same observation in an essay on 'Development of the Ego-Psychology' contained in Sandor Lorand's *Psychoanalysis Today*.

He writes: 'Patients often admit without great resistance objectionable tendencies which the psychoanalyst shows them are in their unconscious and outside their actual ego. Just because these condemned and repressed tendencies are outside the actual personality they can be admitted, and the patient can comfort himself by saying: "These strange things are in my unconscious but not in me, i.e. not in the part of my personality which I feel to be my ego".' It appears that in Horney's method of analysis as in Adler's what is dealt with is not primitive or infantile material, except in so far as this reveals contemporary tendencies; it is rather an analysis of present defects in interpersonal relationships as revealed in the patient's attitudes towards the analyst. In her own experience as in that of many other psychotherapists it was found that what causes anxiety and resistance in the patient is not always the making conscious of perverse or incestuous tendencies but such things as being told that what they believe to be genuine affection for the analyst is based upon a neurotic and compulsive need for affection to fend off anxiety. There can be little doubt that Freudians have exaggerated the resistance felt by people to accepting their primitive nature as such. It is only when the primitive drives have to be integrated into the ego, when the patient has to admit 'these are really *my* desires', that conflict begins to arise, and even so many people find it equally difficult to accept certain tendencies which in themselves contain nothing particularly shocking or obscene.

Although Horney makes no mention of the anthropological theories discussed in Chapter 6, she makes it clear that she considers neurosis to be a social manifestation in the sense that if a symptom or mechanism is an accepted way of behaving within a particular culture, it can be regarded as 'normal' for individuals within that culture. But if it is used to solve intrapsychic conflicts then, even if it is a 'normal' form of behaviour in other societies, it is 'neurotic' for that individual. In *The Neurotic Personality of Our Time* she blames neurosis upon the contradictions of contemporary American life; conflicts are ready-made by the 'American way of life' and, of course, by other 'ways of life'. There exists a contradiction between competition and success on the one hand ('never give a sucker an even break'), and brotherly love on the other ('love your neighbour as yourself'), between the stimulation of needs by advertising ('keeping up with the Joneses'), and the inability of the individual to satisfy them; between the assertion that the individual is free, and his increasing limitation by the environment. All these factors result psychologically in the individual's feeling that he is isolated and helpless.

Unfortunately, as Patrick Mullahy points out, Karen Horney never sufficiently clarified her basic concepts, and although accepting Freud's doctrine of psychic determinism, she herself gives a very inadequate account of the actual details of psychic structure. For example, we are told of the various neurotic traits but are given no understanding as to why that particular combination of traits arose rather than any other. We are struck by the number of observations which her theory does not explain—the symbolism of dreams, the meaning of symptoms, the reason why one type of neurosis rather than another has developed, mythology, and so on. In this respect too Horney reminds one of Adler, while lacking Adler's virtue of clarity and simplicity. Her theory is essentially an empirical account of the structure of a neurosis from the standpoint of the analysis of the ego, and as such is of more interest to the psychotherapist than the scientist. As a frame of reference for the scientific description of personality it seems almost useless, but Horney's observations and criticisms are often brilliant and may well in the future and in other hands bear fruit.

CHAPTER 8

The Theories of Erich Fromm

IF the theories of Karen Horney have been strongly influenced by the work of Freud and Adler, those of Erich Fromm show on the psychological side the influence of Freud and Rank, on the sociological side the influence of Marx. Trained both as a social psychologist and a Freudian analyst, Fromm is primarily interested in the problem of the relationship between the individual and his society —a trend which is in accord with the American tendency to regard individual psychology to a greater or less extent as an offshoot of social psychology. Like Karen Horney he was born in Germany, and we have seen that the two had exchanged ideas before coming to the United States. There they met H. S. Sullivan, and finding that they had many interests in common, the three worked in close association for several years. In 1941, Fromm's book *Escape from Freedom* was published in America, and a year later appeared in Britain under the title of *The Fear of Freedom*. *The Fear of Freedom* is a study of the psychology of authoritarianism, but in dealing with this problem Fromm has to range widely and thus develop a theory of personality which, while based upon that of Freud, differs from orthodox psychoanalytic theory in many important respects. As Fromm points out Freud accepted the traditional beliefs that, firstly, there exists a basic dichotomy between man and society, and secondly, that human nature is at the roots evil. Man is 'naturally' antisocial and it is the function of society to domesticate him. Some expression of biological drives may be permitted, but ordinarily the instincts must be checked or refined, and through the thwarting of the sex-impulse and its deflection to symbolic ends there arises by the process described by Freud as 'sublimation' what we know as civilization. If we grant this assumption, it follows as already noted that there must exist an inverse relationship in any society between the satisfaction of man's drives and his level of cultural attainment, such that the more suppression the more elaborate the culture and the greater the incidence of neurosis, and the less suppression the less neurosis but also the less civilization. Neurotics in fact are those who have fallen by the wayside in the drive towards a civilized society. Freud's picture of society is static, and he means by human nature the human nature he knew from his own social background: '[In Freudian theory] those passions and anxieties that are characteristic for man in modern society were looked upon as eternal forces rooted in the biological constitution of man.' Fromm criticizes Freud's biological orientation, giving examples similar to those already discussed in the last chapter (the Oedipus complex, the castration complex, etc.), but unlike Horney he goes on to make an analysis of Freudian theory in more or less Marxian terms: '[Human] relations as Freud sees them are similar to the economic relations to others which are characteristic of the individual in capitalist society. Each person works for himself, individualistically, at his own risk, and not primarily in cooperation with others. But he is not a Robinson Crusoe; he needs others, as customers, as employees, or as employers. He must buy and sell, give and take. The market, whether it is the commodity or the labour market, regulates these relations. Thus the individual, primarily alone and self-sufficient, enters into economic relations with others as means to one end: to sell and to buy. Freud's concept of human relations is essentially the same: the individual appears fully equipped with biologically given drives which need to be satisfied. In order to satisfy them, the individual enters into relations with other "objects". Other individuals are always a means to one's end, the satisfaction of strivings which in themselves originate in the individual before he enters into contact with others. The field of human relations in Freud's sense is similar to the market—it is an exchange of satisfaction of biologically given needs, in which the relationship to the other individual is always a means to an end, but never an end in itself.'

Fromm disagrees with these implications of Freudian theory, and bases his own theory on the two assumptions: (a) that the fundamental problem of psychology has nothing to do with the satisfaction or frustration of any instinct *per se*, but is rather that of the specific kind of relatedness of the individual towards his world, and (b) that the relationship between man and society is constantly changing and is not, as Freud supposed, a static one. The Freudian view that we have on the one hand the human individual innately equipped with a specific set of biological drives, and on the other human society which is capable of either satisfying or frustrating his basic instincts, is incorrect. On the contrary, although there are certain organic drives (hunger, thirst, sex, and so on) which are *common* to all men, it is obviously the case that those traits which make for the *differences* between individuals (sensuality, puritanism, love, hate, the desire for power, or the wish to submit) are produced by the social process. Society not only suppresses—it also creates, and what we know as human nature is a cultural product which may be limited by, but cannot be completely explained in terms of, his biological nature.

Man in fact has created 'human nature', and if we wish to understand this process of creation we must turn to history. Why is it, Fromm asks, that certain quite definite changes have taken place in human personality at particular historical epochs? Why, for example, is the outlook of the Renaissance different from that of the Middle Ages? There are some writers who attempt to describe all sociological problems in terms of individual psychology (as is the case with Freud, Klein, and Róheim), and on the other hand there are those who try to explain individual behaviour in basically sociological terms (Durkheim, Marx, and many modern American social psychologists). Both these approaches are rejected by Fromm, who not only refuses to accept Freud's biological and individual approach but also will have nothing to do with those theories with a sociological bias which 'reduce the psychological factor to a shadow of culture patterns'. He wishes to show '...not only how passions, desires, anxieties, change and develop as a *result* of the social process, but also how man's energies thus shaped into specific forms in their turn become *productive forces, moulding the social process.*' 'Man is not only made by history—history is made by man.'

Freud's concept of 'instinct' requires, in Fromm's opinion, to be further clarified, since it is not sufficiently realized that the word may be used in at least two quite different ways: (1) it may refer to a specific action pattern which is determined by the physical structure of the nervous system (much of the complex behaviour shown

by ants, bees and wasps, fish, and birds comes into this category);
(2) it may be used to refer to what are now generally described as
'biological needs' or 'drives'. When we say that the nest-building
habits of birds, the migrating cycle of the salmon, or the social
behaviour of ants is 'instinctive', we are using the word in the
first sense to imply that the behaviour in question is inherited, more
or less automatic, and has little or nothing to do with intelligence.
In this sense of the word, man has no 'instincts' unless with the
Behaviourists we include the reflexes in this category, and most
biologists agree that such behaviour is disappearing in man and
the higher animals, since intelligent and flexible learned behaviour
is replacing inborn, inflexible, and unlearned behaviour. In the
second use of the word we are discussing *needs* such as sex, hunger,
thirst, and so on, and the fact that men have instincts in this sense
of the word—that is to say biological drives—does, indeed, explain
why they *initiate* certain actions (e.g. why they want to eat, drink,
or obtain sexual satisfaction), but it does not in any way explain
how, *when*, or even *if* they do these things. Man shares his biological needs with the other animals, but the manner in which
these needs are satisfied is culturally or socially determined. That
man possesses certain needs is a biological fact; how he satisfies
them lies in the realm of culture. To recapitulate: the main problem of psychology is to consider the manner in which the individual relates himself to society, the world, and himself, but his
particular mode of doing so is not innate, it is acquired in the process of learning or acculturation. Human behaviour cannot be
understood purely in terms of the satisfaction or frustration of
biological drives because the social process generates new needs
which may be as powerful or even more powerful than the original
biological ones. That men give away their last piece of bread, permit themselves to be destroyed rather than give up their convictions, are patriotic, religious, and so on—these forms of behaviour
cannot be explained biologically but only in terms of society and
culture.

Evolution involves not merely a re-arrangement of what was
already there but the production of entirely new qualities, and in
man certain traits have emerged which have had the effect of
widening the gulf between himself and the other animals. Man,

unlike any other creature, is aware of himself as a separate being, is able to store up the knowledge of the past in symbolic form and visualize the possibilities of the future, and by his imagination he can reach far beyond the range of his senses. Instead of the relatively fixed action patterns by which an animal adapts to its environment, man has no ready-made solutions and requires to adapt himself consciously through the use of his reason. He is an anomaly, a 'freak of the universe', '...a part of nature, subject to her physical laws and unable to change them, yet he transcends the rest of nature. He is set apart while being a part; he is homeless, yet chained to the home he shares with all creatures. Cast into this world at an accidental place and time, he is forced out of it, again accidentally. Being aware of himself, he realizes his powerlessness, and the limitations of his existence. He visualizes his own end: death. Never is he free from the dichotomy of his existence: he cannot rid himself of his mind, even if he should want to; he cannot rid himself of his body as long as he is alive—and his body makes him want to be alive'.

These fundamental facts of existence—that we are born without choice and must ultimately die, that we are here for only a brief period of the whole historical process, that our abilities can never reach far beyond the limits set by the level of culture attained at that time, are described by Fromm as 'existential dichotomies' and contrasted with 'historical dichotomies' which, given time and the will to solve them, may possibly be overcome (e.g. the problem of war, of hunger in the midst of plenty, of disease, and so on). According to Fromm, those members or classes of society who benefit from historical dichotomies attempt to convince others that they are an unavoidable and inevitable part of human life—that, in fact, they are existential dichotomies.

It is one of the properties of the human mind that it cannot remain passive in the face of contradictions, puzzles, anomalies, and incompatibilities. Inevitably it wishes to resolve them. From this it follows that if men are to be prevented from rebelling against the contradictions and anomalies of social life (the historical dichotomies), the existence of the contradictions must be denied. In social life an ideology, which is to society what 'rationalization' is to the individual, may serve this purpose. Thus during the

Middle Ages the theory of a static society ordained by God with fixed classes served as a rationalization to explain why it was that 'the rich man in his castle, the poor man at the gate' should be accepted as a natural state of affairs. In early capitalist society the rationalization was that in a free market the best man would inevitably reach the top, and consequently that the poor were lazy individuals who did not choose to work hard in order to improve their condition. As Mosca and other political thinkers have pointed out, the ideologies of various communities are not to be taken as scientific hypotheses or laws, but 'they answer a real need in man's social nature... of knowing that one is governed not on the basis of mere intellectual or material force, but on the basis of a moral principle'. The unconscious function of an ideology is to satisfy this need.

Since the existence of such dichotomies generates such complex needs as the need to restore the sense of equilibrium between himself and nature and the need to understand the why and wherefore of the universe, an orientation or frame of reference becomes necessary. Such a frame of reference, described as a 'frame of orientation and devotion', may take the form of some sort of supernatural religion or, as in the case of the Communist ideology, a secular religion. All religions, metaphysical systems, or all-inclusive ideologies serve the same fundamental need: to relate man significantly to the universe, to himself, and to his fellow-men. This observation leads Fromm to reverse the opinion of Freud that religion is a form of universal neurosis—on the contrary, he says, neurosis is a form of private religion. Whereas a religion is a generally accepted frame of orientation and devotion, a neurosis is a personal non-socially patterned one designed by the individual in order to explain his relationship to 'life'. In Fromm's opinion, as in Jung's, the need for a frame of this sort is man's most fundamental and all-inclusive desire. He needs, as William James pointed out, to 'feel at home in the universe'.

The individual is born into a world in which the stage is already set for him. Requiring to eat and drink, he must work, and the conditions and methods of work are determined by the kind of society into which he is born. Thus his need to live and the social system in which he must live are, in principle, unalterable by him as an individual. Yet these are the factors which determine his social traits and the type of personality he may develop: '...the mode of life, as it is determined for the individual by the peculiarity of an economic system, becomes the primary factor in determining his whole character structure, because the imperative need for self-preservation forces him to accept the conditions under which he has to live. This does not mean that he cannot try, together with others, to effect certain economic and political changes; but primarily his personality is moulded by the particular mode of life, as he has already been confronted with it as a child through the medium of the family, which represents all the features that are typical of a particular society or class.' (Fromm is careful to distinguish between 'economic conditions', which, as the above quotation indicates, he believes to influence personality development, and 'subjective economic motives' such as the wish for material wealth. Thus all societies, however primitive, have some sort of economic structure and therefore 'economic conditions', but by no means all societies are characterized by the possession of 'subjective economic motives'—there are, for example, societies which abhor material wealth or are indifferent to it.)

The belief that significant changes have taken place in the human personality at certain historical epochs is elaborated in great detail in *The Fear of Freedom*. Briefly, Fromm sees the historical process as manifesting a progressive growth of individuality on the part of human beings. The history of man begins with his emergence from a state of oneness with the rest of nature, the state of primitive animism described by some anthropologists, during which he is only vaguely aware of his existence as a separate being. In this state of primitive animism he exists in a condition of 'cosmic unity', not only with his fellow-men, but also with the physical universe around him—the earth, the sun and stars, trees and animals. The fact that he has this feeling of complete identity protects him from loneliness, but on the other hand it has the defect that it binds him to nature and his social group and blocks his development as a free, self-determining productive individual. In such circumstances, man may suffer in many ways, but, says Fromm, 'he does not suffer from the worst of all pains—complete aloneness and doubt'. If social development had been harmonious, both sides of the process, the ever-increasing strength and control over nature, and the growing individuation, would have gone on alongside each other. But this did not happen and each increase in individuation led to new conflicts and insecurity. By the Middle Ages, man had largely lost his feeling of unity with nature, but he still possessed his social solidarity. During this period, as Jacob Burchardt has pointed out: 'Man was conscious of himself only as a member of a race, people, party, family, or corporation—only through some general category' (*The Civilization of the Renaissance in Italy*). The social order was static and each individual was tied to the role and status into which he had been born; for until the rise of the merchant class there existed little opportunity to move from one social level to another. Geographical mobility, owing to the primitive methods of transport, was limited and most people lived all their lives in the towns or villages where they had been born. Dress was largely determined by social status and occupation, and personal, economic, and social life were controlled by rules and obligations laid down by the Catholic Church. In the economic sphere for instance the rule of the 'just price' prevailed (this meant, in practice, that the price of an article was determined by what was felt to be 'fair', rather than by the fluctuations of a free market) and usury was forbidden. The economic sphere, like any other, came under the control of religion. In spite of dirt, disease, and misery in the physical environment, suffering and pain were made tolerable by the 'frame of orientation and devotion' supplied by the doctrines of the Church, which, while it certainly fostered a sense of guilt, also assured the individual of her unconditional love to all her children and offered a way to acquire the conviction of being forgiven and loved by God. The universe, too, at this time seemed limited and easy to understand: the earth and man were its centre, heaven or hell lay in the future, and 'all actions from birth to death were transparent in their causal interrelation'.

In these circumstances the human individual might well be supposed to have lived in bondage. But such was not the case. 'Medieval society did not deprive the individual of his freedom, because the "individual" did not exist', being still bound to his society by primary ties, and full awareness of himself and others as separate beings had not yet developed. In the late Middle Ages, however, the structure of society began to change and with it the personality of the individual. The rise of a new merchant class based upon private capital, competition, and individual enterprise disrupted the static unity of feudalism, and a growing individualism began to make its appearance in other spheres. This process came to a peak at the time of the Renaissance, when 'a growing individualism was noticeable in all social classes and affected all spheres of human activity, taste, fashion, art, philosophy, and theology'. Whereas the builders of the Gothic cathedrals had been content to remain for the most part anonymous, the architect in the new era wished to be known to his public; clothing was no longer a conventional sign of one's class or trade, but became bizarre, ornate, and elaborate; art began to take a new pleasure in the representation of the naked human body, and the pagan philosophers of Greece and Rome once more came to be studied as their books became available. The old static society of fixed classes became one in which status was mobile and one could move more or less freely up—and, of course, down—the social ladder. Birth and origin became less important than wealth. For geographical and other reasons these developments first took place in Italy, and to quote Burchardt: 'In Italy this veil [of faith, illusion, and childish prepossession] first melted into air; an *objective* treatment of the state and of all the things of this world became possible. The *subjective* side at the same time asserted itself with corresponding emphasis; man became a spiritual *individual* and recognized himself as such.'

But the new individualism was paralleled by a new despotism, and in gaining freedom and self-awareness emotional security was lost. From this time onwards social life became to an ever-increasing extent a life-and-death struggle for supremacy and those who failed in the fight were regarded with contempt rather than pity. Economic life, freed from the moral control of the Church, developed a life of its own, controlled no longer by ethical considerations but solely by the limits permitted by the law of the land. The individual could no longer depend upon the security of his traditional status and became acutely aware that everything depended upon his own efforts. Freed from the bondage of tradition and fixed status and role, he was also freed from the ties which had given him security and a sense of belonging. With the Reformation similar attitudes appeared in the field of religion, and Protestantism and capitalism came to be closely associated. If capitalism meant individual enterprise in the economic sphere, Protestantism was individual enterprise in the religious sphere. Man now stood naked before God, alone, and without the Church to intercede on his behalf; he was a powerless tool in God's hands who might be saved, if at all, not as the result of any understandable process, but (in Calvinist theory) by the mere whim of the Deity. The individual was told to accept his powerlessness and the essential evilness of his nature, to consider his whole life an atonement for his sins, and to submit completely to the will of God; and, whereas in the Middle Ages the poor had been thought to be particularly the object of God's love, it was now believed that wealth was a sign of God's approval and poverty a disgrace. The later developments of capitalism are traced by Fromm up to the present day, and he describes modern totalitarianism as a reaction against the aloneness of man cut off from his primary ties of family, guild, and religion. In the totalitarian state, artificially created secondary bonds are substituted for the primary ones in a self-conscious attempt to submerge the individuality which so terrifies man. Modern industrial society lacks any universal frame of orientation and devotion, hence the individual is unable to impose any rational order upon the universe to explain his position in relation to himself, his fellow-men, or the world in general.

Faced by these pathological conditions in his social world, the individual attempts to escape from his intolerable feelings of helplessness and aloneness. Fromm describes certain 'psychic mechanisms' analogous to the 'neurotic character traits' of Karen Horney by which man tries to relate himself to society and solve this problem. These are moral masochism, sadism, destructiveness, and automaton conformity.

(1) Moral masochism corresponds to Karen Horney's category of 'the neurotic need for affection'. Such individuals may complain of feelings of inferiority and inadequacy, but these traits are an expression of a *need* to be dependent and to rely on others in a weak and helpless manner. Masochistic feelings of this type are

often disguised by the individual as 'love', 'devotion', or 'loyalty', but they are based on a neurotic compulsion and bear no relation to genuine affection.

(2) Sadism, which might seem the reverse of masochism, nearly always goes together with it; it is 'the other side of the penny', which may be compared with Horney's 'neurotic striving for power'. Sadism as a neurotic trait shows itself in numerous ways: in the wish to make others dependent upon oneself, to exploit them, or to make them suffer either physically or mentally.

(3) Destructiveness is not in a completely separate category from sado-masochism, but the destructive person is described as one who, in order to escape his unbearable feelings of powerlessness and isolation, attempts to eliminate any possible threat or basis of comparison. His attitude is: 'I can only escape the feeling of my own powerlessness in comparison with the world outside of myself by destroying it' (*The Fear of Freedom*).

(4) Automaton conformity, corresponding to Horney's 'neurotic submissiveness', is a mechanism by which the individual attempts to wipe out by conformity the differences which exist between himself and others and by so doing escape his sense of helplessness. The ecstatic submissiveness of some individuals to totalitarian régimes is often motivated by the need to conform: 'I am exactly like you, and shall be as you wish me to be.' Thus a pseudo-self is substituted for the real self.

In the process of history man has developed from a state of 'cosmic unity' with nature and society, through an intermediate state in which he was separated from nature but remained integrated within society, to the present state when he has become isolated from both. As Rank saw the situation, he now has the choice of conforming completely and willingly to the standards of society (the usual solution), secretly rebelling while outwardly conforming (the neurotic solution), or realizing himself as an individual (the creative solution). His loss of 'oneness' with society was brought about by largely economic causes, and predominantly by the rise of capitalism, which set one man against another as competing units, and changed the static medieval society into a dynamic one. It should be noted that Fromm's interpretation of history is not his own creation, since it can be traced in the works of Burchardt, in Tawney's *Religion and the Rise of Capitalism*, in the sociologists Max Weber and Brentano, and more recently in Alfred von Martin's *Sociology of the Renaissance* and Lewis Mumford's *The Condition of Man*. Lewis Mumford, who gives no evidence of having read Fromm, has the following statement to make concerning the Reformation: 'Thrift, foresight, parsimony, order, punctuality, perseverance, sacrifice: out of these austere protestant virtues a new kind of economy was created, and within it, a new kind of personality proceeded to function' (*The Condition of Man*). The views of Fromm on human history are best summarized by Gardner Murphy in his *Personality: a Biosocial Approach*: 'Fromm and Horney make the point that with the loss of security in the medieval system, the primary problem has become the struggle for status, the struggle to be somebody.... (They) both suggest that we have paid a terrific price for freedom to come and go, to rise and fall. Not that we should wish to give it up. But we live competitively only at great cost; and in times of grave stress many of us strive to "escape from freedom" through recourse to a pattern of authority.'

In the process of living man relates himself to the world in two ways: (1) by acquiring and assimilating things. (2) by relating himself to other people and to himself. 'Man can acquire things by receiving or taking them from an outside source or by producing them through his own effort. But he must acquire and assimilate them in some fashion in order to satisfy his needs.... Man can relate himself to others in various ways: he can love or hate, he can compete or cooperate; he can build a social system based on equality or authority, liberty or oppression; but he must be related in some fashion and the particular form of relatedness is expressive of his character.' We have seen that there are five methods of relating oneself to others: masochism, sadism, destructiveness, automaton conformity, and, not so far mentioned, the normal approach, which is love. Corresponding to these methods of socialization, there are five methods of assimilation, five basic character types: these are the receptive, the exploitative, the hoarding, the marketing, and the productive. The various character types are ideal constructions which are not found in the pure form, since everyone is a mixture of several, although one is likely to pre-dominate.

Character is defined by Fromm as 'the [relatively permanent] form in which human energy is canalized in the process of assimi-lation and socialization'. It is influenced by the inherited factor of temperament (classified by Fromm, in the terminology of Hippo-crates, as choleric, sanguine, phlegmatic, and melancholic) which of course does not determine *what* method of assimilation or socialization is used by the individual but does determine how he reacts—whether he is quick or slow, introverted or extroverted, easily aroused or phlegmatic. Character is moulded by the family, which is described as the 'psychic agency of society'. The family is a factory which produces characters, but it produces them accord-ing to definite specifications supplied by the society within which it is functioning. While a certain degree of latitude may be allowed in character-formation, it is generally the case that if a society is to function well its members must acquire the kind of character which makes them *want* to act appropriately as members of the society or of a special class within it. 'They have to *desire* what ob-jectively is necessary for them to do. *Outer force* is replaced by *inner compulsion*, and by the particular kind of human energy which is channelled into character traits' (Fromm: 'Individual and Social Origins of Neurosis', *American Sociological Review*, LX, 1944). Another analyst, Erik Erikson, notes that in primitive societies: '...systems of child training... represent unconscious attempts at creating out of human raw material that configuration of attitudes which is (or once was) the optimum under the tribe's particular natural conditions and economic-historic necessities' (quoted in David Riesman's *The Lonely Crowd*). Thus each society develops in its members a 'social character' common to all and derived from its dominant social and cultural patterns, and upon this are im-posed the variations of the individualized character permitted in that society.

(1) *The receptive character.* The receptive character believes that everything he wishes, whether goods, knowledge, pleasure, or love, must come from an outside source which is passively ac-cepted. He is dependent and wants someone to take care of him,

has a great fondness for food and drink, and is related to others in terms of 'moral masochism', thus representing Horney's individual with a 'neurotic need for affection'. There is also an obvious relationship between this type and Freud's 'oral receptive' character.

(2) *The exploitative character.* The exploitative character tries to satisfy his desires by force or cunning, is aggressive, exploits others, and prefers what he can take or steal to what he can produce by his own efforts. His method of relating himself is by sadism, and he represents Horney's personality with a 'neurotic need for power' or Freud's 'oral aggressive' character.

(3) *The hoarding character.* Security in this type of individual is based upon saving and hoarding, or keeping what one has; he has no use for what he has not produced for himself. The hoarder is orderly, punctual, pedantic, and tends to insulate himself from the outside world. This character-type bears a resemblance to Horney's 'neurotic withdrawal' type and to Freud's 'anal-erotic' character.

(4) *The marketing character.* This is based upon the 'automaton conformity' approach to socialization which represents a tendency to exist by 'adapting oneself' or 'selling oneself' to others. 'People of this kind feel that their personalities are commodities to be bought and sold like a bale of hay' (Mullahy). Possibly this type may be compared with Horney's 'neurotic submissiveness' or Freud's 'phallic' character.

(5) *The productive character.* This is the normal person who is capable of genuine love-attachments to others, and demonstrates '...man's ability to use his powers and to realize the potentialities inherent in him'. He corresponds to Freud's 'genital' character.

In dealing with love Fromm expresses the view mentioned elsewhere that self-love and love for others, so far from being polar opposites as supposed by Freud, are inevitably associated. To Freud love for others means so much the less affection for ourselves, but to Fromm they are not alternatives or contradictory — on the contrary, they are basically conjunctive. 'Love, in principle, is indivisible as far as the connexion between "objects" and one's own self is concerned. Genuine love is an expression of productiveness and implies care, respect, responsibility, and knowledge. It is not an "affect" in the sense of being affected by somebody, but an active striving for the growth and happiness of the loved person, rooted in one's own capacity to love.' In general the trouble with modern culture is not that people are too much concerned with their self-interest, but '...that they are not concerned enough with the interest of their real self; not in the fact that they are too selfish, but that they do not love themselves'.

The Oedipus complex is interpreted by Fromm in a manner very similar to that of Rank, which was described in Chapter 5. The myth of King Oedipus represents, not the incestuous relationship between mother and son, but the rebellion of the son against the authority of the father of the patriarchal family. That Oedipus later marries Jocasta is a secondary elaboration symbolizing the son's victory when he takes over his father's place and privileges. The whole Oedipus trilogy (*Oedipus Rex*, *Oedipus at Colonus*, and *Antigone*) relates basically to the struggle between matriarchal and patriarchal forms of society. This theory, based upon Bachofen's concept of 'Mutterrecht', visualizes a time when matriarchy was the normal form of rule and before men defeated and subdued women to become themselves the rulers of the social hierarchy. In the individual the Oedipus complex is symptomatic of the patriarchal society; it is not universal, and the rivalry between father and son does not occur in societies where patriarchal authority does not exist. In non-patriarchal societies, infantile sexuality is not directed towards the mother, but is ordinarily autoerotic or directed towards other children. The pathological dependence upon the mother arises from her compensatory dominating attitude, which makes the child more helpless and in greater need of her protection. The Oedipus complex and neurosis are related, as Freud clearly saw, but not in terms of cause and effect; rather is it the case that both arise from the frustration of man's wishes to be free and independent of the patriarchal or authoritarian social arrangements which frustrate his strivings for self-fulfilment, independence, and happiness. The frustrations imposed by a particular type of social organization create in man a drive to destruction which, again, has to be suppressed by further force, so producing more frustration and aggression. Once man had left his animal ancestry behind, he began to find problems and contradictions and became involved in an unending search for new solutions if his species were not to die out, unending because each new solution created new contradictions. But this state of affairs does not depress Fromm, who believes that, in so far as we are able to accept individuation and realize the nature of our problems, we can be happy in productive work and truly loving relationships. 'Uncertainty is a necessary condition to compel man towards further development, and... if he faces the truth without panic he will recognize that there is no meaning to life except the meaning man gives his life by the unfolding of his powers' (*Man for Himself*). Innate traits do not exist, so there is neither innate social feeling nor antisocial feeling, neither Eros nor Thanatos, and man's sole advantage is the flexibility of his nervous system. Moreover the Freudian opposition between individual and social drives is unreal precisely because there is no fundamental contradiction between self-love, when it is genuine and not a neurotic defence, and altruism. These views are, of course, interesting, but the general validity of the Neo-Freudian position will be discussed later.

CHAPTER 9

Harry Stack Sullivan and Others

THE last theory of personality to be discussed here is that of Harry
Stack Sullivan, a former colleague of Karen Horney and Erich
Fromm, who died in Paris in 1948. Like most of the other writers in
this book, Sullivan presented a self-contained theory, which,
however much it diverged from the Freudian system, had clearly
been influenced by Freudian assumptions. Also mentioned here
are a number of other important writers who have criticized various
aspects of Freudian theory without necessarily having founded
schools of their own: Theodor Reik, a former colleague of Freud,
J. F. Brown, a psychologist at the Menninger clinic, and David
Reisman, a sociologist, are amongst those we shall discuss in this
connexion.

Harry Stack Sullivan was a native American psychiatrist who
first became known for his success in dealing with young schizophrenic patients. But it is unfortunately the case that his system is
particularly difficult to summarize and describe, firstly, because he
wrote rather little (apart from articles in psychiatric journals, the
only formal presentation of his views is in a book entitled *Conceptions of Modern Psychiatry* published in 1947), and secondly
because he tended to make use of neologisms and technical jargon
even when explaining matters not in themselves particularly complex or difficult. Sullivan's theories are primarily those of a psychotherapist and therefore, according to Mullahy, retain something of
the odour of the clinic. Whether or not we accept this view, there
can be no doubt that they represent the completest statement by a
psychiatrist of the views of the modern school of social psychology,
which regards the self as being made up of the reflected appraisals
of others and the roles it has to play in a given society. The Italian
novelist Carlo Levi expresses this viewpoint concisely when he
describes personality as *'il luogo di tutti rapporti'* —the meeting-
place of all relationships. But this statement is not meant to convey
the belief that the self merely contains, or is influenced by, attitudes

developed in personal relationships—what we are asked to accept is that in quite a real sense the self *is* one's personal relationships. We have tended in the past to suppose that we are self-contained individuals looking out from a tower in our own private castle from which we proceed on periodic excursions in order to satisfy physical, emotional, and mental needs and desires. We assumed that our contacts with the world left us relatively untouched, the same person as before. In the opinion of Sullivan, this is a complete fallacy; we do not merely *have* experiences—we *are* our experiences.

All 'human performances', says Sullivan, may be divided into two categories: the pursuit of satisfactions and the pursuit of security. Satisfactions are the drives or physical needs for sleep, food and drink, and sexual fulfilment. Loneliness is classified as a 'middling example', since in addition to the feeling of loneliness there appears to be an earlier need to touch one another, to be physically close. The pursuits relating to security, on the other hand, are cultural in nature. They are '... all those movements, actions, speech, thoughts, reveries, and so on which pertain more to the culture which has been embedded in a particular individual than to the organization of his tissues and glands'. From his earliest days, at first through the process of 'empathy' (which will be discussed later) and then by deliberate indoctrination, the child is brought into contact with his culture. He is taught to do and think what in that culture is regarded as right and 'good', and to avoid what is wrong and 'bad', under threat of punishment or withdrawal of approval. It therefore comes about that the achievement of satisfactions according to the approved patterns comes to be associated with a feeling of being 'good' and a sense of well-being and security. When on the other hand the biological drives cannot be satisfied according to the culturally approved patterns with which the individual was indoctrinated in early life, there arises a feeling of being 'bad', and a sense of insecurity and discomfort. This state is what is generally described as 'anxiety'. The two categories of securities and satisfactions may conveniently be used for purposes of description, but, as the above account should make clear, they are in practice inextricably bound up together.

Sullivan's account of anxiety makes use of psychosomatic concepts. He points out that the satisfaction of biological drives is ordinarily accompanied by a decrease of tension, particularly in the involuntary muscles of the internal organs, but also in the voluntary skeletal muscles of the body. This process, as we saw in an earlier chapter, is brought about internally by the action of the parasympathetic section of the autonomic nervous system, and since satisfaction reduces the need for further action, the skeletal muscles which are under the control of the central nervous system tend to relax also. 'The securing of satisfactions [produces] a relaxation of this tone [in the involuntary muscles] with a tendency towards the diminution of attention, alertness, and vigilance, and an approach to sleep'. Anxiety and insecurity or the craving for satisfactions produce the opposite effect, and sympathetic stimulation leads to heightened tone in the involuntary muscles, accompanied by tension of the skeletal muscles resulting from the action of the central nervous system. In the very young infant the natural cycle is: sleep—hunger (accompanied by contractions of the stomach muscles or 'pangs of hunger')—crying—satisfaction—sleep. The skeletal muscles are relatively unimportant at this stage because the infant's crying is enough to secure the mother's attention and the satisfaction of its needs. In other words, at this period of life the apparatus which is utilized to obtain satisfaction of the basic needs is not, as it will be at a later stage, the muscular system but rather what Sullivan describes as the 'oral dynamism', which includes the respiratory apparatus and the food-taking apparatus from which the speaking apparatus is evolved. This is the channel for performances needed to appease hunger, pain, and other discomforts. However, a stage soon arrives when the mother no longer satisfies the child's every need and she begins to show overt approval or disapproval at its behaviour—when in short the child's education begins. The oral dynamism of crying is much less effective than it once was and the skeletal muscles become proportionately more important, since the child is no longer passive but is expected to do things. The pattern of crying comes gradually to be inhibited, but although the actual cry is no longer expressed, the increase in tone in the appropriate muscles may still occur in the presence of anxiety-producing situations and is said to give them some of their characteristic feeling-tone (cf. the Freudian account of asthma).

During the early months of life the infant shares a peculiar emotional relationship with those who take care of him. Particularly between the sixth and twenty-seventh months, it is said, the child becomes aware of the attitudes of his mother or nurse by a sort of 'emotional contagion or communion' which Sullivan describes as 'empathy'. For example, if the mother is angry or upset about feeding-time the infant may have great difficulty with feeding, and since the mother's attitudes are to a large extent socially conditioned, Sullivan considers that this process is of great importance in understanding early acculturation. Empathy is said to occur in certain animals, to be biological in nature, and not to occur through the ordinary sensory channels. It is of interest to note that C. G. Jung seems many years ago to have thought along similar lines, since in a lecture at Clark University as early as 1909 he made the following comments on childhood experiences: 'It is not the good and pious precepts, nor is it any other inculcation of pedagogic truths that have a moulding influence upon the character of the developing child, but what most influences him is the peculiarly affective state which is totally unknown to his parents and educators. The concealed discord between the parents, the secret worry, the repressed hidden wishes, all these produce in the individual a certain affective state with its objective signs which slowly but surely, though unconsciously, works its way into the child's mind, producing therein the same conditions and hence the same reactions to external stimuli.... The father and mother impress deeply into the child's mind the seal of their personality, the more sensitive the child, the deeper is the impression. Thus even things that are never spoken about are reflected in the child. The child imitates the gesture, and just as the gesture of the parent is the expression of an emotional state, so in turn the gesture gradually produces in the child a similar feeling, as it feels itself, so to speak, into the gesture.'

Empathy, according to this view, causes the child to become aware of its mother's emotional states relating both to pleasure and anxiety, approval and disapproval. Since a considerable part of early education consists in learning to control urination and defaecation it is possible that empathized anxiety due to parental disapproval of failure in this respect may play some part in training, and on the other hand empathized comfort when such control is successful comes to be added to the physical relief experienced from release of the tension at the 'correct' time. Anxiety, in the opinion of Sullivan, is always experienced in relation to interpersonal situations, and what he describes as the 'power motive' is based on the individual's capacity to avoid anxiety and obtain and maintain a feeling of ability. The ability to obtain satisfactions and security is synonymous with possessing power in interpersonal relations, and this leads to respect for oneself and others. Self-respect therefore arises originally from the attitudes of those who care for the child in early life, but in later life his attitude towards others is determined by his attitude towards himself. The importance of empathy lies in its capacity to produce in the child the two opposite states of anxiety or euphoria, tension or relaxation, comfort or discomfort, through emotional contagion from the parent, so that, for example, a chronically hostile or anxious mother cannot help, whatever she does, producing anxiety in her child.

Sullivan compares the mind to a microscope which, while permitting minute observation of a limited field (namely that field which relates to those performances which are the cause of approbation and disapprobation), interferes with noticing the rest of the world. The individual's self-awareness arises originally from anxiety, which as other psychologists have pointed out has the effect of narrowing the field of attention. Thus a large area of the mind comes to be, or rather remains, unattended to. Accordingly, what Freud described as 'the unconscious' and thought of in topographical terms is seen by Sullivan in functional terms of 'selective inattention' and 'disassociation', between which the difference is only a matter of degree. To put the matter rather crudely, Freud depicted the unconscious as a place containing mental states which were permanently out of awareness, and the preconscious as a place containing those mental states which at a given moment were out of awareness but were capable of being recalled at will, while Sullivan prefers not to think in terms of mental locations, and his picture of the mind is rather like the state of affairs seen by the driver of a car on a dark night. The headlamps of the car only focus on that part of the landscape which is of immediate importance to the task in hand, although the driver could, if he wished, cause his lights to shine on other parts of the road which are at the moment being ignored by 'selective inattention' or are, in Freudian terms, preconscious. But behind the car lies the area of total darkness which cannot be lighted up by any simple manoeuvre on the part of the driver and this dark area of unconsciousness or disassociation consists of mental states to which the self refuses to grant awareness. Like Freud, Sullivan accepts the theory that motivational systems or complexes existing in disassociation may find expression in dreams, in everyday errors, in phantasies, and in one's relationships with others. If this were not so, he says, the self would disintegrate as the result of intolerable pressure from its unconscious motivations.

It is characteristic of the self that once it has developed it tends to maintain its own form and direction as a system whose basic function it is to avoid anxiety. Although the earliest experiences of approbation or disapprobation occur long before the child is capable of discrimination or reasoning, it is precisely the attitudes acquired at this time which for reasons already discussed are the most deep-seated and pervasive. At a later stage the individual acquires the ability to question and compare his experiences, but he never escapes the potent influences developed during childhood without thought or discrimination. What maintains the self in this relatively fixed form is the fact that any experience which threatens to disrupt or conflict with its organization provokes anxiety and leads to behaviour calculated to nullify its significance. The experience may be selectively ignored, disassociated, or its meaning wilfully misunderstood. In Freudian terms, the ego-defences will be brought into action. Sullivan pictures the mind as rather like the amoeba in a laboratory tank which absorbs particles of meat extract and digests them completely, wholly rejects particles of glass, and when given glass coated with meat extract, absorbs the meat and rejects the glass. We have built up a self-structure throughout our formative years and are resolved at all costs to maintain its integrity and to keep its original form and direction. This is the case even when the self appears to be a poor and wretched thing: 'Even when the self is a derogatory and hateful system it will inhibit and misinterpret any disassociated feeling or experience of friendliness towards others; and it will misinterpret

any gestures of friendliness from others. The direction and characteristics given to the self in infancy and childhood are maintained
year after year, at an extraordinary cost, so that most people in this
culture, and presumably in any other, because of inadequate and
unfortunate experience in early life become "inferior caricatures
of what they might have been".'

It may be asked why such 'derogatory and hateful' self-systems
should arise if the child is rewarded for being 'good' and punished
in various ways for being 'bad'. This is perhaps best explained if
we recall that, in the psychological system of Suttie, it was
suggested that whatever the child did was done in order to
obtain love. The aggressive child no less than the compliant one
was trying to get parental approval, and only resorted to aggressiveness because being 'good' did not work and aggressiveness
might. In the system of Sullivan, the individual is seen as seeking
freedom from anxiety, the achievement of security, and release
from tension *under all circumstances*. A hateful self no less than a
pleasing one is motivated by the need to avoid anxiety and is said
to arise in situations when the child's need for tenderness is re-
buffed by the parent. When this occurs, the need for tenderness
comes to be associated with parental rebuffs and hence with
anxiety, so that when the child feels tenderness he is manifesting
the 'bad me'. His behaviour in this way may become 'malevol-
ently transformed' and may later show paranoid developments of
a persecutory nature.

In addition to the methods already mentioned there are two
other means of dealing with experiences which collide with the
self-system. The first is sublimation, in which forbidden impulses
which provoke anxiety are unconsciously combined with socially
approved patterns so that the forbidden impulse is partially satisfied without provoking anxiety. Failure of sublimation may lead
to regression or, on the other hand, to reintegration of the impulse into new patterns of behaviour. The second way of dealing
with anxiety is by anger, which has the temporary effect of neutral-
izing anxiety. Many people conceal their anxiety in this way and
even remain unaware of it.

The self-system is that part of the personality which can be observed; the true self is the core of potentialities which exist from the

beginning but may or may not have been developed. Whether or not the individual is able to develop his true self depends in considerable measure upon cultural factors, since man is moulded by his culture and all attempts to break with it produce anxiety. But certain modifications for better or worse may be brought about by the influence of different personalities, particularly the parents and sometimes by teachers and friends in later life. The self being the sum of 'reflected appraisals', it follows that what we think of ourselves depends upon what others have thought of us in the formative years. Nevertheless interpersonal relations do not relate merely to what overtly goes on between two or more real people. There may be 'fantastic personifications' or ideal figures with whom the individual 'interacts', and by a process of what Sullivan describes as 'parataxic distortion' one may attribute to others traits taken from significant poeple in one's past (as in the Freudian transference situation). To some extent this happens in all interpersonal relationships, and one of the main purposes of treatment in this view is to remove such distortions. This may be done by comparing one's evaluations with those of other people; for when a person for whose judgement one has some respect sees the situation in a different way, one may change one's views about it. In therapy, Sullivan attached importance to the analyst as one who is detached, not in the sense that he does not care, but rather in the sense that he is an impartial observer whose views the patient may accept when it is revealed to him what goes on between himself and others, especially in the way of parataxic distortion.

Sullivan described six epochs of personality development: (1) infancy, during which empathy is the important influence, a realization of one's capacities arises, and there develops an increasing awareness of the self as a separate entity; (2) the period of childhood begins where that of infancy ends — with the acquiring of language; cultural indoctrination begins, thought appears, and there are clashes between the interests of the child and the wishes of the parents; (3) the juvenile era arises when cooperating with compeers becomes a possibility; group solidarity, competition, and the desire to belong are typical of this period; (4) pre-adolescence, from $8\frac{1}{2}$ or 12 to early puberty, is the time when egocentricity changes to a fully social state; personal friends are found who really become as important as oneself; (5) adolescence, divided into (a) early adolescence, (b) mid-adolescence (the beginning of genital behaviour), and (c) late adolescence (the establishment of durable patterns of intimacy). Lastly, of course, is the period of maturity.

Theodor Reik, an old colleague of Freud's now resident in the United States, has criticized many aspects of Freudian theory — particularly those relating to masochism (in *Masochism and Modern Man*) and the nature of love (in *A Psychologist Looks at Love*). As we already know, Freud believed (a) that love is sublimated sexuality, and (b) that the original object of love is the self. Reik strongly disagrees with both of these theses since he considers that romantic love has little to do with sex, and that there is no such thing as primary narcissism. Sex is a biological need originating in the body, dependent upon internal glandular secretions, localized in the genitals and the other erotogenic zones, aiming ultimately at the removal of physical tension, and originally objectless. In sexual desire the sexual object is simply the means by which the tension is eased. Love, on the other hand, possesses none of these characteristics. 'It certainly is not a biological need, because there are millions of people who do not feel it and many centuries and cultural patterns in which it is unknown. We cannot name any inner secretions or specific glands which are responsible for it. Sex is originally objectless. Love certainly is not.' Now precisely these views were put forward many years ago by a brilliant young German writer, Otto Weininger, in his book *Sex and Character*, and although acquaintance with his work is not admitted by Reik, we may take a quotation from his book to illustrate Reik's argument: '[How obtuse is the view] of those who persist with unconscious cynicism in maintaining the identity of love and sexual impulse. Sexual attraction increases with physical proximity; love is strongest in the absence of the loved one; it needs separation, a certain distance to preserve it... Then there is platonic love, which professors of psychiatry have such a poor opinion of. I should say rather, there is only "platonic" love, because any other so-called love belongs to the kingdom of the senses: it is the love of Beatrice, the worship of Madonna; the Babylonian woman is the symbol of sexual desire'. But if 'love' is not sexual in origin, how are we to explain it? Reik here takes issue with the Freudian concept of primary narcissism: 'The infant does not love himself because he does not exist originally as a separate individual. He is an egoist without an ego, he is selfish without a self.' Although he is favourably impressed by Suttie's views that love and sex are not the same, Reik refuses to believe that love is an innate quality. On the contrary, the young child is the recipient of his mother's love and care, and learns to love himself from his mother's example, and in later years, he will be the mother's substitute in loving himself. It is a striking fact, says Reik, that falling in love often follows a mood of self-distaste: Faust before he meets Gretchen, Romeo before he meets Juliet, are both discontented. Love is not a crisis but the way out of a crisis which has arisen from a state of dissatisfaction with oneself. Having fallen short of his ego-ideal, the individual makes use of love as a means of finding it in someone else and, in this way, achieving wholeness. The beloved person is a substitute for the ideal ego, and two people who fall in love with each other are interchanging their ego-ideals. Love, therefore, is not love of oneself but love of one's better self or ego-ideal as seen in someone else. To quote Weininger once more: 'In love, man is only loving himself. Not his empirical self, not the weaknesses and vulgarities, not the failings and smallnesses which he outwardly exhibits; but all that he wants to be, all that he ought to be, his truest, deepest, intelligible nature, free from all fetters of necessity, from all taint of earth'. Reik prefers the word 'ego-ideal' to 'superego' and believes that it is an acquisition of later childhood, a result of our growing awareness that we are not as we should like to be. It is conditioned by the attitude shown towards us by others, by the contrast felt by the child between what he does and what, to fulfil the expectations of his mother, he ought to do.

There is, therefore, a constant nagging dissatisfaction between these contrasting aspects of our selves—a dissatisfaction which, says Reik, can only be resolved in one of four ways: by falling in love (i.e. by possessing another who seems to have some of the qualities we lack), by 'falling in hate' (i.e. by nourishing hostile feelings for those who are more satisfied with themselves), by moderating our demands upon ourselves, or by doing something creative which entitles us to a better opinion of ourselves. Love therefore originates in unconscious envy of another person who has qualities which we ourselves wish to possess. Friendship is the result of a calmer estimation in which we wish to possess only certain intellectual, mental, emotional, or physical qualities which appear desirable to us. Love wants all, friendship only a part. Reik accordingly denies the existence of primary narcissism, denies that love and friendship arise from aim-inhibited sexuality, and doubts Freud's account of the origin of the superego.

J. F. Brown, Professor of Psychology at the University of Kansas and Chief Psychologist at the Menninger Clinic, has written two interesting books: *The Psychodynamics of Abnormal Behaviour* and *Psychology and the Social Order*. His views are based primarily upon Lewin's topological psychology, but he has been deeply impressed by Freudian theory and has, indeed, undergone a training analysis. Some of his criticisms of psychoanalysis are worth noting here as representing the views of an academic psychologist on Freud's scientific methods. In general, Brown does not disagree with Freud's observations or statements—what he objects to is the manner in which they are expressed. As others have done before, he criticizes Freud's use of the biological instinct theory, which he holds to be out of date, since there are no basic instincts in man which lead to definite behaviour independent of the existing environment. Most psychologists today, he says, are quite prepared to accept the facts of erotic and aggressive behaviour, but they attribute these behaviours to a combination of biological and cultural influences. This is a matter of some importance; for if aggression is innate, war is presumably inevitable, and if it is not innate but due rather to the frustration of constructive impulses, there is still hope. It is true, of course, that aggression is universal, since the frustration which produces it is also universal, but if frustration is the sole source of aggressiveness, then a decrease of frustration will materially reduce it. In Brown's view, Freud himself played a large part in destroying the old instinct theory, since if we are to limit instincts to self-preservative and self-destructive, or race-preservative and race-destructive, we might as well say that there are no basic instincts which lead to definite behaviour independent of the environment.

In reply to the criticism of others that Freud has allowed sociological or cultural factors no role in the determination of personality structure, Brown denies that this is so. Since, he says, the superego is almost completely sociologically determined, this type of criticism is not to be taken seriously. In other words, the superego is Freud's way of talking about the influence of culture. (In this instance, Brown is too generous to Freud; for, as we have already seen, Freud does *not* picture the superego as representing the influence of *contemporary* society. It represents, on the contrary, moral prohibitions which have been handed down from one generation to the other, and the superego of each generation is based on the superego of the generation before.) However, Brown is on firmer ground in his criticism of Freud's tripartite divisions of the mind into ego, superego, and id, conscious, preconscious, and unconscious. He writes: 'although it is undoubtedly true that there is an underlying difference between the structure of immediate sensory perception and the structure of deeply repressed emotional experience it is probably quite unlikely in reality that three definite regions of consciousness and only three are to be distinguished.' The concepts of ego, superego, and id leave one with the impression that there is a selfish homunculus, a nasty homunculus, and a moral homunculus who are always fighting each other. Just as Freud paved the way for overthrowing the instinct theory but failed to overthrow it completely, so he prepared the way for a functional theory of personality without ridding it entirely of all the characteristics of demonology.

Horney complained of the psychoanalytic tendency to assume that later developments were a literal repetition of earlier ones, and Brown similarly complains of the assumption that regression can be considered as a direct reversal of a total process. For example, the behaviour of an extremely regressed psychotic patient is not by any means the exact equivalent of the behaviour of a very young child, although quite frequently psychoanalysts speak as if it were because the process of regression is inadequately defined. Finally, he says, logic demands that any scientific theory must be expressed in such a way that it may be proved or disproved, and the theories of Freud do not always fulfil this condition. If we take, for example, the mechanism of reaction formation, it appears that opposite behaviours are accounted for as a continuation of the same basic mechanism. The aggressive man is aggressive because he is aggressive, but the non-aggressive man also is non-aggressive for the same reason. The boy who loves his mother deeply has an Oedipus complex, the boy who does not has an Oedipus complex too which he is said to be repressing. This, says Brown, in effect, may very well be true, but it gives the scientific psychologist no means whereby he may prove it to be so. But, he concludes, 'We must say of the Freudian theory that even if it does not have all the answers, it does pose all the questions'.

David Riesman is an American sociologist who has written an interesting study of the changing American character entitled *The Lonely Crowd* which, in a sense, may be described as a continuation of the argument in Fromm's *The Fear of Freedom*. With Riesman's argument as a whole we shall not be concerned here, but he has developed an interesting theory concerning the nature of moral controls which both illuminates the Freudian concept of the superego and implies a criticism of it. Like Fromm, Riesman supposes that basic character types change as society develops, and, in particular, the methods of social control in a society alter from one place and time to another. He correlates the historical sequence of character types with trends in population growth, which in long-industrialized countries tend to show an S-shaped curve. This curve begins at a point where the number of births and deaths are fairly equal, both being high (the phase of high growth potential); it passes through a period of rapid population increase when, with improvements in hygiene, death rates go down and birth rates remain high (the phase of transitional population growth), and finally arrives at a stage when birth and death rates are again equal, both being low (the phase of incipient decline). The first stage corresponds to the medieval period of European history, the second to the early industrial period, and the last to modern times in both Europe and the United States. According to Riesman, a society of high growth potential develops in its typical members a social character in which conformity is brought about by their tendency to follow tradition—they are in his terminology 'tradition directed'. The society of transitional population growth develops in its members a social character in which conformity is brought about by their tendency to acquire in early life an internalized set of goals (this, of course, is the Freudian superego). Lastly, the industrial society of modern times with low birth and death rates produces a social character controlled by its sensitization to the expectations and preferences of others. Whereas the society of transitional population growth produces 'inner-directed' individuals, the modern society of incipient population decline is producing a new type of individual who is 'other-directed'.

Ignoring the question of population trends, we can see that the method of social control in medieval society (and presumably in other predominantly agrarian societies) is through the mechanism of tradition; the method of social control in early industrial society is through the mechanism of internalized controls—the conscience or superego—and in modern mass society social controls arise from a sensitivity to the reactions of others. We shall now discuss these mechanisms in greater detail.

(1) *Tradition direction.* The tradition-directed society is a relatively static one, because such a form of control must be dependent upon rules and customs which retain their validity over long periods of time. Tradition controls all aspects of behaviour minutely, and from birth to death each member of society knows exactly what is expected of him in all situations. Science (such as it is), religion, law, economic life, and custom are all in accord, so that there exists what Fromm has described as a universal frame of orientation and devotion. Of this type of society Karen Horney has pointed out that the possibilities of mental conflict are much fewer than in the case of a society in transition, which inevitably has a relatively fluid ethical system full of potential conflicts. Although individuality is undeveloped, each person in a tradition-directed society 'belongs'—illegitimate children, the poor, and the aged, are all cared for by the family or village; they do not, as is the case in modern or early industrial society, become 'surplus'. Finally, the queer or eccentric individual is also fitted into society, such deviants often being given institutionalized roles. The epileptic, the insane, or the individual who would be regarded as a rebel in modern times may be fitted into such positions as that of shaman, medicine-man, or sorcerer.

(2) *Transitional growth.* With the improvement of sanitation and communications, and the decline of infanticide and other forms of

institutionalized violence, the expectation of life is longer while the birth-rate remains high. Population commences to increase as it did in Europe between 1650 and 1900. At this stage, there is increased personal mobility both geographically and up and down the social scale. Capital accumulates rapidly, and there are vast technological changes resulting in an increased production of goods, expansion, and imperialism. Such a society finds tradition-direction no longer adequate—firstly because it is fighting the traditional views, and secondly because they are, in any case, breaking down with a changing technology. Old concepts in religion, the family, science, and ethics no longer fit the changing scene. A new type of individual is necessary who can manage to live socially without traditional controls; he is the inner-directed type whose controls are implanted early in life by the elders of the society and are directed towards generalized but fixed goals. As Riesman says, a new psychological mechanism is devised by society, which takes the form of a 'psychological gyroscope'—the superego. This does not mean to say that tradition plays no part in the life of the inner-directed individual, but being aware, as he inevitably must be in industrial society, of the existence of competing traditions, the superego gives his actions a greater flexibility and independence of the weakened external controls.

(3) *Incipient decline.* At this stage, the death-rate has already declined and the birth-rate begins to go down also. There are many reasons for this decline in births, but the most obvious one is that children are no longer an economic asset (as they were in the pastoral family or during the period when child-labour was permitted in factories); on the contrary they become an economic liability, since they cannot be put to work for many years. The economy is no longer expanding, for production has outrun consumption—or, at any rate, the ability to absorb the goods produced under existing economic circumstances: 'Hours are short. People may have material abundance and leisure besides. They pay for these changes however—here, as always, the solution of old problems gives rise to new ones—by finding themselves in a centralized and bureaucratized society and a world shrunken and agitated by the contact—accelerated by industrialization—of races, nations, and cultures' (Riesman, op. cit.). Under these

circumstances, the toughness and enterprise of the inner-directed types is less necessary and increasingly *other people* rather than the material environment form the problem confronting the individual. Traditions are still further destroyed, social change is increasingly rapid, and a new mechanism of social control becomes necessary. The new character type is described in detail in Riesman's book, which sees it arising predominantly in America. Briefly, the modern individual who is emerging from the new society is what Fromm has described as the 'marketing character' —shallow, friendly, demanding of approval, willing to 'sell himself' ('I am as you wish me to be'), and uncertain of himself and his values. His conduct is regulated by observing that of others, and failure to live up to these standards leads to anxiety.

Riesman's views are mentioned here, firstly, because they seem to be important and interesting in themselves, and secondly, because they clearly supply another example of the type of criticism of Freudian theory which claims that Freud's views do not have universal application but are related to the times in which he lived. How far such criticism is justified the reader will have to decide for himself, but it is worth while pointing out that Bateson and others have made the point that a strong superego can only be formed when three conditions are satisfied:

(1) There must be some individual adult who makes it his or her business to teach the child how to behave.

(2) This teaching must be backed by punishment.

(3) The child must love the adult in question.

Since these conditions are not, in fact, fulfilled in all cultures, there is good reason to suppose that the superego as described by Freud is not a universal phenomenon. Margaret Mead, in two chapters of Kluckhohn's *Personality*, has made the same point: 'Comparative studies demonstrate that this type of character—in which the individual is reared to ask first, not "Do I want it?", "Am I afraid?", or "Is it the custom?", but "Is this right or wrong?"—is a very special development, characteristic of our own culture, and of a very few other societies. It is dependent upon the parents personally administering the culture in moral terms, standing to the children as a responsible representative of right choices, and punishing or rewarding the child in the name of the *right.*'

Sullivan, Horney, Fromm, and Kardiner together formed what came to be known as the Neo-Freudian school of analysts. Although differing in detail, they are united in the following beliefs:

(1) That social and cultural, rather than biological, factors are basic to the understanding of human nature.

(2) That the instinct and libido theories are outdated; e.g. the Oedipus complex, the formation of the superego, and the alleged inferiority of women are cultural and non-universal traits, and, although there may be a biological foundation for oral and anal stages, these can be greatly modified by cultural factors.

(3) Emphasis is placed upon 'interpersonal relationships' in the formation of character, in the production of anxiety, and in neurosis.

(4) Instead of character arising from sexual development, it is asserted that sexual development is an index of character. 'In this view it is not sexual behaviour that determines character, but character that determines sexual behaviour' (Fromm).

Fenichel, as an orthodox analyst, makes the following reply to these claims: '... insight into the formative power of social forces upon individual minds does not require any change in Freud's concepts of instincts, as certain authors (Fromm, Horney, Kardiner) believe. The instinctual needs are the raw material formed by the social influences; and it is the task of a psychoanalytic sociology to study the details of this shaping. It is experience, that is, the cultural conditions, that transforms potentialities into realities, that shapes the real mental structure of man by forcing his instinctual demands into certain directions, by favouring some of them and blocking others, and even by turning parts of them against the rest' (*The Psychoanalytic Theory of Neurosis*).

Here then are a number of different views: those of Horney, Fromm, and Sullivan, those of Freud's old and relatively orthodox pupil Reik who seems to attach more importance to the ego and to cultural factors than most Freudians, those of J. F. Brown who is quoted here mainly as one of the more vocal psychologists voicing criticisms such as one might expect many psychologists to voice if they studied Freud, and those of Reisman as a sociologist who has attracted popular attention and, together with Fromm and Horney, become somewhat of a best-seller. The phenomenon of the psychological best-seller leads one to wonder whether the scientific standards of the masses have gone up or whether the academic standards of the psychologists have gone down, and, quite apart from the content of these books, one cannot help wondering for whom they were written in the first instance. The works of Horney and Fromm or Riesman are extremely competently written, but they are not beyond the ability of any reasonably educated person even without any special knowledge of Freud, and, above all, they are not *academic* in the sense that they really do not seem to be directed towards experts. Experts write popular books of course, but rarely to the exclusion of serious ones, unless they have nothing further to say.

Fromm's position is particularly puzzling because, although nearly all that has been said here comes from his two earlier books *The Fear of Freedom* and *Man for Himself*, his later works, *The Forgotten Language* (a study of dreams which criticizes in various respects the dream theories of both Freud and Jung), *The Sane Society*, *The Art of Loving*, and *Sigmund Freud's Mission*, really say very little more. We may pick up each book as it appears ready for some new revelation, but, alas, very little has changed but the colourful title. Those whose interest was aroused by Fromm's criticisms of Freud and had hopes of something concrete to replace 'discarded' notions will soon find that the new ones are even more metaphysical than the old. Psychology, according to Fromm, must be based upon 'an anthropologico-philosophical concept of human existence', but a great many people will feel that if this is the case, so much the worse for psychology. For if the word 'psychology' has many possible meanings, 'anthropologico-philosophical' has none whatever save that which Fromm himself has chosen to give it, and if his position is relativist with respect to man's changing problems and circumstances his views derive more from his historical perspective than from anthropological data pertaining to contemporary cultures. Of course philosophical concepts of any sort are precisely what the modern psychologist has been doing his best to avoid since psychology first became a science by leaving metaphysics behind, and although we may all possess philosophical beliefs, it is usually counted a virtue and even a positive necessity that they should be left aside when studying phenomena scientifically. Freud's metapsychology was part of the general world-picture of his own times and one which his own work seemed to support; Fromm's gives the impression of having been forced upon his observations rather than derived from them. But disagreement with Freud's outlook and the giving of new titles to personality types described by Freud in terms of libidinal fixations and by Fromm and Horney in terms of interpersonal relationships does not in itself seem to justify the formation of a new school. Freud always denied that he had philosophical views or a *Weltanschauung*, and in so far as we see that he did, it is because our own have changed and the ones we now possess and fail to recognize will appear equally strange a generation hence. In Freud's day nearly all scientists were sure that the universe with man himself was a vast machine, that such entities as spirit, mind, soul, and God did not exist, and that an individual either did or did not have a disease which, if it existed, must ultimately have a physical basis. The belief was not a carefully worked-out philosophy but rather a series of conclusions which seemed to follow from the new scientific discoveries, and it is only the influence of Engels's historical materialism that causes us to regard the 'common sense' of a culture as an unconscious ideology justifying the existing state of affairs. Future generations will know which of these elements to discount in Freud's theories, just as we know how far Dalton's atomic theory was limited by contemporary views and the available knowledge; but Fromm's views are a self-conscious ideology, and although it is necessary and justifiable to criticize Freud we can have no confidence that alternative views unsubstantiated by direct observation are anything but representatives of another ideology—the more so as Fromm makes no reference to any facts observed by himself, quotes no cases, and nowhere describes his own technique of analysis.

The fact is that the vast majority of psychoanalysts are interested in treating their patients and are no more interested in anthropology, culture, or human nature and psychology than the busy physician is interested in the chemical structure of penicillin or the history of the germ theory of disease. They have their own political, moral, and religious views which arise in the same way as those of other people and need bear no logical relationship whatever to their psychoanalytic theories. Indeed nobody would have been more surprised than Freud if they did, and one recollects in this connexion the reply of Ernest Jones to someone who after a lecture asked whether Freud expected all analysts to become atheists: 'Freud was not given to expecting anything of other people.' Doubtless if the psychoanalyst is attacked about certain of Freud's assertions he will tend to support the orthodox viewpoint even if the matter under discussion is something he personally has devoted little thought to working out, but for a considerable time now psychoanalysts have quietly been modifying dated trends in the theory without supposing for one moment that they were initiating a new school of thought. Nor, looking back upon the past history of psychoanalysis, is it too far-fetched to suppose that frequently the differences which led up to the formation of a new sect were more personal and temperamental than scientific and rational. In Fenichel's orthodox text-book *The Psychoanalytic Theory of Neurosis* various findings of the Neo-Freudians, Rank, Stekel, Ferenczi, and others are reported without any special reference to their membership of a different school of thought, and this is what one might expect since in the practice of analysis specific observations are of more interest than general theories. An adherent of Horney pays relatively more attention to the ego, to interpersonal relationships and the contemporary situation—but so does Anna Freud, without adopting a new language with which to describe her emphasis. No analyst would fail to take the cultural background of his patient into account, but for obvious reasons most patients in a psychoanalytic practice belong not only to the same culture as the analyst himself but even to the same subculture of class or religion, so the need to write a book about how the Trobriand Islanders prove Freud wrong does not arise. Nothing can alter the fact that Freud discovered the importance of the family constellation in influencing the growing child, not only by the parent's overt example and command, but more significantly by the conclusions the child draws from the parents' deeds and the concealed implications of their words; that he described the complex in terms of the family as it was known to himself hardly needs emphasizing if it does not justify later Freudians in denying that other types of family situation can exist. Here again Fenichel claims as an orthodox Freudian that the Oedipus complex is biologically founded, but he does so in a way that few of those who are said to be its critics can possibly complain about. Pointing out that the human infant is biologically more helpless than other mammalian offspring and therefore needs prolonged care and love, he observes that at the simplest level: 'He will always ask for love from the nursing and protecting adults around him, and develop hate and jealousy of persons who take this love away from him. If this is called Oedipus complex, the Oedipus complex is biologically founded.' He then adds that the Freudian combination of genital love for the parent of the opposite sex and jealous death wishes for the parent of the same sex is a highly integrated combination of emotional attitudes which is the climax of the long development of infantile sexuality. '... In this sense the Oedipus complex is undoubtedly a product of family influence. If the institution of the family were to change, the pattern of the Oedipus complex would necessarily change also.' Interpretations to the effect that the complex is caused by parental overstimulation, that it is used as an excuse for failing in life, that it is sexual or asexual, are not necessarily wrong so much as one-sided and narrow, just as are interpretations of the transference situation which insist that it reveals the patient's attitude to his father, that it reveals his typical ways of dealing with current interpersonal situations, or that it is an attempt to get the better of the analyst. It is, of course, all of these things and the observations are complementary rather than mutually exclusive.

So too with the motive forces behind behaviour as described by the various schools; to Freud, dealing with the ultimate biological level, it is the satisfaction of appetitive drives and the destruction of whatever hinders satisfaction, to Adler it is power to satisfy drives, to Horney it is the overcoming of basic anxiety and to Rank overcoming the trauma of birth (in both cases anxiety regarding forces which control drive satisfaction—competence in dealing with others and individuation from others), to Suttie it is fear of loss of love, as it is to many modern Freudians. Freud speaks in terms of drives to be satisfied, the others in terms of overcoming handicaps to satisfaction, because man can only satisfy his drives through the intervention of people. The Neo-Freudians are self-consciously socially orientated, Freud mainly by implication since he lived at a period when the individual was regarded as the unit of society in a sense that he no longer is today. As a thorough-going evolutionist Freud emphasized the development of complex from simpler forms, the general from the particular, and therefore deduced the development of general obstinacy from obstinacy over bowel control; Fromm makes the latter a sequel to the former but without explaining what other significant behaviour at that age reveals the presence of general obstinacy or how his thesis can be put to the test. Horney's analysis of interpersonal relationships is extremely interesting and unlike Fromm she quotes many cases, but it is difficult to see how an analysis of these alone, which ignores earlier and more primitive trends, can help the patient who might, for all we know, be just as much helped and convinced of his defects by reading a book.* People *are* relieved of symptoms in this way as any psychiatrist knows, but in the more severe neuroses patients continue to have their phobias and obsessions although well aware of their origins: indeed, awareness of a neurotic attitude such as those described by Horney may well be the cause of increased anxiety about it rather than a basis for giving it up.

The concept of the unconscious is treated by the Neo-Freudians rather cavalierly. It is obvious that mental states can be 'unconscious' in a number of quite different ways and it is no use criticizing Freud for holding views about states he never considered as relevant to his own work. When Marx and Engels pointed out that changing human motives may be a response to changing economic situations of which the individual is only dimly aware, in the sense that he is not necessarily conscious of their true nature or complete implications as they affect himself and might indignantly reject them if he were told, they were dealing with one kind of unconscious

* In fact, as the title of her book *Self Analysis* indicates, Horney did believe that under certain circumstances this was possible.

motivation. The nineteenth-century industrialist who thought it wrong to help the poor because this would be going against the doctrine of the survival of the fittest would have been genuinely indignant had he been accused of being mean-spirited or sadistic, when he was merely accepting what he had been taught to regard as one of life's inevitable hardships. This type of motive is noted by Fromm who does not, however, make much of the fact that its absence from awareness may be due not only to ignorance but even to a kind of repression. Horney and Sullivan, on the other hand, describe as 'unconscious' trends which (a) we may vaguely note without understanding the full extent of their potency in day-to-day life, and (b) we choose to disregard by a process of 'selective inattention' similar to that described by Stekel as 'scotomization'. That this process occurs is beyond doubt, but that it bears any relationship to the unconscious as described by Freud is manifestly absurd, although doubtless some Freudian observations could be explained in this way. For example, many hysterics when they are not under attack can be brought to recall events they have chosen to forget or can be brought to admit their distaste for the situations from which the symptoms protect them, but this has little relationship to the unconsciousness of events nearer the biological level which may never have existed in consciousness in a verbalized form—precisely the events to which Freud devoted most attention and Horney chooses to ignore. We are told very little about the actual details of analyses conducted by the Neo-Freudians, but it is not easy to understand how Horney, an orthodox analyst for many years, could seriously believe that the concept of the unconscious was exhausted in the sort of data discussed by her own school. Of course, the real mystery of mind is not that certain mental processes should be unconscious, but that we should be aware of any at all; for it is clear that consciousness illuminates only that part of reality which is significant to the organism's purposes at a given moment of time and even of that part only a minute portion is sharply focused. Facts may be ignored because they have never been put into words, because they are utterly out of accord with the organization of the mind as a whole, because they are out of accord with certain aspects of the mind, because they have not been seen in their true significance, because the frame of reference containing them is unfamiliar, or because they are ignored as irrelevant or temperamentally inconsistent as happens when, as Jung and Anna Freud have noted, thinking is rejected by an emotional type or feeling by a thinking one. The problem of the unconscious is not a simple one, and whilst one is entitled to say that *for therapeutic purposes* the important aspect is that concerning the ego-defences (although not all psychoanalysts would agree), this is no good reason for ignoring *for scientific purposes* data which relate to the origin of personality. One cannot help being struck by the fact that those analysts whose avowed intent it was to broaden the scope of psychoanalytic theory have ended by removing a great deal more than they have put in. Jung, for instance, presents us with the collective unconscious, but his psychology of the individual becomes a vague and misty version of static Herbartian psychology; Fromm makes many valid criticisms of the Freudian position, but ends up with a theory of personality which seems to imply that between the temperament with which the individual is endowed at birth and the predominant ways by which he relates himself to society in later life little of any significance happens. Sullivan's theories have really very little bearing on the present discussion; for although the above criticisms have some relevance to his views and he is ordinarily described as a Neo-Freudian, he was comparatively little influenced by Freudian thought except in the sense that it has permeated all psychiatry. His true spiritual ancestry is the American tradition in psychology from William James onwards through the social psychologists C. H. Cooley and G. H. Mead, and American psychiatry as represented by Adolf Meyer, founder of the school of psychobiology, and perhaps the greatest of American psychiatrists in the older tradition. Like Meyer's approach, Sullivan's is essentially empirical and this perhaps explains his great practical ability combined with his relative failure to put his method into words—Sullivan's is not a neat theory with all the loose ends tied and no ragged edges, but it was not intended to be. This native American tradition ran parallel with Freud's rather than followed it, and embodies a vast amount of information and observations—almost too vast for systemization. The real difference between Sullivan and Freud is the difference between empirical thought and the thought of a brilliant theoretician: what Sullivan and the Neo-Freudians have in common is a denial of the primacy of the more specific biological demands which are seen as secondary in importance to interpersonal relations and efforts at self-maintainance. This is the real crux of the matter in considering the Neo-Freudians, for, as Gardner Murphy points out, if the conflicting entities in neurosis are socialized trends, we shall have to explain what original bodily activities are frustrated in society. Adler tells us that weakness is intolerable, but he never tells us why; others talk glibly of ego needs without saying why so passionate a demand for status should exist or why one cannot simply sit down quietly and happily accepting the existing position—as many people, in fact, do. This is rather like discussing a theory of famine without first explaining why people need to eat. There is no reason why the Neo-Freudians should not concern themselves with interpersonal relations, but that does not absolve them from the necessity of considering the biological foundations from which they arise.

CHAPTER 10

Assessments and Applications

ONCE it is realized that acceptance of the general standpoint of psychoanalysis no more commits us to Freud's philosophy or the commonly held assumptions of his time than acceptance of Newton's theory commits us to his peculiar theological doctrines or his views on alchemy, the way is opened to a consideration of psychoanalytic theory as both a theoretical and an applied approach in psychology. Science is a hard discipline and necessitates an attitude that nobody is capable of maintaining all the time, nor would it be desirable if they could, and Freud's impeccable approach to fact-finding is not invalidated by demonstrating that he was also a man of his time with strong personal convictions of his own. When in his later years he became interested in telepathy and, in fact, published some papers on the subject, Freud wrote in reply to a letter from Jones inquiring whether telepathy would now be included as part of psychoanalysis: 'When anyone adduces my fall into sin, just answer him calmly that conversion to telepathy is my private affair like my Jewishness, my passion for smoking, and many other things and that the theme of telepathy is in essence alien to psychoanalysis.' The real criticism of psychoanalytic orthodoxy is not that there was anything wrong with Freud's methods or observations but that there was something very far wrong indeed with the attitude of the group which kept his *explanations* fixated at the level of Herbert Spencer's sociology, an anthropology which was half speculative, half travellers' tales, and an extremely naïve moral and political philosophy; that there was an arrogance bordering on dottiness in the assertion that only members of this body were qualified to criticize its theories, when we know that hardly one trusted the insight of another or was capable of distinguishing between personal feelings of loyalty and devotion to scientific truth. In fact, in terms of generally accepted criteria Freud's is an extremely good theory which explains an immense number of facts with a minimum number of assumptions, and on the whole does so both economically and convincingly. It poses many new questions, invites further applications, and in this way differs from an open-and-shut theory such as Adler's, which has no further applications outside the clinical sphere for which it was designed and is economical at the expense of adequate detail. Whatever criticisms may be made of Freud's theories the fact remains (and this is perhaps the supreme instance of his tremendous genius) that, whilst making no claim to know all the answers, he was well aware of the right questions psychology should ask. By the single assumption of psychic determinism Freud brought every manifestation of the irrational into the sphere of scientific investigation, showing that no matter what an individual said or did was always the truth—not necessarily about reality but about the individual himself. Sane or insane, drunk or sober, literate or illiterate, genius or idiot, rational or irrational, sick or healthy, the individual's projections or the projections of social groups are scientific facts capable of being interpreted. The old criticism that Freud took his material from a relatively small group of Viennese neurotics who were not only unstable in their judgements but were discussing events or alleged events which had supposedly happened many years earlier and did not seem even at the time of recounting to be inherently likely ones, shows a complete misunderstanding of his approach. Thus, when it was found that the sexual seductions in early life reported by his patients had never in fact occurred, Freud, after an initial period of frustration, came to realize that the fact that the patients felt *as if* they had occurred was equally significant. Individuals and groups give themselves away by the material they project upon external reality, and of course the fact that they do so is the basis of projective techniques in the personality tests which are widely used by psychologists today. Myths, fairy-tales, literature, political and religious beliefs, or art, become scientifically meaningful to the psychologist precisely to the degree that they do *not* correspond with the facts of external reality, and from this there follows the converse proposition that to the extent they do so correspond they are none of the psychologist's business. Unfortunately this has not always been realized by psychoanalysts, and we have seen how Rank and others made the most far-fetched interpretations of cultural objects such as jugs and bowls, spears and swords, whose significance is adequately accounted for purely in terms of utility. That such objects may *come to assume* a different significance from the original one is self-evident, but it is difficult to imagine a container with any shape that does not betray the fact that, like the womb, it is intended to contain, and if swords and spears were designed *because* they are phallic symbols we shall have a good deal of strain put upon our ingenuity when we are expected to find a sexual significance in stones, bombs, or poison gas. The fact that objects with a similar function tend to possess a similar form does not entitle us to assume with the Freudians that the chronologically earliest example of the object *caused* the development of subsequent examples, or with Jung that they are all imitations of an archetypal object or idea. Generally speaking, physicians make poor scientists because a scientist must be a good theoretician, a physician a good practitioner and empiricist, and the fact that an explanation or method works in practice has not the slightest bearing on its scientific truth. In an address to the British Medical Association in 1959 the eminent neurologist Lord Adrian described the immense revolution Freudian theory had brought about in the field of medicine, but pointed out that its therapeutic results could not be adduced as evidence for its truth since the whole history of medicine shows that the scientific validity of a particular line of treatment has not always much to do with its success. 'In the past, success in the treatment of neurotic complaints has been claimed for methods as different as the removal of the colon, the anchoring of a wandering kidney, and the laying on of hands', he asserted, and it is impossible to deny that this is so, since even orthodox psychoanalysts have been vociferous in claiming that the successes claimed by other schools are due to nothing but the patient's suggestibility. Nevertheless a major reason why psychoanalysis proved acceptable to the man in the street, to the artist and novelist (who could not conceive of an Adlerian theory of art), to the social worker or the psychiatrist (who realized that the content of schizophrenic phantasies could be understood in Freudian or even Jungian terms but never in Adlerian ones), is precisely the fact that it can be applied to real situations whereas the undoubtedly important results obtained by experimental psychologists in general cannot. They can of course be applied in very many situations—in testing and selection for jobs, in industry, in education, and so on—but in few that press closely upon the individual as a person. The adolescent with sexual problems, the psychiatrist who needs to understand his patient, the novelist, or for that matter the advertising firm making use of motivational research, would get cold comfort from a textbook of psychology, but (Freud showed how many forms of behaviour, ranging from the home life of the ordinary man or woman to the lives of the gods, from an isolated act of assault to general warfare involving millions, could be fitted together within a common frame of reference that made some sort of sense. The pattern was found satisfying (a) because it had an inner consistency, (b) because it seemed to explain behaviour adequately, and (c) because, once one had got used to the unfamiliar jargon, Freudian theory appeared to be saying things that one had vaguely known all along.) Professor Notcutt *(Psychology of Personality)* points out that even those who regard dream symbolism as far-fetched or ridiculous often know perfectly well what symbolism means. A man dreamt that he came into the kitchen and, on opening the electric oven, saw that there was a bun inside on the tray; on waking up the dream seemed to him to be completely meaningless; yet, when at the local bar a soldier said to him, 'My wife has a bun in the oven,' he had no difficulty whatever in knowing what he meant. As Notcutt says, 'anyone who has spent a few hours leaning on a bar counter listening to dirty jokes will have heard in conscious form all the sexual symbols that Freud "discovered" in *The Interpretation of Dreams*. With the leer in the voice and the gleam of glasses to define the context, it is not difficult to interpret most of the symbols which at other times would be deeply hidden.' Many of the Freudian mechanisms of defence are so familiar to us that they have for long been enshrined in everyday speech: 'There are none so blind as those who don't want to see' (repression or dissociation), 'kicking the cat' (displacement), or the man who sees the mote in his brother's eye when he cannot see the beam in his own (projection), are examples. The ordinary man or woman *knows* that from an early age the child is interested in the mystery of birth, in its genitals and bowel motions, that one commonly refers to 'daddy's little girl' or 'mummy's little boy' rather than the reverse, that dreams mean something (although exactly what is another matter), that people frequently make mistakes 'on purpose', that protestations of sexual innocence or pacific propensities are most frequently made by those in whom one suspects the reverse, and no amount of criticism from the scientific psychologist is going to make him think otherwise. If psychology cannot encompass such everyday observations, so much the worse for psychology. Nor does it take a great effort of imagination to see that the children of fervent atheists or agnostics are as likely to become fervent Catholics as to adopt the views of their parents but are unlikely to be indifferent to religious issues, or to note that their attitude is likely to depend more on their basic filial attitude than their intellect. That such conclusions are intuitively arrived at and are therefore not always expressed in a form that appeals to the scientist or put forward with what he would regard as adequate supporting evidence may be granted; that adequate supporting evidence is provided by Freud may be denied; but that they are to be rejected as inherently non-scientific because of their nature is peculiarly a conception of the experimental psychologist. Professor H. J. Eysenck, in an essay entitled 'What is wrong with Psychoanalysis?' *(Uses and Abuses of Psychology)*, supports this view and notes the distinction made by German philosophers between *verstehende* psychology (i.e. a common-sense psychology which tries to *understand* human beings) and *erklärende* psychology (which tries to describe and *explain* their behaviour on a scientific basis), pointing out that the former category is the one to which psychoanalysis rightly belongs. He then states 'quite briefly and dogmatically' that consequently 'it is essentially non-scientific and to be judged in terms of belief and faith rather than in terms of proof and verification; and that lastly its great popularity among non-scientists derives precisely from its non-scientific nature, which makes it intelligible and immediately applicable to problems of "understanding" other people. This judgement I believe to be a statement of fact, rather than a value judgement.' This point of view is worthy of note but it must be said equally dogmatically that it is not one which is widely held by psychologists in general, that the contrast between *verstehende* and *erklärende* psychology is inapplicable to the present issue, since Freud's methods were entirely in accord with the ordinary scientific approach, and that if Freud introduced an irrelevant metapsychology it would be equally easy to show that strict use of the scientific method by psychologists has frequently led to results which vie for absurdity with any conclusions of the psychoanalytic schools, although for precisely the opposite reason: that not enough attention was paid to the wider context of the object of study. (The contrast between *verstehende* and *erklärende* in German is not that between mere understanding and explaining, which in English signify pretty much the same process in the sense that when something is properly *explained* it is reasonable to say that it has been *understood;* the implied contrast in German is between *intuitive understanding* (as when one says, 'I understand how you feel') and *scientific explaining in terms of 'laws'* —which are not, of course, laws in the usual sense but statements of probability arrived at by a process of induction from a large number of individual observations. When confirmation of many such observations leads to a high degree of probability we speak of a scientific law, when it is of a lower degree we speak of a theory, and when it is lower still we speak of a hypothesis; between the extremes of law and hypothesis there is a quantitative, not a qualitative difference. This is so (1) because it is never possible to test all cases that would validate a law, and (2) because it is never possible to investigate every hypothesis that would explain a given phenomenon and therefore, other things being equal, a hypothesis is likely to be preferred in so far as it complies with the criteria already mentioned. Nor is any law universally 'true' regardless of circumstances, for even physical laws such as Boyle's or Charles's equations dealing with the interrelationships between volume, temperature, and pressure of gases are true only within a quite narrow range of temperature or pressure; in the same way the Oedipus complex as described by Freud was the one he observed in bourgeois Vienna at the turn of the century, and as Fenichel points out, Malinowski's findings in the Trobriand Islands do not show that there are places where the Oedipus complex does not exist, but rather that the form taken by the complex varies from one culture to another. Circumstances alter cases in both physics and psychology, and it is one of the commonest failings of the strict experimental scientist to ignore the fact that they do or to ignore how widely 'circumstances' may be spread. For example there has been, and perhaps still is, an extraordinary inability on the part of some psychologists to see that where human beings are concerned the very fact that they are being experimented upon becomes an additional factor which inevitably affects the result; so, prior to Mayo, industrial psychologists simply assumed (wrongly, as he was able to show) that any change in the physical environment of the workshop which was followed by alterations in mood or productivity on the part of the workers must be the sole cause of the alteration. Early studies of perception were carried out on the fallacious assumption that perceptions exist uninfluenced by expectations, social norms, needs, complexes, and other emotional factors which form an important circumstance of any experiment. In place of the psychoanalyst's frequently inaccurate and inexact mode of expressing himself, his bad logic and worse metaphysics, the psychologist often presents us with a view of the scientific method so naïve as to confound the critic who wants to reject what is unscientific in Freudian theory. That two American psychologists should ask college students to recall at random pleasant and unpleasant experiences on the assumption that, if repression were a fact, more of the former than the latter would be recalled is bad enough; that, as Professor Eysenck assures us, a group of strong and presumably normal individuals were persuaded to starve themselves for an appreciable period in order to prove that Freud's theory of dreams as wish-fulfilments was false because they did not dream of food, strains one's credibility; but that an eminent educational psychologist should solemnly 'prove' the Oedipus complex to be a myth by the simple expedient of asking a number of other professional psychologists about the preferences of their own children towards one parent or the other baffles comprehension. Freud at no time said that unpleasant experiences as such were likely to be forgotten; he said that experiences which might conflict with other dominant tendencies of the personality were likely to be repressed whether as experiences they were pleasant or not; he did not say that for any appreciable period a child showed overt preference for the parent of the opposite sex, because the very word 'complex' refers to *unconscious* attitudes which are unconscious precisely because they are forbidden; he did not assert that hunger made one dream of food, although explorers and others subjected involuntarily to hunger have said that it did, and he would certainly have seen through the fallacy of supposing that voluntary and experimental subjection to starvation bears any resemblance in its emotional significance to the involuntary situation in which the basic issue is not primarily lack of food but imminent proximity of death. 'Do you think that I am easier to be played on than a pipe?' asked Hamlet, and apparently some psychologists believe that the answer to what was intended as a rhetorical question is in the affirmative. Without any further nonsense Hamlet should be asked the simple question: 'Do you, or do you not, have an Oedipus complex?' (Perhaps, on second thoughts, it would be more scientific to ask his mother the Queen, who was naturally in a better position to observe Hamlet's childhood reactions and is clearly an intelligent and unbiased witness.) Dr Eysenck rejects the psychoanalytic concept of reaction-formation which, as he says, allows a person who theoretically should show behaviour pattern A to react away from this pattern to such an extent that he shows the opposite pattern Z (as violent aggressiveness leading to compulsive gentleness by a process of repression). This, he complains, allows the hypothesis to be verified regardless of whether the individual is timorous or aggressive. Possibly the hypothesis is badly expressed in terms of Aristotelian logic, although entirely in conformity with Hegelian dialectic, but the fallacy lies in supposing that compulsive gentleness and aggressiveness are opposites rather than variations along a scale of 'conflict about aggression' which in a truly gentle person is poorly represented. What the proposition says is that conflict over authority in early life predisposes to conflict over authority in later life—that there is a type of 'pseudo-gentleness' recognized by most people without psychological theorizing and sharply distinguishable from the genuine article which is the result of absence of such conflict. The attitude of the experimental psychologist to the measurement of personality traits is incomprehensible to those whose approach is fundamentally a dynamic one. For instance the supposed 'trait' of suggestibility is investigated by observing the reaction of an individual when, with eyes shut and feet together, it is suggested to him that he is swaying, the degree of sway being measured although there seems to be not the slightest *a priori* reason to suppose that suggestibility is a unitary trait that some people have a lot of and others just a little, still less reason to suppose that if there were it could be correlated with sway, and no reason at all to think that suggestibility is independent of who is doing the suggesting, what is suggested, or the mental and physical state of the subject at the time of the test. Here again it is assumed that a subject *pretending* to do something in an experiment responds in the same way as in a real situation, and it is far from clear what the psychologist proposes to do with his results once he has succeeded in plastering a framework of personality with all its traits in specified amounts, like the numbered areas on the head of a phrenologist's dummy. What happens then? One must be forgiven for supposing that the answer appears to be that, so long as the traits never interact, nobody cares very much what they do. Dr Raymond Cattell of the University of Illinois is another eminent psychologist who is dazzled at the prospect of founding psychology on a basis of measurement, since nothing, it appears, is truly scientific unless it makes use of mathematics. But our initial enthusiasm—unless we are exceptionally credulous—is quickly damped by the discovery that although figures and symbols appear in plenty in his works they are based on the answers to such questions as the following: 'Are you attentive in keeping appointments?', 'Would you feel embarrassed on joining a nudist colony?', 'Have people called you a proud, stuck-up, self-willed person?', 'Do you think people should observe moral laws more strictly?', 'Do you crave travel?' Surely the compiler of such a questionnaire must be aware that anybody who answered these questions truthfully (except in the interests of pure research) conveys to the tester one single piece of information: that the testee ought to see a psychiatrist. For the questions imply value judgements and nowhere more so than in the United States where they are in use, and nobody but a fool would do other than answer them in the way that revealed himself in the best possible light. Furthermore they refer to subjects about which most people are a great deal more touchy than the most intimate details of their sexual life, because they feel greater responsibility for them. Many people would admit to perverse sexual practices sooner than admit that others regard them as proud and stuck-up or that they are careless about appointments, and any American male who admitted failure to live up to the national stereotype of 'maleness' of the red-blooded rather than the blue-blooded variety, extreme sociability and distaste for being alone, punctuality, broadmindedness except about 'homosexualists' and Communists, generosity, and support for the Church 'or some other worth-while cause' — which, incredible as it may seem, is one of the questions asked of him in the name of science—would already be under psychoanalytic treatment.

These views are by no means typical of psychology as a whole, and it is broadly true to say that, although psychologists do not ordinarily deal with the sort of material which concerns the psychoanalyst and are likely to leave the whole subject of personality severely alone, their reaction to Freudian theory has been favourable if not uncritical. One thing however is certain, and that is that few text-books of psychology ignore Freud and many are built around his theories, whereas none have ever been built around Adlerian or Jungian theory, and the other schools are rarely even mentioned. Adler is likely to be mentioned in connexion with the mechanism of compensation and Jung in connexion with the word-association test or the introversion-extraversion dimension of personality, but their theories as such are not recognized as serious contributions to scientific knowledge. The reason for this discrimination is clear. It is that Freud alone amongst the founders of analytic schools understood and made thorough use of the scientific method in his investigations. Freud's approach was as logical and his findings as carefully tested as Pavlov's but he was able to deal successfully with phenomena inaccessible to Pavlov; for in spite of denials the fact remains that the foundations of his method—psychic determinism and the relentless logic of free association—are scientific, and are so over a wider area of experience than anything before or since. It is worth while repeating that, so far from implying intuition, Freud's method was to take everything anybody said at any time or place regardless of truth or falsity in terms of external reality to be used as basic data in revealing the dynamics of the personality in precisely the same way that meteorological data might be used to chart the weather map of a geographical area. Since the data are subsequently referred back to fundamental mental processes, it is beside the point to say that they were initially obtained from Austrian middle-class Jews suffering from hysteria (if, in fact, this is true), because even at that time it was clear that they were equally applicable to British working-class Gentiles or Andaman Islanders. It is curious that those who would not be prepared to assert that the physiology of digestion or respiration recognizes national, religious, or class boundaries are prepared to make an exception in the case of the fundamental dynamics of the mind. The differences noted by the cultural schools are variations which do not affect the basic issues, and if we wish to reject Freudian theory we must either reject determinism and the validity of the technique of free association, thereby admitting that there exists an area of experience to which the rules of science do not apply, or else—and this attitude rests on firmer ground—we may deny the validity of Freud's interpretation of the data. Freud's work does not represent a limited theory of the type beloved by experimental scientists and cannot therefore be compared with the laws of Boyle and Charles, of Ohm, or of Weber and Fechner, which deal mathematically with the relationships between a small number of data within a narrow range of observations; it is a hypothesis covering a wide range of facts with correspondingly less overall accuracy in matters of detail. In this respect it is comparable in form to Newton' s hypotheses which made an imaginative leap into space on the basis of a few observations of the behaviour of falling objects on earth—although fortunately for Newton nobody was foolish enough to complain that he had not tested out his hypothesis on the extragalactic nebulae. Newton's and Freud's propositions were inadequate to explain every phenomenon, which is why they are described as hypotheses, but Freud still awaits his Einstein. The relative status of Freud in the eyes of the world is significantly shown in the number of books written by orthodox psychoanalysts or written about his work by non-psychoanalysts. Their number, of course, is legion. Yet from a reasonably wide acquaintance with the literature of the other analytic schools it would be difficult to think of even half a dozen significant commentators on Adler in the last twenty years, and although Jung himself had been a most prolific writer his commentators in English and German over the same period have been only slightly more numerous, even if his work has frequently been discussed in articles and to some extent in books by intellectuals who were not psychologists. British or American psychiatrists make no mention of Jung in standard text-books except for the now historical work on schizophrenia contained in his earliest publications long before his break with Freud. In fact, of all those discussed here only Freud (including Anna Freud and Melanie Klein) and Jung have any considerable influence in Europe so far as theory and psychotherapeutic practice is concerned, and the Neo-Freudians have had as little influence here as Klein in America. Perhaps the clearest picture of their relative significance, if not necessarily of their scientific validity, can be obtained from a brief account of the distribution of the schools in Europe and America which as we have seen are the main centres. Neo-Freudianism in America is centred in New York, where Horney formed a group known as the Society for the Advancement of Psychoanalysis, which has its own Institute for training. Sullivan's group began in Washington and Baltimore and is known as the William Alanson White Foundation, which also has an Institute in New York with which Fromm has been associated although most of his work has been in the direction of teaching and writing. Nevertheless by far the greatest number of analysts in the United States remain more or less orthodox Freudians, as is the important Institute in Chicago under Franz Alexander, and excluding the Neo-Freudians, most of the other schools have a relatively insignificant following. There are small Adlerian and Jungian groups scattered throughout the country, but practically speaking Adlerian psychology as a system is dying out, not so much by rejection as by absorption, so far as medically-trained analysts are concerned. It is, however, still in use by lay workers in education, child guidance, and counselling. The strongest Jungian groups are in England and Switzerland, but by reason of its larger population America possibly possesses a greater total number of Jungian analysts than either of these two countries. Almost alone amongst non-Freudian groups the Jungians have maintained their position and may even in recent years have improved it, particularly outside the medical and scientific spheres. Jung has come to be regarded by many as a sage or a prophet of our times, particularly by those whose real aim is to discover some sort of religious viewpoint and find Freud too materialistic. A few analysts in both Europe and America still make use of the methods of Rank, Reich, and Stekel, but these schools have never had the slightest appeal to the scientific psychologist.

In considering the various schools discussed here, the following points have to be borne in mind if we wish to avoid the mistake of assessing all by the same standards: (1) all took their origin largely from Freud and frequently begin their exposition with a criticism of the orthodox viewpoint; (2) there is little—indeed surprisingly little—divergence of opinion about actual clinical observations and the main disagreements occur in relation to their immediate interpretation, their relative importance, the framework of reference into which they are fitted, and their significance for psychotherapy; (3) they do not in all cases cover the same group of phenomena (e.g. Jung, Rank, and Freud discuss cultural phenomena at length, Adler and Horney concentrate on the individual ego); (4) not all set out to present a scientifically coherent account of personality but rather those aspects of personality relevant to a method and theory of psychotherapy as practised by the school; this in turn is not unrelated to such factors as the temperament of the founder, the type of patients treated, and the therapeutic limits he has set himself. Clearly, when a theory is of this nature it would be futile to criticize it in terms of scientific personality theory when it can only be counted 'wrong' if it fails therapeutically or if it bases itself on assumptions which the psychologist has good reason for believing to be false. For the most part psychologist have recognized this significant distinction. They have taken Freud's theories on his own estimate of them as serious contributions to scientific psychology, and they have largely ignored Jung, because, whatever Jung's intentions, his theories are not expressed scientifically nor are they subject to scientific proof or disproof. This is not a value judgement and it is not in the least inconsistent with the conviction held by many people that Jung is a great and profound thinker; it is merely an admission that his work can no more be scientifically assessed than that of Kierkegaard or Sartre, Nietzsche or Pascal. So far as the other schools are concerned, the psychologist concerned with personality theory has been prepared to accept, or at any rate to take note of, the criticisms of Freudian theory by the Neo-Freudians; he is interested in Jung's theory of personality types (which can theoretically be tested), in Adler's account of certain ego defence mechanisms, and perhaps in Suttie's or Klein's accounts of the origins of love and hate in early life, because unlike the psychoanalyst he is not committed to an almost total acceptance of Freudian orthodoxy. Generally he is prepared to take psychoanalytic theory as a useful frame of reference, to be modified or corrected on scientific grounds, because there actually exists a Freudian *normal* psychology, social psychology, and anthropology represented today by such authorities as Anna Freud, Melanie Klein, Róheim, and Kardiner. Again, this is not a value judgement and interest in their works is not inconsistent with believing that the views expressed are largely mistaken, but it is a fact that no child psychologist today ignores the theories of Freud and Klein and no anthropologist ignores Róheim or Kardiner however much he may disagree with them. Yet although there exist Neo-Freudian schools in America described as Horneyian, Frommian, and Sullivanian, it is not easy to see wherein their specificity lies or on the basis of what new and objective clinical data their divergence from Freud or from each other rests. No systematic account amounting to a new theory has been presented by any of the three, and one is left with the general impression that Fromm is a man of broad if not particularly original learning who disagrees with Freud in numerous respects and, reasonably enough, attempts to bring his thought into closer alignment with modern views; that Horney disagrees with Freud on similar grounds and produces an Adlerian-type theory which does not deny the unconscious but largely ignores it in favour of an analysis of the patient's interpersonal relationships; that Sullivan says little in criticism of Freud, who, in any case, was not a fundamental influence—or at any rate *the* fundamental one—in the development of his psychology, but that he too is mainly concerned with distortions of personal relationships, judgements, and behaviour as revealed in the transference situation. What we do not know is what parts of Freudian theory Fromm *does* accept since, had we not been informed to the contrary, we should have thought that he was an ordinary Freudian who saw that Freud's cultural outlook was outdated or at least not universally applicable. Nor do we know very much about Horney outside the consulting-room except what most people would be prepared to accept as an interesting and illuminating account of what goes on in interpersonal relationships at a fairly superficial level, described as it might be by a sensitive behaviourist observing the reactions of individuals without any sort of analysis whatever. Of other forms of behaviour she tells us nothing. Sullivan is even more puzzling because, while he apparently feels dissatisfied with Freudian mechanistic modes of description, his own in terms of 'dynamisms' is expressed in an excruciatingly tortuous language, which is the more irritating in that it complicates rather than simplifies and even gives the impression that the complexity is a deliberate 'show-off'. At one moment he is expressing himself with all the directness of a quaintish old-timer leaning over the bar of a saloon—no nonsense about 'libido', it must be 'lusts', and *they* come into action as everybody knows at puberty not with earlier oral or anal stages—the next moment he is inventing neologisms with all the aplomb of a Mid-West vendor of patent medicines whose classical education began and ended with a year's study of dispensing to enable him to write and read prescriptions. In this respect he goes one better than other American scientific text-books which tend to be either out-and-out 'folksy' or so full of detail and novel words and phrases as to be downright incomprehensible (in fact, the works of one eminent sociologist have been hailed with respect here largely because, although it would be difficult to find many who understand even a single page, the general feeling has been that anyone who takes so much trouble to invent a new laguage must have something to say). Sullivan uses both methods, from the archaic 'middling example' and the wrong use of ordinarily used words such as 'euphoria' to the half-pompous, half-popular definition of dynamisms as 're-latively enduring configurations of energy which manifest themselves in characterizable processes in interpersonal relations' and are not 'some fanciful substantial engines, regional organizations, or peculiar more or less physiological apparatus about which our present knowledge is nil'. The realization that Sullivan's style is peculiar is not a purely personal one; it is commented upon by many critics, and another American, Ruth Munroe, finds in it 'the precarious summit of a brilliant display of fireworks', which, however, has not been the general impression it has made on others.

What is obvious about these three schools is that they are socially rather than biologically orientated, that they overtly or by implication criticize Freud's metapsychology and social psychology, and that Horney and Sullivan are almost entirely concerned with clinical problems, Fromm with sociological ones. It is, in fact, impossible on the basis of his major works to discover where Fromm's analytic followers obtain their specifically Frommian clinical data, since even in earlier papers published in German his main concern seems to have been with moral and social issues of the kind already described rather than with patients. A characteristic feature is their emphasis on the ego and its relationships in a social background, while the unconscious is proportionately disregarded save as a means of explaining how distortions of relationships and reality sense arose in early experiences. Analysis of the transference as a sample interpersonal situation is a logical consequence of this attitude. It is noteworthy, too, that there is less emphasis on biological factors and that the personality is regarded—particularly by Sullivan—as the resultant of social relationships, although Fromm pays some attention to temperament and Horney rather vaguely speaks of a 'real' self in spite of the fact that on any interpersonal theory of personality the 'neurotic' self must have started to develop from the earliest days. From a practical point of view the main failing of these schools is their lack of system and detail, in which they stand in direct contrast to Freud's unremitting attention to both or even to Adler's logic, which simply ignored aspects of behaviour which did not fit the pattern or were regarded by him as irrelevant. Those who like clear-cut logical statements are likely to feel irritated when Sullivan, having presented a perfectly reasonable if limited theory, proceeds to throw in other concepts which are outside the mainstream of his argument—for example, the vaguely-defined 'power dynamism', and his appeal to 'empathy' which apparently lacks any analysable sensory foundations and has been found unnecessary by every other school save that of Jung. The Neo-Freudians all too frequently attack an orthodoxy which no longer exists, and so far as analytic procedure is concerned we are never told wherein their attitude to the ego differs from that of Anna Freud, save that she thinks in terms of analysis of the defence mechanisms and resistances which keep repressed unconscious attitudes of sexualized hostility and distort personal relationships in the process. Most European analysts, however, would agree with Miss Freud that defence mechanisms or parataxic distortions cannot be dealt with without investigation of their unconscious roots. Similarly, although Sullivan's concept of parataxic distortion possibly gives a clearer picture of a process which *distorts* contemporary relationships as a result of unsatisfactory early ones, it is fully comprehended in Sigmund Freud's concept of projection, which in its wider connotation is used to explain the same observations; the sole difference is that Freud is concerned about causes, Sullivan about results.

The divergences of opinion between all the schools represented here are perhaps more apparent than real because they are based on clinical material accepted by all. In the early days Freud did not disagree with Rank's concept of the birth trauma but with its application in the form of separation anxiety as an explanation of psychic phenomena in general; he did not disagree with Adler's theory as applied to ego psychology but with its over-enthusiastic use outside this sphere; he did not disagree with Jung's group unconscious or his interest in mythology but appears to have become rather impatient when Jung's concern with these subjects seemed to interfere with the more practical issues of therapy and with his preparation for assuming the role of Joshua to Freud's Moses within the psychoanalytic movement. In the case of Ferenczi, Freud was furious as one might expect him to be over Ferenczi's conviction that the analyst should show a human and loving attitude towards the patient in place of the orthodox impersonal and mirror-like one, and Stekel's active therapy had a similar reception. But in all these cases the initial clash was one between personalities rather than any direct clash of ideas. We have seen that a theory of psychotherapy must to some extent reflect the temperament of the person who devises it, the type of patient he most frequently sees, and the more material issues such as time and money. Stekel, Rank, and Ferenczi were in part trying to solve the ever-pressing problem of how to shorten the course of analysis without reducing its effectiveness, Stekel by direct attack on the neurotic system, Ferenczi by cooperation and sympathy, and Rank by setting a time limit from the start. The temperamental factor which influences the individual's approach to reality particularly impressed Jung, who has said that his theory of types originated from his observations of the reactions of Freud, Adler, and himself in the days of the early dissensions, and he has even asserted that some patients are best treated along Freudian lines, some along Adlerian lines, and others by his own method. No doubt the fact that Jung's patients have been predominantly schizophrenics whose condition in former times was likely to prove static for long periods, or older people whose mental dynamics are likely to be set, has some connexion with the generally static impression conveyed by the Jungian system, which Glover does not even regard as a dynamic psychology but rather as a derivative of the old faculty school on which a mystical philosophy has been superimposed. From personal observation it would appear that even those who describe themselves as Jungians or Adlerians make very considerable use of Freudian concepts when it suits their convenience. Jung shares with Rank the disconcerting attitude towards scientific truth and reality noted earlier; for example, a Jungian analyst will refer to witches or other entities ordinarily regarded as supernatural or pure superstition, and it is not always easy to discover just what is meant when they are said to be 'real'. Is a 'witch' 'real' (a) in the straightforward medieval sense when both the individual claiming the title and the rest of society accepted it, (b) as a member of some modern sects who claim to practise witchcraft but are not believed by society in general to be other than foolish exhibitionists, (c) in the sense of a patient who claims the title but in fact is deluded and requires psychiatric treatment? Since the first category no longer exists in civilized communities, the second is no concern of the psychiatrist, and the third, one might suppose, would be better explained in other and simpler terms and better treated than by agreeing with the patient's own diagnosis, it would appear to be confusing the issue to use the word witch to describe her or him (since witches, it seems, are of both sexes) save in a highly metaphorical sense. This would still be true if, as a Jungian would probably say, the concept refers to an archetype which is by definition real; for as Róheim has pointed out similarities in thought and belief are quite adequately explained in terms of shared experience and tradition, and to describe an idea as real is misleading even to a Platonist outside his study. Rank's contribution to this confusion—and his distinction, shared with Sullivan, of being the other worst writer in the analytic field—is revealed in the following quotation from the last page of *Will Therapy*, *Truth and Reality:* 'Questions which originate from the division of will into guilt consciousness and self-consciousness cannot be answered through any psychological or philosophical theory for the answer is the more disillusioning the more correct it is. For happiness can only be found in reality, not in truth, and redemption never in reality and from reality, but only in itself and from itself.'

Other differences between the schools arise because of differing ways of describing the same observations or from semantic confusions. The former is a problem common to all psychologists and arises in part from the fact that the more complex forms of behaviour can be described either from a determinist and behavourist point of view, which emphasizes drives or conditioned reflexes, or from a hormic and striving point of view, which emphasizes aims, goals, and purpose. From the one standpoint the organism is seen as being pushed from behind, from the other as being drawn from in front, and whether or not this leads to any significant difference in ultimate conclusions, it obviously leads to considerable differences in the way the situation is described. The semantic problem in psychology is that the psychologist has inevitably to make use of many words in everyday use which have widely divergent meanings and frequently emotional overtones which are liable to be ignored. Thus all that the general public knew of Freud in the early years was that he was the man who said that everything was sex —a statement which at that time was not entirely untrue but which disregarded Freud's special use of the word and seriously underestimated the emotional overtones the word held (guilt, 'rudeness', etc.) for the ordinary man. Now the most obvious difference between Adler's and Freud's theories is that the former describes in terms of goals and sees neurosis in terms of fictive goals, whilst the latter describes in terms of *Triebe* or drives seeking satisfactions which, when blocked, seek substitute satisfactions or produce neurotic symptoms. A swimmer returning to the beach who makes use of a large wave to be swept in quickly and without exertion behaves in a way which can be described scientifically by the laws of physics and hydrodynamics and psychologically in terms of psychic structure and dynamics; but Adler admitted the concept of purpose regarded with suspicion by scientists and saw the swimmer making use of external circumstances to attain a deliberately-sought end. The neurotic is distinguished from the normal person in seeking unrealistic goals which, however, are not unconscious in the Freudian sense but disregarded as reflecting little credit on himself (cf. Sullivan's 'selective inattention' and Stekel's 'life-lie'). The facts are not at issue, the interpretations are, and there is no means available to science save the criteria already mentioned of proving one interpretation right and the other wrong. Nor are Adler and the more superficial analytic shools necessarily contradicting the massive body of Freudian data relating to early experiences; what in effect they are doing is declaring them unnecessary to the psychotherapist. Because Freud does not think in terms of conscious or subconscious purpose he attaches relatively little significance to secondary gains, regarding them simply as superficial adjustments the patient makes on the basis of his neurosis to the problems set by his environment; because Adler does, the concept of secondary gains is broadened and becomes the major issue in treatment. Both are right within their own limits because as every psychiatrist knows the more superficial neuroses are 'cured', in the sense that their symptoms disappear, either when their obvious purpose is pointed out to the patient or when the environment is so altered that it is no longer possible to gain advantage from them. This of course is not a cure from the Freudian standpoint nor indeed from that of the psychiatrist, who would agree that a normal person does not resort under stress to hysterical symptoms or become anxious in the face of what are not generally regarded as anxiety-producing situations, but it is a social cure; and he is apt to become impatient with the perfectionism of the psychoanalyst when it is suggested that, for a patient who has lived in what his associates and himself regard as 'normal' health for twenty or thirty years before developing overt symptoms, the only cure is a complete Freudian analysis. It is impossible to doubt that of the soldiers one saw during the war with neuroses a very large number would not have broken down had it not been for what, after all, were not ordinary circumstances. Were they neurotic before? Were they prone to wet the bed at a late stage of childhood, recognized as mummy's boys, afraid of enclosed spaces, worried about exams or teacher, shy with girls? Or were they rather bombastic and boastful, liable to get drunk more often than is thought usual, given to telling tall stories, or getting in trouble with the law? Perhaps they were, and so perhaps in many of these respects were the psychiatrists who treated them or the commanding officers who wanted to have them court-martialled. But whereas we laboriously investigated the past of our patients we were not so quick to investigate our own or that of the men who did not develop an overt neurosis as a basis for comparison. Nor did we investigate the characters of that deservedly honoured group which superficial inspection would suggest to contain a very high percentage of psychopaths and neurotics—the men who won decorations for bravery or for undertaking dangerous exploits, or the not inconsiderable number of men who positively enjoyed war. Neurosis is in part socially defined, so neurotic character traits which prove socially useful are not often regarded as abnormalities and even the more irritating ones such as dependency, fussiness, or mild hypochondria are not looked on as anything more than ordinary idiosyncrasies. It is not unreasonable for the individual who has broken down in later life or after being exposed to stress of a more or less severe nature to say in effect: 'Take away my symptoms and leave my traits alone, because if I was not always happy or always as competent as I might have been I nevertheless got on quite well; other people thought me normal and I thought so too.' The mild chronic neurotic often does not think of himself as such and in the course of time develops a régime suited to his problems; he does not worry because he is claustrophobic in the underground, he takes the bus instead; he does not worry about his occasional attacks of functional dyspepsia, he takes a dose of baking soda and forgets about it; his periods of depression or anxiety are interpreted as signs of being run-down, and he takes a pharmacologically inert 'nerve tonic' to 'build himself up', as of course it frequently does.

If he is asked about his symptoms, he will expatiate about them at length, because after all he has 'studied himself', but if he is told of their psychological significance he will become really worried, and if psychoanalysis is suggested he will think his adviser unreasonable— and many psychiatrists would agree with him. As a rule the psychiatrist does not see this type of patient, although it is far commoner than the more florid case he may come to regard as typical; but the family doctor does and, thinking along Adlerian lines without necessarily having heard of Adler's name, will ask himself: 'What's old Jones's problem now? The factory? No, everything seems all right there. His home? Well, it has been quite happy lately and there has never been any serious difficulty anyhow—except...of course, this is the beginning of the fortnight when his mother-in-law comes for her yearly visit—he had the same symptoms this time last year!' So Jones is given a nerve tonic in which he has great faith, although the doctor almost blushes to sign a prescription for it, and is advised to 'get out a bit more for a couple of weeks or so', which is the official authorization for being out more often than not during the critical period. This is successful psychotherapy for this case and it would be unsuccessful or at the least unhelpful to attempt to bring Jones's guilt-laden incestuous longings for his mother-in-law and his earlier incestuous longings for his own mother as a child into consciousness, even if they existed. The vast majority of people in the world are not rootless intellectuals free to range about in the realm of ideas at will and tied to no particular social norms; they are ordinary individuals living in communities with very strict social and religious codes of behaviour which are highly resistant to novel ideas. Their churches teach that incestuous and other forbidden desires are a grave sin, and their laws that, no matter what a man may feel or think, there are certain things he must not do, and to cause anyone to think otherwise will result in maladaptation to his community whatever it may do to his mind. Psychoanalytic theories are the most useful device for understanding the human personality we possess, and so far as detail is concerned they are really the only one; psychoanalysis is a valuable method of treating the type of case so carefully specified by Freud himself, the fairly severe and persistent neurosis which proves disabling to a youngish individual of high intelligence and otherwise strong character—in fact, a rather small proportion of all neuroses; the psychoanalytic approach is a helpful one in understanding the dynamics of social movements and planning social schemes and policies, provided the actual planning is not left to those whose proper concern is treating the abnormal rather than advising the normal. Repression and the irrational lie at the very foundations of society and the wise policy may sometimes be to play along with them, lightening the burden they may cause here, supporting their edicts there, because no psychologist or psychoanalyst, much less psychiatrist, can give a better reason for *not* stealing, *not* killing, *not* committing incest (all antisocial acts in any society) than the ingrained belief that in the beginning it was said, 'Thou shalt not'. It may be possible to explain in psychological terminology why this was said, but such an explanation is unlikely to convince simple people or children or have the same prohibitive power. Those who deal with the mentally sick are not always realistic in their appraisal of social realities; both by reason of their work itself and sometimes by reason of that law of compensation which, as Adler showed, attracts people to employments which have a morbid personal interest, their views may be narrow and emotionally biased. The employer may be very sorry to hear that his factory manager suffers from an anxiety neurosis, but what he really wants to know is why it should be that this man's symptoms demand rest at home specifically at times when important problems are cropping up, and why he remained at work without absence for nearly a whole year when a rumour was going about that the new trainee might fill his place—the rumour was incorrect but it nevertheless seemed to have an effect on what the psychiatrist had assured the employer was 'an illness, just like other illnesses'. The magistrate or judge may understand perfectly when he is told by a psychiatrist that the men arrested for importuning have always been practising homosexuals, that the respectable lady found stealing pencils was symbolically stealing love (or even something more concrete if the psychiatrist has strong Freudian leanings), that the man who attacked a policeman was in effect attacking the drunken father who beat his mother each Saturday evening, but he is unlikely to see what all this has to do with breaking the law, because in the eyes of most people explaining is not the same as condoning, and the fact that one has a desire for a thousand pounds is not ordinarily regarded as a reason for stealing it no matter how easy it would be to do so. In cases such as these it is sometimes the psychiatrist or the psychoanalyst who is wrong, because he does not realize that one cannot apply conclusions derived from a quasi-scientific discipline concerned only with describing objectively, explaining objectively, and treating scientifically *without reference to personal responsibility or guilt or appeal to 'will-power'* to a totally different sphere which, except in unusual individual cases, accepts these concepts as forming the very foundations of human society. Of course he would be entirely within his rights and perhaps logically justified if he explained that he could conceive of a society where employers thought not in terms of laziness or incompetence but in practical ones of suitability or unsuitability for a particular job; where judges thought, not in terms of crime and punishment, but of maladaptation to social demands and its treatment; but he does not explain whether or not this is his position and therefore necessarily limits himself to a kind of double-talk which makes the worst of both worlds. Any moderately educated person without a specialist axe to grind can see for himself that mental illness is not 'just like other illnesses', that in fact with the exception of cases which are in effect organic diseases with psychic complications it is not an illness at all but a form of social maladjustment; he can see that serious forms of madness or insanity are frightening to all of us (regardless of whether or not they can be cured or whether they are more scientifically or considerately described as psychoses) because they change the personality and the sufferer becomes a different person in a way that does not happen if, for instance, he loses both legs. Intelligent people in positions of authority can observe that aspect of a neurosis which leads the individual to evade responsibilities and behave in a way which his associates may interpret as malingering, and they may note too the equally significant fact that when evasion is not permitted the individual's condition may even in some cases improve; the apparent failure of some psychiatrists to note the same facts or to draw logical conclusions from them is likely to result in their being regarded as simpletons. Those connected with the law are often well aware when the accused pleads loss of memory that

what people forget is what it suits them to forget and that there are
degrees of loss of memory right up to that experienced by the
ordinary man, but in court the psychiatrist frequently speaks of it
as if it were a brain tumour, something that is just there, a fixed and
circumscribed disease rather than a self-protective mechanism.
Having thus taken up a rather foolish position, he is asked
foolish questions—does the accused recall the name of his school,
does he remember how to tie his bootlaces, if he does not know he
is married why did he after the crime go to collect his family
allowance—which are all based on the assumption that a large
block of 'memory' has been destroyed by a pathological condition which has little to do with the person himself. The psychiatrist does not always admit that there are no means available
to him which are not equally available to the ordinary man
by which he can tell whether the loss of memory is genuine
and is quite likely to suffer the indignity of finding himself confronted by one of his colleagues who will swear precisely the opposite of all that he has given in evidence. These examples are not
given in order to discredit the psychiatrist who, according to his
own lights, is behaving quite correctly and arguing perfectly
rationally, but to show once more the dangers of arguing from a
discipline which eschews moral judgements and responsibility to
circumstances where they are assumed to be valid. In such circumstances his refusal to consider them may be accepted as a value
judgement in itself, as indeed it sometimes is when the official
nomenclature is strained to breaking-point in order to bring into
the category of sick those who are simply sad, worried, or bad. In
some circles it is almost impossible to mourn the loss of a loved
one without being labelled as suffering from 'reactive depression',
impossible for a wealthy embezzler to be worried about the prospect of appearing in court without the authorities being informed
that he is suffering from 'severe nervous shock', and difficult for
the pacifist called up for military service to avoid being described
as an 'inadequate psychopath'. But the psychiatrist's real position is that he judges nobody, because it is not his business to do
so, and it is extremely dangerous if he is to be expected to attach
medical tags where they do not properly belong and by so doing
decrease the area within which people are to be regarded as fully

responsible for their behaviour. It is equally dangerous, one might think, that so many people have been led to believe that the ordinary emotions of worry, anxiety, depression, boredom, and tiredness in normal degree or in situations to which they would appear a natural response, should require, not that problems should be actively dealt with or some discomfort tolerated, but some form of medical treatment, with the result that a large proportion of the population is more or less constantly under the influence of stimulating or sedative drugs. Freud devised a means of diagnosing man's troubles, not of suppressing them, and the emotions we are so desirous of suppressing are the mental equivalents of body symptoms which may give warning that all is not well. Obviously there is a gap somewhere between the important knowledge of man and society we already possess and the ignorant and half-baked way in which we apply it. But the way of dealing with this situation is not that we should wait until one-half of the world's population, looking back sadly to the good old days when their ancestors were worried about where the next meal would come from, sits in marvellously-equipped clinics waiting for the other half to come and treat it, but rather that we should set about wondering what is wrong with our outlook and what is wrong with our way of life that we should have need of so much psychiatry and often-misapplied psychology. It took the best part of forty years for industrial psychologists to make the staggering discovery that the best way to get people to do a good day's work is not some special technique of applied science but simply to treat them as responsible individuals whose group life at their job is an important aspect of their life as a whole. We spend heaven knows how much on treating delinquency as an individual problem when research has shown that, as common sense would suggest, it is frequently a function of the group which has to be treated *as* a group rather than a function of the individual requiring individual therapy. Psychologists conspire to produce tests for the selection of officers in the services or managers in industry, and, while nobody who knew the amount of scientific forethought lavished upon them would wish to deny that they test *something*, many of us are still wondering what that something is; for there is not much use in testing people to find out if they will make good officers or managers unless we know what it is that makes the good ones good. Of this we may be quite sure: that they would exclude from the service, let alone a commission, every single military or naval leader of note in the whole of British history, not only such noted eccentrics as Lawrence and Wingate but also Nelson, Marlborough, Wolfe, and Montgomery, that they would exclude from industry every important leader from Ford, Hearst, and Morgan right up to the present day. Psychoanalysts and psychologists are at one in supposing that it is a good thing to be normal, in spite of the fact that it is almost as difficult to discover a 'normal' genius as it is to discover a 'Nordic' blonde one, that it is a good thing to be happy and contented, although probably the largest number of happy and contented people are either in mental hospitals or in institutions for the mentally defective—Dr Jones indeed expresses regret that Oscar Wilde, Dr Johnson, Schopenhauer, and Swift were unable to resort to medical treatment for their mental conditions. They would, he says, have had happier lives had they done so. But neither in the history of psychoanalysis nor today is there any evidence whatever to suggest that psychoanalysts are happier, more normal, or more free from prejudice than other men and quite a lot of evidence that might suggest the contrary—which would be no great matter were it not for their own claims. The sort of questions one has asked psychiatric patients and the conclusions one has drawn from the answers are almost embarrassing to recollect; for what useful conclusions is one to draw from the knowledge that X did not do well at school where he was lazy and indifferent, that he was inhibited about sex, that he was shy and ordinarily solitary, that his father was an alcoholic and he is still over-attached to his mother on whom he continually sponges, that he has never settled down to a steady job although now over thirty? That X is an inadequate psychopath, a case of schizophrenia simplex, or that in less than ten years his name, George Bernard Shaw, will be world-famous? Yet had even one of these facts been known to a psychological tester or a psychiatrist, very considerable significance would have been attached to it and subsequent revelations—save the last—would have been seen in the light of the earlier ones. Freudians are perhaps less likely than non-Freudian psychiatrists to attach weight to facts taken in isolation, but this has to be counterbalanced by their extraordinary lack of any sense of reality shown, for example, in a document intended for official consumption where it is stated that unrest in the coalfields must have some connexion with the miner's unconscious conflicts aroused by the fact that he has to use his phallic pick on 'mother earth', thus committing symbolic incest! As in the case of an earlier example, the question is not whether this astonishing statement is true or false as a statement, but whether anyone could seriously believe it to have the slightest relevance in the circumstances and how anyone could expect it to be accepted by management. On the other hand it is not necessarily more peculiar than the picture of the 'normal' Britisher arising from the conspiracy between psychologists and psychiatrists and deducible from the stock questions of their clinical examinations and personality tests. This paragon, we are led to suppose, is hale in body and limb and never gave his parents a moment's anxiety during childhood years; he loved them both equally (but not excessively) and was liked (but not too much) by both brothers and sisters. His ability to get on with people was shown at school, where he was a conscientious if not brilliant scholar, and on the playing field, where his prowess on the football—i.e. Rugby football—field and at cricket led to his captaincy of both First Fifteen and First Eleven in his final year; he was *never* interested in politics nor, although a regular attender at church, was he 'morbid' about religion. Taking a good First in Modern History at Oxford, he has fulfilled his early promise both in military and civil life, is popular amongst his many friends and full of sympathy for the underdog in a non-political way, since as a moderate member of the Conservative Party he naturally remains politically unbiased. This account, if exaggerated, is not wholly a parody, because it is undoubtedly the case that definite views on political or religious subjects or unconventional views about anything, strong emotions generally, anything suggesting conflict in early life or later, a tendency to shyness or unsociability, excessive studiousness, and any interest at all in sex or 'culture' incur the suspicions of both the clinician and the psychological tester in Britain and America, although in America the suspicion of studiousness or culture is perhaps greater. Since this conception of normality is consciously or unconsciously present in the minds of those who wish to get on, many of the questions in personality tests

answer themselves, so that 'do you read many books?' does not
mean what it says but, according to one's outlook, either 'are you
one of the ignorant and semiliterate masses who never opens a
book?' or 'are you one of those unsociable so-and-sos who never
takes his nose from a book and thinks he is an intellectual?' The
trouble is not that psychologists and psychiatrists in practice make
value judgments, but that they are not aware they are doing so.
Psychoanalysts again are much less prone to this danger, but this is
at least partly due to the fact that their opinion in matters involving
such issues is less frequently sought, and they cannot be absolved
from spreading by implication a view of man's nature which to the
intelligent outsider seems to infer that all problems are individual
problems which are not only individual but infantile. Hence
battle neuroses are caused, and industrial unrest is initiated, by the
Oedipus complex and have really little to do with war or fear of unemployment, and the world of experience is not simply liable to
emotional distortion but is actually a completely individual creation. All these eccentricities arise from the 'tunnel vision' which
so many specialists sooner or later seem to develop, by becoming so
intent on their special fraction of a special subject that they cannot
see the obvious or their own observations in proper perspective in
a wider context—no doubt much of the popular success of
writers such as Fromm, Horney, and Riesman, or, to a lesser
extent, Jung, arises from the fact that successfully or otherwise
they try to avoid this danger. It is true that orthodox Freudians
have also written on the wider implications of Freudian theory,
but to the lay mind their contributions are more likely to cloud
than to clarify the issue; analytic theory can hardly probe deeper
into the past than Klein has done and is unlikely to go beyond Jung
in search of man's superstructure of myths and archetypes; so unless we are to be restricted to the mere filling-in of details, any
future advance must be in the direction of the analysis of social
and cultural phenomena and its application in the light of modern
knowledge from related fields. The general acceptability of a
scientific theory is not wholly dependent upon its validity as science,
because history shows that its relevance to the contemporary situation and the degree to which it conforms to the contemporary
approach are equally important. In a world which increasingly sees

all human problems as social problems psychoanalysis as a method of treatment may well fall into desuetude, not because it does not work, but simply because it is inapplicable to the problems of the day. Even now, the knowledge that thousands of citizens of New York or London are being analysed by hundreds of psychoanalysts begins to seem more incongruous than sad, as we are likely to argue that lying individually on a thousand individual couches talking in the presence of a thousand individual analysts seems a peculiar method of attacking a social problem. This is not a criticism of psychoanalytic theory, which is likely to become increasingly recognized as the greatest single advance in our understanding of the human personality so far conceived, but it is an expression of doubt whether under changing conditions it will continue to be important in its original form as a therapy. It was Freud, after all, who showed that neurosis is not an illness in the classical sense but a form of social maladaptation, that it is not either present or absent in a given individual but present in varying degrees, and that psychoanalysis as a treatment is applicable to a relatively small proportion of the population; but his followers have failed to draw the logical conclusions that, if this is so, it must be dealt with socially on the basis of a psychoanalytic understanding of personality and the nature of society, and that on the same basis it must be treated in individual patients when this is necessary by methods which are brief and do not strive for perfectionist goals. There is no logical contradiction involved in seeing that, although every neurosis has deep-seated roots, its immediate causes are often superficial and environmental, and when these are dealt with the symptoms disappear. The very real danger today is that neuroses may cease to be dealt with by psychological methods based on understanding at all, and that with new pharmacological and medical or surgical methods we shall be 'cured' by being made insensible to conflicts rather than facing up to them and trying to understand what is wrong with our way of life. Instead of realizing that there are circumstances which justify attitudes of guilt, remorse, shame, anxiety, or injustice, we shall treat them as inconvenient 'symptoms' to be dispelled by a tranquillizer or thymoleptic drug. Freud's work will make an even greater impact in the future when it is removed from the category of an expensive and prolonged method of treatment for a minute portion of the population carried out by practitioners who often have very little interest outside their own speciality and sometimes adopt a paranoid and contemptuous attitude towards the rest of the world. It is a scientific anomaly that it should be possible for a psychoanalyst to have his own private social psychology which never comes into contact with ordinary social theory because those to whom the truth has already been revealed have no need of such trivialities. Psychoanalysis has so much to offer that it is absurd that it should be restricted in this way, and it is to the credit of the Americans, whether we agree with their conclusions or not, that they should have been the first to make the attempt to break down the barriers. For the explanation of the irrational is a special task of the twentieth century.

BIBLIOGRAPHY

Bibliography

FREUD: *The Interpretation of Dreams* (Allen and Unwin); *The Psycho-pathology of Everyday Life* (Benn); *New Introductory Lectures in Psychoanalysis* (The Hogarth Press); *Totem and Taboo* (The Hogarth Press). All of these except the Introductory Lectures have been published as Pelicans. Two useful books for the novice are: *Sigmund Freud: a General Selection* and *Civilization, War, and Death*, dealing with Freud's social theories, both edited by John Rickman and published by The Hogarth Press.

BOOKS BY FREUDIANS: O. Fenichel, *The Psychoanalytic Theory of Neurosis* (Routledge); J. C. Flugel, *The Psychoanalytic Study of the Family* (The Hogarth Press) and *Man, Morals, and Society* (Duckworth); E. Jones's biography of Freud and his small book *What is Psychoanalysis?* (Allen and Unwin); Hans Sachs, *Freud, Master and Friend* (Imago); Anna Freud, *The Ego and Mechanisms of Defence* (The Hogarth Press); M. Klein, *The Psychoanalysis of Children, Contributions to Psychoanalysis*, and Klein and Rivière's *Love, Hate, and Reparation*, all published by The Hogarth Press.

THE NEO-FREUDIANS: E. Fromm, *The Fear of Freedom, Sigmund Freud's Mission, The Art of Loving* (Allen and Unwin); K. Horney, *The Neurotic Personality of Our Time, New Ways in Psychoanalysis, Our Inner Conflicts, Self-Analysis* (Routledge and Kegan Paul); H. S. Sullivan, *Conceptions of Modern Psychiatry* (Tavistock).

JUNGIANS, ADLERIANS, AND OTHERS: A. Adler, *The Practice and Theory of Individual Psychology* (Routledge and Kegan Paul) and many other books; *Individual Psychological Treatment* by E. Wexberg (The C. W. Daniel Co.); Lewis Way, *Man's Quest for Significance* (Allen and Unwin), *Alfred Adler; an Introduction to his Psychology* (Penguin Books); C. G. Jung, *The Integration of the Personality* (Routledge and Kegan Paul); G. Adler, *Studies in Analytical Psychology* (Routledge and Kegan Paul); F. Fordham, *An Introduction to Jung's Psychology* (Penguin Books); G. Groddeck, *The Book of the It* (Vision Press) and others; I. Suttie, *The Origins of Love and Hate*

(Penguin Books); T. Reik, *From Thirty Years with Freud, Listening with the Inner Ear* (Allen and Unwin); W. H. R. Rivers, *Instinct and the Unconscious, Conflict and Dream* (Routledge and Kegan Paul); F. Alexander, *Fundamentals of Psychoanalysis* (Allen and Unwin); J. L. Halliday, *Psychosocial Medicine* (Heinemann); J. A. Hadfield, *Dreams and Nightmares* (Penguin Books).

GENERAL: Gardner Murphy, *Historical Introduction to Modern Psychology* (Routledge and Kegan Paul); J. C. Flugel, *A Hundred Years of Psychology* (Duckworth); D. Riesman, *The Lonely Crowd* (Yale University Press); M. Mead, *Coming of Age in Samoa* (Penguin Books); R. Benedict, *Patterns of Culture* (Routledge and Kegan Paul); *The Chrysanthemum and the Sword* (Secker and Warburg), o.p.; John Wisdom, *Philosophy and Psychoanalysis* (Blackwell); N. O. Brown, *Life against Death* (Routledge and Kegan Paul).

INDEX

Index